Thomas A. Bronikowski
Marquette University

Student Supplement
Volume 1: Chapters 1–11

to accompany

Swokowski's

Calculus *with analytic geometry*

Third Edition

 Prindle, Weber & Schmidt *Boston*

PWS PUBLISHERS

Prindle, Weber & Schmidt • ❦ • Duxbury Press • ♠ • PWS Engineering • ⋏ • Breton Publishers • ⚙
20 Park Plaza • Boston, Massachusetts 02116

PWS Publishers is a division of Wadsworth, Inc.

Portions of this text previously appeared in the Student Supplement
Volume I: Chapters 1-11, to accompany Swokowski's Calculus with
Analytic Geometry, Alternate Edition, copyright © 1983 by PWS
Publishers, and in the Student Supplement Volume I: Chapters 1-12,
to accompany Swokowski's Calculus with Analytic Geometry, Second
Edition, copyright © 1979 by Prindle, Weber & Schmidt.

89 88 87   - 10 9 8 7 6 5 4 3

Printed in the United States of America.

Cover image by Rene Burri/Magnum Photos, Inc.

ISBN 0-87150-446-4

INTRODUCTION

This supplement to the third edition of Earl W. Swokowski's <u>Calculus</u>
<u>with Analytic Geometry</u> has been written to help you, the student, develop the
skill and art of solving problems in Calculus. I have included the solution of
every third problem (numbers 1, 4, 7, 10, etc.) from every section of the text.
Occasionally this sequence is modified slightly to provide a greater variety of
solved exercises. However, theoretical problems involving proofs are sometimes
not included because many instructors use such problems as special assignments
and prefer to have no more than a hint given. In sections of the text concerned
with applications of the definite integral I have included, in addition to solutions of exercises in the normal sequence, integral answers to the remaining odd-
numbered exercises. In this way you can quickly check to see if a wrong answer
is due to setting up the problem incorrectly or to merely making an error in
evaluating the correct integral.

Clearly, not every arithmetic and algebraic detail can be included in every
solution if the size of this book is to remain reasonable. You will find
enough detail in all solutions to see how the correct answers are obtained. The
symbols " $\Longrightarrow$ " and " $\Longleftrightarrow$ " are used frequently and are to be read "implies" and
"if and only if" respectively. All other symbols will be familiar to you from
the text or from other courses. The author would appreciate being informed of
errors or misprints in this work. A note to me at the address below will be
promptly acknowledged with thanks.

I would like to express my appreciation to the staff of PWS Publishers,
especially David Pallai, for prompt assistance and advice, to my friend and
colleague, Earl W. Swokowski, for his thoughtful concern and recommendations, and
to Sally Canapa for her excellent job of typing the original manuscript and its
revisions. To my family I owe a special debt of gratitude for assistance and
encouragement in the preparation of this edition. Particular thanks to my sons,
Joseph and Michael, for assistance in proofreading and preparation of new sketches
and to my wife, Irene, for her good-natured, generous participation in all phases
of the preparation of this manuscript.

Thomas A. Bronikowski
Departments of Mathematics,
    Statistics and Computer Science
Marquette University
Milwaukee, WI 53233

TABLE OF CONTENTS

CHAPTER 1

PREREQUISITES FOR CALCULUS

EXERCISES 1.1, page 9

1. (a) $-2 > -5$ since $-2 - (-5) = 3 > 0$. (b) $-2 < 5$ since $5 - (-2) = 7 > 0$.
    (c) $(6-1) = (2+3)$ since $(6-1) - (2+3) = 0$. (d) $2/3 > 0.66$ since $2/3 - 0.66 = 0.666... - 0.66 = 0.006... > 0$. (e) $2 = \sqrt{4}$ by definition of the $\sqrt{}$ symbol.
    (f) $\pi < 22/7$ since $22/7 - \pi = 3.14285... - 3.14159... = 0.00126... > 0$.

4. (a) $|4-8| = |-4| = -(-4) = 4$. (b) $|3-\pi| = -(3-\pi) = \pi-3$. (c) $|-4| - |-8| = -(-4) - (-(-8)) = 4-8 = -4$. (d) $|-4+8| = |4| = 4$. (e) $|-3|^2 = (-(-3))^2 = 3^2 = 9$. (f) $|2-\sqrt{4}| = |2-2| = |0| = 0$. (g) $|-0.67| = -(-0.67) = 0.67$.
    (h) $-|-3| = -[-(-3)] = -3$. (i) $|x^2+1| = x^2+1$ since $x^2+1 \geq 1 > 0$ for all x.
    (j) $|-4-x^2| = |-(4+x^2)| = -[-(4+x^2)] = 4+x^2$ since $-4-x^2 \leq -4 < 0$ for all x.

7. $5x-6 > 11 \iff 5x > 17 \iff x > 17/5$. $\therefore (17/5,\infty)$ is the solution set.

10. $7-2x \geq -3 \iff 10 \geq 2x \iff 5 \geq x$. $\therefore (-\infty,5]$ is the solution set.

13. $3x+2 < 5x-8 \iff 10 < 2x \iff 5 < x$. $\therefore (5,\infty)$ is the solution set.

16. $-4 < 2-9x < 5 \iff -6 < -9x < 3 \iff 2/3 > x > -1/3$. $\therefore (-1/3,2/3)$ is the solution set.

19. $5/(7-2x) > 0 \iff 7-2x > 0$ (since $5 > 0$) $\iff 7 > 2x \iff 7/2 > x$.
    $\therefore (-\infty,7/2)$ is the solution set.

22. $|(2x+3)/5| < 2 \iff |2x+3| < 10 \iff -10 < 2x+3 < 10 \iff -13 < 2x < 7 \iff -13/2 < x < 7/2$ or $(-13/2,7/2)$.

25. $|25x-8| > 7 \iff 25x-8 > 7$ or $25x-8 < -7$. The first yields $x > 3/5$; the second yields $x < 1/25$. Thus the solution set is $(-\infty,1/25) \cup (3/5,\infty)$.

28. $2x^2 - 9x + 7 < 0 \iff (2x-7)(x-1) < 0$. For the product to be negative, the factors must differ in sign. The points where one or the other changes sign are $x = 1$ and $x = 7/2$. Schematically we have

    $(2x-7)$ $-$ $-$ $+$

    ――――――――――――――――――― x

    $(x-1)$ $-$ 1 $+$ 7/2 $+$

    Thus $(1,7/2)$ is the desired solution set.

31. $1/x^2 < 100 \iff 1/|x| < 10 \iff |x| > 1/10 \iff x > 1/10$ or $x < -1/10$. Thus $(-\infty,-1/10) \cup (1/10,\infty)$ is the solution set.

34. It is convenient to look at the inequality separately on $(-\infty,-2)$, $(-2,9)$, $(9,\infty)$. On the 1st, both denominators are negative and $3/(x-9) > 2/(x+2) \iff (3x+6)/(x-9) < 2 \iff 3x+6 > 2x-18 \iff x > -24$. Since $x \in (-\infty,-2)$, we get $(-24,-2)$. On the 2nd interval the left side is < 0, the right side is > 0, and, so, no number here can satisfy the given inequality. On the 3rd, $(9,\infty)$, both denominators are positive and, as above, we obtain $x > -24$. Since every

$x \in (9,\infty)$ satisfies this, we get the entire interval $(9,\infty)$. Combining results we get $(-24,-2) \cup (9,\infty)$ as the solution set.

37. $F = 4.5x = \frac{9}{2}x$, $10 \leq F \leq 18 \implies 10 \leq \frac{9}{2}x \leq 18$. Now multiply through by $\frac{2}{9}$ to obtain $\frac{20}{9} \leq x \leq 4$.

40. $g = 980 \implies T = \frac{2\pi}{\sqrt{980}} \sqrt{\ell}$. $98 \leq \ell \leq 100 \implies \sqrt{98} \leq \sqrt{\ell} \leq 10$. Now, multiply by

$2\pi/\sqrt{980}$ to obtain: $\frac{2\pi\sqrt{98}}{\sqrt{980}} \leq \frac{2\pi\sqrt{\ell}}{\sqrt{980}} \leq \frac{20\pi}{\sqrt{980}} \implies \frac{2\pi}{\sqrt{10}} \leq T \leq \frac{20\pi}{\sqrt{980}} \implies 1.99 \leq T \leq 2.01$.

43. Hint: If $0 < a < b$, multiply first by $1/a$ and then $1/b$, both of which are positive. If $a < b < 0$, do the same, but now both multipliers are negative.

46. No. The result is true if all numbers are positive, but the reverse inequality is true if all are negative. In mixed cases, anything can happen.

EXERCISES 1.2, page 18

1. (a) $d(A,B) = \sqrt{(2-6)^2 + (1-(-2))^2} = \sqrt{(-4)^2 + 3^2} = \sqrt{16+9} = \sqrt{25} = 5$. (b) Midpoint is $((6+2)/2,(-2+1)/2) = (4,-1/2)$.

4. (a) $d(A,B) = \sqrt{(4-4)^2 + (5-(-4))^2} = \sqrt{0+9^2} = 9$. (b) Midpoint is $((4+4)/2,(5-4)/2) = (4,1/2)$.

7. Since $d(A,B)^2 = 5^2 + 5^2 = 50$, $d(B,C)^2 = 7^2 + 7^2 = 98$, $d(A,C)^2 = 12^2 + 2^2 = 148$, it is a right triangle with legs AB and BC and hypotenuse AC. The area is $\frac{1}{2}d(A,B)d(B,C) = \frac{1}{2}\sqrt{50} \sqrt{98} = (5\sqrt{2})(7\sqrt{2})/2 = 35$.

10. P is on the perpendicular bisector of AB if and only if $d(A,P) = d(B,P) \iff$ $\sqrt{(x+4)^2 + (y+3)^2} = \sqrt{(x-6)^2 + (y-1)^2}$. Squaring and simplifying, we obtain: $x^2 + 8x + 16 + y^2 + 6y + 9 = x^2 - 12x + 36 + y^2 - 2y + 1 \iff 8x + 6y + 25 = -12x - 2y + 37 \iff 20x + 8y - 12 = 0$, or $5x + 2y - 3 = 0$.

16. A point (x,y) satisfies $y = -3$ if and only if it is 3 units below the x-axis. Thus the graph is a horizontal line 3 units below and parallel to the x-axis.

19. $|x| < 2 \iff -2 < x < 2$ and $|y| > 1 \iff y > 1$ or $y < -1$. Thus the graph consists of the two vertical strips shown between the vertical lines $x = \pm 2$. The upper strip corresponds to $y > 1$; the lower to $y < -1$.

NOTE: In graphing the equations in #21-38 of the text, all you can do now is tabulate some points, plot them and connect them smoothly. Only after Chapters 3, 4 and 12 will you have the mathematical background to sketch graphs accurately with only a few significant points plotted. The graphs for the odd-numbered exercises are in the text.

22. For y = 4x-3, we obtain the table of points and then
     plot to obtain the line shown.

x	-2	-1	0	1	2
y	-11	-7	-3	1	5

     There are no symmetries in this graph.

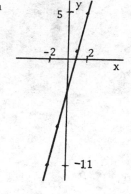

25. For $y = 2x^2 - 1$, we plot

x	±2	±1	0
y	7	1	-1

     to obtain the graph in the text, a parabola. If we replace x by -x and use
     $(-x)^2 = x^2$, we obtain the same equation. Hence, the graph is symmetric with
     respect to the y-axis.

28. Rewrite the equation as $y = -x^2/3$ and tabulate as above.

x	±3	±2	±1	0
y	-3	-4/3	-1/3	0

     As above, the graph is symmetric with respect to
     the y-axis.

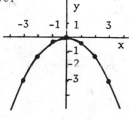

31. For $y = x^3 - 2$, we obtain

x	-2	-1	0	1	2
y	-10	-3	-2	-1	6

     There are no symmetries.

34. For $y = \sqrt{x} - 1$, x must be ≥ 0 and we get

x	0	1	4	9
y	-1	0	1	2

     There are no symmetries.

37. By (1.13) the graph is a circle of radius 4 with center at (0,0), symmetric
     with respect to both axes and the origin.

40. Directly from (1.13) the equation is $(x-(-5))^2 + (y-2)^2 = 5^2$ or
     $(x+5)^2 + (y-2)^2 = 25$.

43. Since the center has y-coordinate 2, the radius must be 2 for the circle to
     be tangent to the x-axis. Thus the equation is $(x-(-4))^2 + (y-2)^2 = 2^2$,
     which reduces to the answer given.

46. The center must be 2 units from each axis for the circle to have radius 2
     and to be tangent to both axes. Since it is in the 1st quadrant, the center is
     at $(2,2)$ and $(x-2)^2 + (y-2)^2 = 2^2$ is the equation.

49. We solve by completing the square:
$$(x^2 + 6x \quad) + y^2 = 0$$
$$(x^2 + 6x + 9) + y^2 = 9$$
$$(x+3)^2 \qquad + y^2 = 3^2$$
$$\Longrightarrow \quad C(-3,0), \ r = 3.$$

52. We start as before but then divide through by 9 to convert the coefficients
     of x^2 and y^2 to 1.
$$(9x^2 - 6x \quad) + (9y^2 + 12y \quad) = 31$$
$$(x^2 - \tfrac{2}{3}x \quad) + (y^2 + \tfrac{4}{3}y \quad) = \tfrac{31}{9}$$
$$(x^2 - \tfrac{2}{3}x + \tfrac{1}{9}) + (y^2 + \tfrac{4}{3}y + \tfrac{4}{9}) = \tfrac{31}{9} + \tfrac{1}{9} + \tfrac{4}{9}$$
$$(x - \tfrac{1}{3})^2 \qquad + (y + \tfrac{2}{3})^2 \qquad = \tfrac{36}{9} = 4$$
$$\Longrightarrow \quad C(\tfrac{1}{3}, -\tfrac{2}{3}), \ \text{and} \ r = 2.$$

EXERCISES 1.3, page 24

NOTE: In some of the solutions below, m_{AB} will denote the slope of the line
through points A and B.

1. $m_{AB} = (18-6)/(-1-(-4)) = 12/(-1+4) = 4.$

4. $m_{AB} = (4-4)/(2+3) = 0.$

7. $m_{AB} = (12-15)/(11-6) = -3/5$ and $m_{CD} = (-5+8)/(-6+1) = -3/5.$ Thus AB $\parallel$ CD.
    Also, $m_{AD} = 20/12 = 5/3$ and $m_{BC} = (-20)/(-12) = 5/3$ and AD $\parallel$ BC. Thus the
    figure is a parallelogram and since the slopes of adjacent sides are nega-
    tive reciprocals, these sides are $\perp$ and the figure is a rectangle.

10. Let E, F, G, H be the midpoints of the segments AB, BC, CD, DA, respectively.
     Then
$$m_{EF} = (\frac{y_2+y_3}{2} - \frac{y_1+y_2}{2}) \Big/ (\frac{x_2+x_3}{2} - \frac{x_1+x_2}{2}) = (y_3-y_1)/(x_3-x_1) \quad (\text{if } x_1 \neq x_3).$$
$$m_{HG} = (\frac{y_3+y_4}{2} - \frac{y_1+y_4}{2}) \Big/ (\frac{x_3+x_4}{2} - \frac{x_1+x_4}{2}) = (y_3-y_1)/(x_3-x_1).$$

Thus EF $\parallel$ HG since, if $x_1 \neq x_3$, the slopes are equal and if $x_1 = x_3$ both lines are vertical. Similarly $m_{EH} = m_{FG} = (y_2-y_4)/(x_2-x_4)$, if $x_2 \neq x_4$.

13. $m_{AB} = \dfrac{(-4-(-7))}{(3-(-5))} = \dfrac{3}{8}$. Using this slope and the point A(-5,-7) in the point-slope formula (1.16), we obtain: $y-(-7) = (3/8)(x-(-5))$ or $8(y+7) = 3(x+5)$ or $3x - 8y - 41 = 0$.

16. Using m = 6, and the point (-2,0), we get $(y-0) = 6(x-(-2))$ or $y = 6(x+2)$.

19. The given line, $2x - 5y = 8$, has slope 2/5 (obtained by writing it as $y = (2/5)x - (8/5)$). Thus the desired slope is -5/2 and the equation is $y + 3 = (-5/2)(x-7)$.

22. The desired line must pass through the origin and must have inclination 135°. Since tan 135° = -1, the equation is $y = -x$.

25. Rewriting the given line as $y = (3/4)x + 2$, we read off the slope, 3/4, and y-intercept 2.

28. Rewriting as $y = -(8/4)x + 1/4$, the slope is seen to be -2 and y-intercept $\dfrac{1}{4}$.

31. Rewriting as $y = -(5/4)x + 5$, the slope is seen to be $-\dfrac{5}{4}$ and y-intercept 5.

34. Rewriting as $y = x = (1)x + 0$, the slope is 1 and the y-intercept 0.

37. HINT: Use the 2 points (a,0) and (0,b) to compute the slope, then use (1.16). Dividing $4x-2y = 6$ by 6 (to get the right side 1) we get
$\dfrac{2}{3}x - \dfrac{1}{3}y = 1$ or $\dfrac{x}{(3/2)} + \dfrac{y}{(-3)} = 1$.

40. $m = \dfrac{(3t+1)-t}{t-(1-2t)} = \dfrac{2t+1}{3t-1}$. Because the denominator, 3t-1, is 0 at t = 1/3, we consider the problem separately on the two intervals t > 1/3, where 3t-1 > 0, and t < 1/3, where 3t-1 < 0. First, then, if t > 1/3, m > 4 $\Longleftrightarrow$ (2t+1)/ (3t-1) > 4 $\Longleftrightarrow$ 2t+1 > 12t-4 $\Longleftrightarrow$ 5 > 10t or t < 1/2. Since t > 1/3 also, we have (1/3,1/2) as part of the solution set. Secondly, if t < 1/3, then 3t-1 < 0 and m > 4 $\Longleftrightarrow$ 2t+1 < 12t-4 $\Longleftrightarrow$ 5 < 10t or t > 1/2. (The inequality sign changed when we multiplied by 3t-1 < 0.) Since no numbers satisfy t < 1/3 and t > 1/2 no new solutions are obtained. Thus (1/3,1/2) is the entire solution set.

EXERCISES 1.4, page 32

1. $f(x) = x^3 + 4x - 3$. (a) $f(1) = 1^3 + 4 \cdot 1 - 3 = 2$. (b) $f(-1) = (-1)^3 + 4(-1) - 3 = -1 - 4 - 3 = -8$. (c) $f(0) = 0^3 + 4 \cdot 0 - 3 = -3$. (d) $f(\sqrt{2}) = (\sqrt{2})^3 + 4\sqrt{2} - 3 = 2\sqrt{2} + 4\sqrt{2} - 3 = 6\sqrt{2} - 3$.

4. $f(x) = 1/(x^2+1)$. (a) $f(a) = 1/(a^2+1)$. (b) $f(-a) = 1/((-a)^2+1) = 1/(a^2+1)$. (c) $-f(a) = -1/(a^2+1)$. (d) $f(a+h) = 1/((a+h)^2+1)$. (e) $f(a) + f(h) = (1/(a^2+1)) + (1/(h^2+1))$.

(f) $\dfrac{f(a+h) - f(a)}{h} = \dfrac{1}{h}\left(\dfrac{1}{(a+h)^2+1} - \dfrac{1}{a^2+1}\right) = \dfrac{1}{h}\left(\dfrac{(a^2+1) - ((a+h)^2+1)}{((a+h)^2+1)(a^2+1)}\right) =$

$\dfrac{1}{h}\dfrac{a^2+1-a^2-2ah-h^2-1}{((a+h)^2+1)(a^2+1)} = -\dfrac{(2a+h)}{((a+h)^2+1)(a^2+1)}$.

7. The domain consists of all real numbers x for which $3x-5 \geq 0$. Solving, we get $3x \geq 5$ or $x \geq 5/3$.

10. Here, the domain $= \{x: x^2 - 9 \geq 0\}$. Since $x^2 - 9 \geq 0 \iff x^2 \geq 9 \iff |x| \geq 3$, the domain is $(-\infty,3] \cup [3,\infty)$.

13. For the 1st part, we solve $f(x) = 4 \iff 7x-5 = 4 \iff 7x = 9 \iff x = 9/7$. For the 2nd part we solve $f(x) = a \iff 7x-5 = a \iff 7x = 5+a \iff x = (5+a)/7$. The range is all of $\mathbb{R}$ for if y is any real number we solve $f(x) = y$ as above to obtain $x = (5+y)/7$. As a check we compute $f((5+y)/7) = 7\left(\dfrac{5+y}{7}\right) - 5 = y$.

16. 1st, $f(x) = 4 \iff 1/x = 4 \iff x = 1/4$. 2nd, $f(x) = a \iff 1/x = a \iff x = 1/a$. The range is $\{y: y \neq 0\}$ for if $y \neq 0$ we solve $f(x) = y$ to obtain $1/x = y$ or $x = 1/y$ and check that $f(1/y) = y$.

19. f is one-to-one since $a \neq b \implies 2a \neq 2b \implies 2a+9 \neq 2b+9$, or $f(a) \neq f(b)$.

22. f is not one-to-one. The graph of f is a parabola opening upward. This suggests that different x values will yield the same functional value. In particular $f(0) = f(.5) = -3$.

25. f is not one-to-one. If $a > 0$ then $a \neq -a$, but $f(a) = a$, $f(-a) = |-a| = -(-a) = a$.

28. $f(-a) = 7(-a)^4 - (-a)^2 + 7 = 7a^4 - a^2 + 7 = f(a)$ $\therefore$ even.

31. f is even since $f(a) = f(-a) = 2$.

34. f is even since $f(-a) = \sqrt{(-a)^2+1} = \sqrt{a^2+1} = f(a)$.

37. As a polynomial, the domain is all of $\mathbb{R}$. The range is also $\mathbb{R}$ since, if $y \in \mathbb{R}$, $f((3-y)/4) = y$.

40. Domain is $\mathbb{R}$; range is $\{3\}$; graph is the horizontal line $y = 3$.

43. Domain $= \{x: 4-x^2 \geq 0\} = [-2,2]$. The graph is that of the equation $y = \sqrt{4-x^2}$, i.e., the upper half of the circle $y^2 = 4-x^2$ or $x^2 + y^2 = 4$. Thus the range is the set of y-values corresponding to this graph, namely $[0,2]$.

46. Domain = {x: x ≠ 4}; the range = {y: y ≠ 0} for
     if y ≠ 0, we can solve 1/(4-x) = y to obtain
     x = 4-1/y so that f(4-1/y) = y. The graph is
     obtained as in Example 6, except when x is near
     4 the ordinate 1/(4-x) is numerically large.

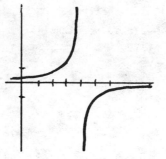

49. Domain = ℝ, range = {y: y ≥ 0} since f(x) ≥ 0
     and for any y ≥ 0, f(y+4) = y.

52. Recalling that |x| = x if x ≥ 0, |x| = -x if x < 0,
     f(x) = 2x if x ≥ 0, 0 if x < 0. Thus Domain = ℝ,
     range = [0,∞), and the graph as shown.

55. Since f(x) = (x-2)(x+2)/(x-2) = x + 2 if x ≠ 2, the graph of f is the point
     (2,3) and the line y = x + 2 from which the point (2,4) is absent. Thus, the
     range of f is {y: y ≠ 4}.

58. From the definition of f, the domain is ℝ, and the range
     is (0,∞) since if y > 0 we can choose x = -y < 0 so that
     f(-y) = y.

61. The graphs are in the answer section.   (a) The graph of f(x) = [2x] is
     obtained by observing:

         -1/2 ≤ x < 0 ⟹ -1 ≤ 2x < 0 ⟹ [2x] = -1
           0 ≤ x < 1/2 ⟹   0 ≤ 2x < 1 ⟹ [2x] = 0
          1/2 ≤ x < 1 ⟹   1 ≤ 2x < 2 ⟹ [2x] = 1, etc.

     Thus, the graph jumps one vertical unit at every integer and half-integer
     value of x.   (b) The ordinates of points on the graph of f(x) = 2[x] are
     just twice those of [x]. Thus, the graph jumps two units at every integer
     value of x.

64. The entire circle is $x^2 + y^2 = 1$, or $y = \pm\sqrt{1-x^2}$. (a) The upper half of this circle requires $y \geq 0$. Thus, the "+" sign must be chosen, and $y = f(x) = \sqrt{1-x^2}$. (b) Now, $y \leq 0$, so that $y = f(x) = -\sqrt{1-x^2}$.

67. $C = 2\pi r \implies r = C/2\pi$. Let r' be the radius after C is increased by 12 inches to $C + 12$. Thus $r' = (C+12)/2\pi$. The increase in the radius is

   $r' - r = \dfrac{C+12}{2\pi} - \dfrac{C}{2\pi} = \dfrac{C}{2\pi} + \dfrac{12}{2\pi} - \dfrac{C}{2\pi} = \dfrac{12}{2\pi} = \dfrac{6}{\pi}$ inches (regardless of the radius!)

70. In an equilateral (indeed, isosceles) triangle, the altitude, a, is perpendicular to and bisects the opposite side. Thus, here, $a = \sqrt{s^2-(s/2)^2} = \sqrt{3/4}\,s = \sqrt{3}s/2$. Then $A = \dfrac{1}{2}as = \dfrac{1}{2} \cdot \dfrac{\sqrt{3}s}{2} \cdot s = \dfrac{\sqrt{3}s^2}{4}$.

73. After t seconds, the balloon will have risen 2t meters. Thus $d = \sqrt{(2t)^2+100^2} = \sqrt{4t^2+10{,}000}$ since d is the length of the hypotenuse of a right triangle with vertical leg 2t m. and horizontal leg 100 m.

76. The 2 ends make a sphere of radius x. (a) V = vol. of cylinder + vol. of sphere $= 10\pi x^2 + \dfrac{4}{3}\pi x^3$. (b) S = surf. area of cylinder + surf. area of sphere $= 10(2\pi x) + 4\pi x^2$.

EXERCISES 1.5, page 38

1. $(f\pm g)(x) = f(x) \pm g(x) = 3x^2 \pm 1/(2x-3)$. $(fg)(x) = f(x)g(x) = 3x^2(1/(2x-3)) = 3x^2/(2x-3)$. $(f/g)(x) = f(x)/g(x) = 3x^2/(1/(2x-3)) = 3x^2(2x-3)$ (if $x \neq 3/2$).

4. $(f\pm g)(x) = (x^3+3x) \pm (3x^2+1)$. $(fg)(x) = (x^3+3x)(3x^2+1) = 3x^5 + 10x^3 + 3x$. $(f/g)(x) = (x^3+3x)/(3x^2+1)$.

7. If $f(x) = 2x^2 + 5$, $g(x) = 4 - 7x$ then $(f\circ g)(x) = 2g(x)^2 + 5 = 2(4-7x)^2 + 5 = 2(16-56x+49x^2) + 5 = 98x^2 - 112x + 37$; and $(g\circ f)(x) = 4 - 7f(x) = 4-7(2x^2+5) = 4 - 14x^2 - 35 = -14x^2 - 31$.

10. If $f(x) = \sqrt{x^2+4}$, $g(x) = 7x^2+1$ then $(f\circ g)(x) = \sqrt{g(x)^2+4} = \sqrt{(7x^2+1)^2 + 4} = \sqrt{49x^4 + 14x^2 + 5}$, and $(g\circ f)(x) = 7f(x)^2 + 1 = 7(x^2+4) + 1 = 7x^2 + 29$.

13. Here, $(f\circ g)(x) = \sqrt{2g(x) + 1} = \sqrt{2x^2+7}$ and $(g\circ f)(x) = f(x)^2 + 3 = (2x+1) + 3 = 2x+4$, for $x \geq -1/2$ (the domain of f).

16. $(f\circ g)(x) = \sqrt[3]{g(x)^2+1} = \sqrt[3]{(x^3+1)^2+1} = \sqrt[3]{x^6+2x^3+2}$. $(g\circ f)(x) = f(x)^3+1 = (\sqrt[3]{x^2+1})^3 + 1 = (x^2+1) + 1 = x^2 + 2$.

19. $(f\circ g)(x) = 2g(x) - 3 = 2(\dfrac{x+3}{2}) - 3 = (x+3) - 3 = x$. $(g\circ f)(x) = \dfrac{f(x)+3}{2} = \dfrac{(2x-3)+3}{2} = \dfrac{2x}{2} = x$.

22. Let $f(x) = a_n x^n + \ldots + a_o$, $g(x) = b_m x^m + \ldots + b_o$, where a_n and $b_m \neq 0$.
     Then $(fg)(x) = a_n b_m x^{n+m} + \ldots + a_o b_o$ and the degree of the product is $n+m$
     since $a_n b_m \neq 0$.

25. HINT: If f is the function, show that $e(x) = (f(x) + f(-x))/2$ is even, that
     $0(x) = (f(x) - f(-x))/2$ is odd, and that $f(x) = e(x) + 0(x)$.

EXERCISES 1.6, page 40

1. $4-3x > 7+2x \iff -3 > 5x \iff -3/5 > x \iff x \varepsilon (-\infty, -3/5)$.

4. Observing that $|6x-7| \leq 1 \iff -1 \leq 6x-7 \leq 1 \iff 6 \leq 6x \leq 8 \iff 1 \leq x \leq 4/3$,
    the desired solution set of $|6x-7| > 1$ is the complement of $[1,4/3]$, namely
    $(-\infty,1) \cup (4/3,\infty)$. (This is equivalent to the method of #25, Sec. 1.1.)

7. If $x > 1/3$, both denominators are positive and $1/(3x-1) < 2/(x+5) \iff x+5 <$
    $\cdot 6x-2 \iff 7 < 5x \iff 7/5 < x$, yielding the partial solution $(7/5,\infty)$. If
    $-5 < x < 1/3$, $3x-1 < 0$, $x+5 > 0$ and every number in $(-5,1/3)$ satisfies the
    inequality. If $x < -5$, both denominators are negative and, as in the first
    part, the given inequality is equivalent to $7/5 < x$ which is not true for any
    $x < -5$. Hence $(-5,1/3) \cup (7/5,\infty)$ is the solution set.

10. $3x-5y = 10$ is a line with slope $3/5$ and y-intercept -2. There are no sym-
    metries since replacement of x by $-x$ and/or y by $-y$ changes the equation
    and the solution set.

13. $|x+y| = 1$ is satisfied if $x+y = 1$ or $x+y = -1$. Thus the graph consists of
    these 2 parallel lines. The graph is symmetric with respect to the origin
    since replacing x and y by $-x$ and $-y$, respectively, we get $|-x-y| = |-(x+y)|$
    $= |x+y| = 1$, the same equation.

16. A point (x,y) satisfies $x^2 + y^2 < 1$ if, and only if, its distance from $(0,0)$
    is < 1. Thus the graph of W is the set of points inside, but not <u>on</u>, the
    circle $x^2 + y^2 = 1$.

19. Since $C(-4,-3)$ is 9 units from the vertical line $x = 5$, the radius is 9 and
    the equation is $(x+4)^2 + (y+3)^2 = 81$.

22. $m_{AC} = (-5-2)/(2-(-4)) = -7/6$ and the equation is $y-6 = (-7/6)(x-3)$ or
    $7x + 6y - 57 = 0$.

25. Any line parallel to the y-axis has equation $x = $ constant. Since it passes
    through $A(-4,2)$, its equation is $x = -4$.

28. Because of the radical in the denominator, the domain is $\{x: 16 - x^2 > 0\} =$
    $(-4,4)$.

31. If $f(x) = 1/\sqrt{x+1}$, (a) $f(1) = 1/\sqrt{2}$, (b) $f(3) = 1/\sqrt{4} = 1/2$, (c) $f(0) = 1/\sqrt{1} =$
     1, (d) $f(\sqrt{2}-1) = 1/\sqrt{(\sqrt{2}-1)+1} = 1/\sqrt{\sqrt{2}} = 1/\sqrt[4]{2}$, (e) $f(-x) = 1/\sqrt{-x+1}$, (f) $-f(x) =$
     $-1/\sqrt{x+1}$, (g) $f(x^2) = 1/\sqrt{x^2+1}$, (h) $(f(x))^2 = (1/\sqrt{x+1})^2 = 1/(x+1)$.

34. If x is close to -1, the numbers $-1/(x+1)$ are very
     large, positive if $x < -1$, negative if $x > -1$. If
     $|x|$ is very large, then $-1/(x+1)$ is nearly 0.

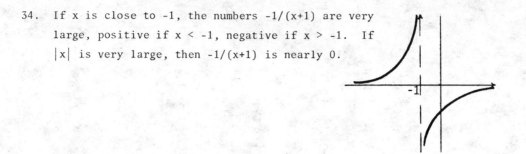

37. $(f+g)(x) = (x^2+4) \pm \sqrt{2x+5}$, $(fg)(x) = (x^2+4)\sqrt{2x+5}$, $(f/g)(x) = (x^2+4)/\sqrt{2x+5}$,
     $(f \circ g)(x) = g(x)^2 + 4 = (2x+5) + 4 = 2x+9$ (for $x \geq -5/2$), $(g \circ f)(x) =$
     $\sqrt{2f(x) + 5} = \sqrt{2x^2 + 13}$.

40. To show f is one-to-one, let $0 \leq a < b$. Multiplying the inequality first by
     a and then by b, we obtain $a^2 < ab$, $ab < b^2$ or $a^2 < b^2 \implies 4a^2 + 3 < 4b^2 + 3$
     or $f(a) < f(b)$. Thus $f(a) \neq f(b)$, and f is one-to-one.

CHAPTER 2

LIMITS AND CONTINUITY OF FUNCTIONS

EXERCISES 2.1, page 45

1. $\lim\limits_{x\to 2} \dfrac{x^2-4}{x-2} = \lim\limits_{x\to 2} \dfrac{(x+2)(x-2)}{x-2} = \lim\limits_{x\to 2} x+2 = 4.$

4. $\lim\limits_{r\to -3} \dfrac{r^2+2r-3}{r^2+7r+12} = \lim\limits_{r\to -3} \dfrac{(r+3)(r-1)}{(r+3)(r+4)} = \lim\limits_{r\to -3} \dfrac{r-1}{r+4} = -4.$

7. $\lim\limits_{k\to 4} \dfrac{k^2-16}{\sqrt{k}-2} = \lim\limits_{k\to 4} \dfrac{(k+4)(k-4)}{\sqrt{k}-2} = \lim\limits_{k\to 4} \dfrac{(k+4)(\sqrt{k}+2)(\sqrt{k}-2)}{\sqrt{k}-2} = \lim\limits_{k\to 4} (k+4)(\sqrt{k}+2)$

 $= (4+4)(\sqrt{4}+2) = 8\cdot 4 = 32.$

10. $\lim\limits_{h\to 2} \dfrac{h^3-8}{h^2-4} = \lim\limits_{h\to 2} \dfrac{(h-2)(h^2+2h+4)}{(h-2)(h+2)} = \lim\limits_{h\to 2} \dfrac{h^2+2h+4}{h+2} = \dfrac{4+4+4}{4} = 3.$

13. $\lim\limits_{x\to -3/2} \dfrac{2x+3}{4x^2+12x+9} = \lim\limits_{x\to -3/2} \dfrac{(2x+3)}{(2x+3)^2} = \lim\limits_{x\to -3/2} \dfrac{1}{2x+3}$, which won't exist since the

 denominator approaches 0 as $x \to -\dfrac{3}{2}$ but the numerator remains 1. The values
 of the function thus get arbitrarily large when x is close to -3/2.

16. $\lim\limits_{t\to 1} \dfrac{(1/t)-1}{t-1} = \lim\limits_{t\to 1} \dfrac{(1-t)/t}{(t-1)} = \lim\limits_{t\to 1} \left(-\dfrac{1}{t}\right) = -1.$

19. (a) As in Example 1, with $P(a,f(a)) = P(a,a^3)$ and $Q(x,f(x)) = Q(x,x^3)$, we

 have $m_{PQ} = \dfrac{x^3-a^3}{x-a} = \dfrac{(x-a)(x^2+ax+a^2)}{(x-a)} = x^2 + ax + a^2$. Then, by (2.2),

 $m = \lim\limits_{x\to a} m_{PQ} = \lim\limits_{x\to a} (x^2 + ax + a^2) = 3a^2.$ (b) With a = 2 we have P(2,8) and

 $m = 3(2^2) = 12$, and the tangent line equation is y-8 = 12(x-2).

22. Here a = 4, and $Q(x,\sqrt{x})$, P(4,2). By (2.2), m =

 $\lim\limits_{x\to 4} m_{PQ} = \lim\limits_{x\to 4} \dfrac{\sqrt{x}-2}{x-4} = \lim\limits_{x\to 4} \dfrac{\sqrt{x}-2}{(\sqrt{x}-2)(\sqrt{x}+2)} = \lim\limits_{x\to 4} \dfrac{1}{\sqrt{x}+2} =$

 $\dfrac{1}{\sqrt{4}+2} = \dfrac{1}{2+2} = \dfrac{1}{4}.$ The tangent line equation is y-2 =

 (1/4)(x-4) or x - 4y + 4 = 0.

25. If P is the origin, then PQ coincides with y=x if Q is to the right of P
 (x > 0), and PQ coincides with y=-x if Q is to the left of P (x < 0).
 As Q approaches P no single limiting line is obtained.

28. HINT: No matter where P and Q are on the graph of f, PQ coincides with the
 graph.

31, 34. The calculations for both exercises are listed in the table below. The
functional values appear as they would on a calculator which displays numbers to 4 decimal place accuracy.

31.

x	$(1 + x)^{1/x}$
.1	2.5937
-.1	2.8680
.01	2.7048
-.01	2.7320
.001	2.7169
-.001	2.7196

34.

x	$(2^x - 2)/(x - 1)$
1.1	1.4355
0.9	1.3393
1.01	1.3911
0.99	1.3815
1.001	1.3868
0.999	1.3858

EXERCISES 2.2, page 52

1. Here $f(x) = 5x-3$, $L = 7$, $a = 2$. Then $|f(x) - L| = |(5x-3)-7| = |5x-10| =$
    $5|x-2|$. Thus $|f(x) - L| < \varepsilon$ if, and only if, $5|x-2| < \varepsilon$ or $|x-2| < \varepsilon/5$.
    So if we choose $\delta = \varepsilon/5$, then for numbers x satisfying $0 < |x-2| < \delta$ we
    have $|f(x) - L| = 5|x-2| < 5\delta = 5(\varepsilon/5) = \varepsilon$, as desired.

4. Here $f(x) = 8x-15$, $L = 17$, $a = 4$. Then $|f(x) - L| = |(8x-15) - 17| =$
    $|8x-32| = 8|x-4|$. Thus $|f(x) - L| < \varepsilon$ if and only if $8|x-4| < \varepsilon$ or $|x-4| <$
    $\varepsilon/8$. So with $\delta = \varepsilon/8$ and $0 < |x-4| < \delta$ we obtain $|f(x) - L| = 8|x-4| < 8\delta$
    $= \varepsilon$.

7. Here $f(x) = 5$, $L = 5$, $a = 3$. $|f(x) - L| = |5-5| = 0$ which is $< \varepsilon$ for all x.
    Thus δ may be any real number here.

9. $|f(x) - L| = |x-\pi|$. So with $\delta = \varepsilon$, $0 < |x-\pi| < \delta \implies |f(x) - L| < \varepsilon$.

10. As in #7 above, δ may be any real number.

13. If $\lim\limits_{x \to -5} \dfrac{1}{x+5} = L$ existed, then given any $\varepsilon > 0$ we could find $\delta > 0$ such that

    if $-5-\delta < x < -5+\delta$, $x \neq -5$ (i.e., $-\delta < x+5 < \delta$, $x+5 \neq 0$) then $L - \varepsilon <$
    $\dfrac{1}{x+5} < L + \varepsilon$ by (2.4). But this is impossible since $1/(x+5)$ can be made
    larger than $L + \varepsilon$ by taking x+5 small enough. (For example, if $L > 0$ then
    $L + \varepsilon > 0$ and $1/(x+5) > L + \varepsilon$ if $0 < x+5 < 1/(L+\varepsilon)$.) Thus, the limit does
    not exist.

16. Informally, with $f(x) = [x]$ if $a < x_1 < a+1$ then $f(x_1) = a$ whereas if $a-1 <$
    $x_2 < a$, then $f(x_2) = a-1$, even if x_1 and x_2 are very close to a. Thus there
    is no single number which all functional values are close to if x is close to
    a. (Compare Figure 1.40.) Formally we prove indirectly that no limit exists.
    If $\lim\limits_{x \to a} f(x) = \lim\limits_{x \to a} [x] = L$ exists where a is an integer, then given any
    positive $\varepsilon \leq 1/2$ we can find $\delta > 0$ such that if $a-\delta < x < a+\delta$, $x \neq a$ then

$|f(x) - L| < \varepsilon \leq 1/2$. Now let x_1 and x_2 satisfy $a-\delta < x_2 < a < x_1 < a+\delta$. Then, as in the 1st sentence $f(x_1) = a$, $f(x_2) = a-1$ and $|f(x_1)-f(x_2)| = |a-(a-1)| = 1$. But, using the triangle inequality we obtain $1 = |f(x_1)-f(x_2)| = |(f(x_1) - L) + (L - f(x_2))| \leq |f(x_1) - L| + |f(x_2) - L| < \varepsilon+\varepsilon < \frac{1}{2} + \frac{1}{2} = 1$ and we have the absurd result, $1 < 1$, which proves our assumption that the limit existed was wrong.

19. We consider the case where $a > 0$. Here, $L = a^3$. The horizontal line $y = a^3-\varepsilon$ intersects the graph of f at the point with abscissa $x_1 = \sqrt[3]{a^3-\varepsilon}$ (obtained by setting $y = a^3-\varepsilon$ in $y = x^3$, and solving for x.) The line $y = a^3+\varepsilon$ intersects the graph when $x = x_2 = \sqrt[3]{a^3+\varepsilon}$. Then any $x \in (x_1,x_2)$ satisfies the condition that the point (x,x^3) on the graph of f lies between the horizontal lines $y = a^3\pm\varepsilon$, i.e. $f(x) \in (a^3-\varepsilon,a^3+\varepsilon)$. To obtain an x-interval of the proper form, $(a-\delta,a+\delta)$, let δ be any number

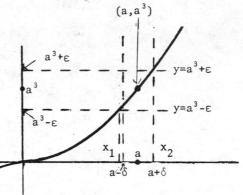

which is positive and less than or equal to the smaller of x_2-a and $a-x_1$. (It can be shown that x_2-a is the smaller.) Then $(a-\delta,a+\delta) \subseteq (x_1,x_2)$ and satisfies (2.4). (The figure shows $\delta = x_2-a$.)

22. Here, $L = (a^2+1)^2$. The horizontal line $y = L-\varepsilon$ intersects the graph of $f(x) = (x^2+1)^2$ when $x = x_1$. To find x_1, we solve $f(x) = L-\varepsilon$ for $x > 0$ (corresponding to the choice of $a > 0$ in the figure). $f(x) = (x^2+1)^2 = L-\varepsilon$ $\Rightarrow (x^2+1) = \sqrt{L-\varepsilon} \Rightarrow x^2 = \sqrt{L-\varepsilon} - 1$ $\Rightarrow x = x_1 = (\sqrt{L-\varepsilon} - 1)^{1/2}$. (NOTE: Since in the discussion of limits ε is a "small" positive number, we may, without loss of generality, assume that $L-\varepsilon > 0$ above.) Similarly, $y = L+\varepsilon$ intersects the graph when $x = x_2 = (\sqrt{L+\varepsilon} - 1)^{1/2}$. Then any $x \in (x_1,x_2)$ satisfies the condition that

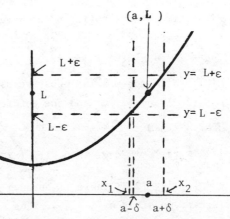

the point $(x,(x^2+1)^2)$ lies between the horizontal lines $y = L \pm \varepsilon = (a^2+1)^2$ $\pm\varepsilon$. Let δ be positive and $\leq$ the smaller of x_2-a and $a-x_1$. Then $(a-\delta,a+\delta) \subset (x_1,x_2)$ and satisfies (2.4).

EXERCISES 2.3, page 60

1. $\lim\limits_{x \to -2} (3x^3-2x+7) = 3(-2)^3 - 2(-2) + 7 = -13$ (by (2.10)).

4. $\lim\limits_{t \to -3} (3t+4)(7t-9) = \lim\limits_{t \to -3} (3t+4) \cdot \lim\limits_{t \to -3} (7t-9) = (3(-3)+4)(7(-3)-9) =$

    $(-5)(-30) = 150$ (by (2.8(iii)) and (2.6)).

7. $\lim\limits_{x \to 7} 0 = 0$ and   10. $\lim\limits_{x \to 15} \sqrt{2} = \sqrt{2}$ both by (2.5).

13. $\lim\limits_{x \to 2} \dfrac{x-2}{x^3-8} = \lim\limits_{x \to 2} \dfrac{x-2}{(x-2)(x^2+2x+4)} = \lim\limits_{x \to 2} \dfrac{1}{x^2+2x+4} = \dfrac{1}{4+4+4} = \dfrac{1}{12}.$

16. $\lim\limits_{x \to -2} \dfrac{x^3+8}{x^4-16} = \lim\limits_{x \to -2} \dfrac{(x+2)(x^2-2x+4)}{(x+2)(x-2)(x^2+4)} = \lim\limits_{x \to -2} \dfrac{(x^2-2x+4)}{(x-2)(x^2+4)} = \dfrac{12}{(-4)(8)} = -\dfrac{3}{8}.$

19. $\lim\limits_{x \to 1} (\dfrac{x^2}{x-1} - \dfrac{1}{x-1}) = \lim\limits_{x \to 1} \dfrac{x^2-1}{x-1} = \lim\limits_{x \to 1} \dfrac{(x+1)(x-1)}{x-1} = \lim\limits_{x \to 1} x+1 = 2.$

22. $\lim\limits_{x \to -8} \dfrac{16x^{2/3}}{4-x^{4/3}} = \dfrac{16(-8)^{2/3}}{4-(-8)^{4/3}} = \dfrac{16(-2)^2}{4-(-2)^4} = \dfrac{64}{-12} = -\dfrac{16}{3}.$

25. $\lim\limits_{h \to 0} \dfrac{4-\sqrt{16+h}}{h} = \lim\limits_{h \to 0} \dfrac{4-\sqrt{16+h}}{h} \dfrac{(4+\sqrt{16+h})}{(4+\sqrt{16+h})} = \lim\limits_{h \to 0} \dfrac{16-(16+h)}{h(4+\sqrt{16+h})} = \lim\limits_{h \to 0} \dfrac{-1}{4+\sqrt{16+h}} = -\dfrac{1}{8}$

28. $\lim\limits_{x \to 6} (x+4)^3(x-6)^2 = (6+4)^3(6-6)^2 = (1000)(0) = 0.$

31. $\lim\limits_{t \to -1} \dfrac{(4t^2+5t-3)^3}{(6t+5)^4} = \dfrac{(4(-1)^2+5(-1)-3)^3}{(6(-1)+5)^4} = \dfrac{(4-5-3)^3}{(-1)^4} = (-4)^3 = -64.$

34. First, from the identity $a^3-b^3 = (a-b)(a^2+ba+b^2)$ we obtain, with $a = \sqrt[3]{x}$ and $b = 2$, $x-8 = (\sqrt[3]{x}-2)(\sqrt[3]{x^2}+2\sqrt[3]{x}+4)$. Thus $\lim\limits_{x \to 8} \dfrac{x-8}{\sqrt[3]{x}-2} = \lim\limits_{x \to 8} (\sqrt[3]{x^2}+2\sqrt[3]{x}+4) = \sqrt[3]{64} + 2\sqrt[3]{8} + 4 = 4 + 2(2) + 4 = 12.$

37. HINT: With $r = m/n$ in lowest terms, recall that $x^r = x^{m/n} = (\sqrt[n]{x})^m$. Then use (2.9) and (2.12) and the conditions there.

40. HINT: $x \neq 0 \Rightarrow x^4 + 4x^2 > 0 \Rightarrow \sqrt{x^4+4x^2+7} > \sqrt{7} > 1 \Rightarrow |x|/\sqrt{x^4+4x^2+7} < |x|.$

43. If $\lim\limits_{x \to a} f(x) = L < 0$, then, if $F(x) = -f(x)$, $\lim\limits_{x \to a} F(x) = -L$ by (2.8(iv)) with $c = -1$. By (2.7) there is an open interval I containing a on which $F(x) > 0$ (except possibly at $x = a$). Thus $F(x) = -f(x) > 0$ or $f(x) < 0$ there and the proof is complete.

EXERCISES 2.4, page 64

1. (a) As $x \to 5^-$, $x < 5$ and $5-x > 0$. Thus such x are in the domain of f.
    $\lim\limits_{x \to 5^-} \sqrt{5-x} = \sqrt{5-5} = 0$. (b) As $x \to 5^+$, $x > 5$ and $5-x < 0$. Thus such x are not
    in the domain of f and $\lim\limits_{x \to 5^+} \sqrt{5-x}$ does not exist. (c) This limit does not
    exist since the right-hand limit does not exist.

4. All three limits exist and equal $(-8)^{2/3} = (-2)^2 = 4$.

7. $\lim\limits_{x \to 0^+} (4 + \sqrt{x}) = 4 + \sqrt{0} = 4$.

10. Note that as $x \to 5/2^-$, $x < 5/2$, $5 - 2x > 0$ and such x are in the domain of f.
    $\lim\limits_{x \to 5/2^-} (\sqrt{5-2x} - x^2) = \sqrt{5-2(5/2)} - (5/2)^2 = 0 - 25/4$. (The right-hand limit,
    however, does not exist for if $x > 5/2$ then $5-2x < 0$, and f is not defined
    for such x.)

13. $\lim\limits_{x \to 2^+} \dfrac{4-x^2}{2-x} = \lim\limits_{x \to 2^+} \dfrac{(2+x)(2-x)}{(2-x)} = \lim\limits_{x \to 2^+} (2+x) = 4$.

16. $\lim\limits_{x \to -10^-} \dfrac{x+10}{\sqrt{(x+10)^2}} = \lim\limits_{x \to -10^-} \dfrac{x+10}{|x+10|} = \lim\limits_{x \to -10^-} \dfrac{x+10}{-(x+10)} = -1$ since, if $x < -10$,
    $x+10$ is negative and $|x+10| = -(x+10)$.

19. $\lim\limits_{x \to -7^+} \dfrac{x+7}{|x+7|} = \lim\limits_{x \to -7^+} \dfrac{x+7}{x+7} = \lim\limits_{x \to -7^+} 1 = 1$ since if $x > -7$ then $x+7 > 0$ and
    $|x+7| = x+7$.

22. The limit does not exist. If $x < 8$ and $x-8$ is small then $1/(x-8)$ is very
    large and negative. See also Exercise 38, Section 2.3 of the text with
    $f(x) = 1$, $g(x) = x-8$ and one-sided limits.

24. $\lim\limits_{x \to 2^-} f(x) = \lim\limits_{x \to 2^-} x^3 = 8$.

    $\lim\limits_{x \to 2^+} f(x) = \lim\limits_{x \to 2^+} (4-2x) = 0$.

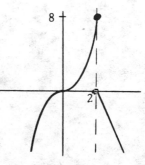

25. $\lim\limits_{x \to -3^+} f(x) = \lim\limits_{x \to -3^+} \sqrt[3]{x+2} = \sqrt[3]{-3+2} = -1$ since if $x > -3$ the second formula in
    the definition of f must be used. $\lim\limits_{x \to -3^-} f(x) = \lim\limits_{x \to -3^-} \dfrac{1}{2-3x} = \dfrac{1}{2-3(-3)} = \dfrac{1}{11}$.

Since the left and right limits differ, $\lim\limits_{x\to-3} f(x)$ does not exist.

28. (a) $\lim\limits_{x\to-1^-} f(x) = \lim\limits_{x\to-1^-} 1-x = 1 - (-1) = 2.$ 28. (graph)

     (b) $\lim\limits_{x\to-1^+} f(x) = \lim\limits_{x\to-1^+} x^3 = (-1)^3 = -1.$

     (c) Since the one-sided limits differ, $\lim\limits_{x\to-1} f(x)$

does not exist.

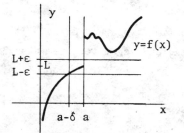

31. Since $(x^4 + x)/x = x^3 + 1$ if $x \neq 0$, all three

     limits exist and equal $0^3 + 1 = 1$.

34. For $n < x < n+1$, $f(x) = 1$ and, thus, $\lim\limits_{x\to n^+} f(x) = \lim\limits_{x\to n^+} 1 = 1$. Similarly, if

     $n-1 < x < n$, $f(x) = 1$ and $\lim\limits_{x\to n^-} f(x) = \lim\limits_{x\to n^-} 1 = 1$. (The value, $f(n) = 0$, has

     <u>absolutely</u> <u>nothing</u> to do with these limits since $x \neq n$ is required for both

     limits.)

37. Recall that if $n < x < n+1$, then $[x] = n$ so that $\lim\limits_{x\to n^+} [x] = n$. If $n-1 < x$

     $< n$, then $[x] = n-1$ and $\lim\limits_{x\to n^-} [x] = n-1$. Thus $\lim\limits_{x\to n^-} x-[x] = n-(n-1) = 1$, and

     $\lim\limits_{x\to n^+} x-[x] = n-n = 0$.

40. Sketch for right-hand limit.   Sketch for left-hand limit.

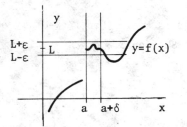

EXERCISES 2.5, page 72

1. $\lim\limits_{x\to4} (\sqrt{2x-5} + 3x) = \lim\limits_{x\to4} \sqrt{2x-5} + \lim\limits_{x\to4} 3x = \sqrt{3} + 12 = f(4).$

4. $f(x) = 1/x$ is continuous at every number $a \neq 0$ **since it is** the

     quotient of the continuous functions 1 and x, and if $a \neq 0$, the denominator

     is nonzero at a.

7. f is defined on [4,8] since $x-4 \geq 0$ for all x there. If $c \in (4,8)$ then

$\lim\limits_{x \to c} f(x) = \lim\limits_{x \to c} \sqrt{x-4} = \sqrt{c-4} = f(c)$ by (2.6) and (2,13). Similarly $\lim\limits_{x \to 4^+} \sqrt{x-4}$

$= 0 = f(4)$ and $\lim\limits_{x \to 8^-} \sqrt{x-4} = 2 = f(8)$. Thus f is continuous on [4,8].

10. If $c \in (1,3)$ then $\lim\limits_{x \to c} f(x) = \lim\limits_{x \to c} \dfrac{1}{x-1} = \dfrac{1}{c-1} = f(c)$ by (2.6) and (2.8)(iii),

valid since $1 < c < 3 \Longrightarrow 0 < c-1$.

13. The domain of f is $\{x: 2x-3 \geq 0\} = [3/2,\infty)$. If $a \in (3/2,\infty)$, $\lim\limits_{x \to a} f(x) =$

$\sqrt{2a-3} + a^2 = f(a)$. Also, $\lim\limits_{x \to 3/2^+} f(x) = \sqrt{2(3/2)-3} + (3/2)^2 = 9/4 = f(3/2)$.

Thus f is continuous throughout its domain.

16. The domain of f is (-1,1), and f is continuous there by the quotient theorem
for continuous functions, valid since the numerator is a polynomial and the
denominator is continuous by (2.13).

19. As a rational function, f is continuous at every number in its domain.
Since the denominator $x^3-x^2 = x^2(x-1)$ is 0 when x = 0 and x = 1, the domain
of f is $\{x: x \neq 0,1\} = (-\infty,0) \cup (0,1) \cup (1,\infty)$.

22. The numerator, $\sqrt{9-x}$, is continuous by (2.13) throughout its domain which is
$\{x: 9-x \geq 0\} = \{x: 9 \geq x\} = (-\infty,9]$. Similarly the denominator, $\sqrt{x-6}$, is continuous on $[6,\infty)$ but is 0 at x = 6. Thus both are continuous and the denominator is nonzero on $(-\infty,9] \cap (6,\infty) = (6,9]$ where f is continuous by the
quotient theorem.

25. From #29, Sec. 2.4, $\lim\limits_{x \to 2} f(x) = \lim\limits_{x \to 2} \dfrac{x^2-4}{x-2} = \lim\limits_{x \to 2} \dfrac{(x-2)(x+2)}{x-2} = \lim\limits_{x \to 2} x+2 = 4$,

whereas f(2) = 3. Since $\lim\limits_{x \to 2} f(x) \neq f(2)$, f is discontinuous at x = 2 but is

continuous at all other real numbers by the quotient theorem.

28. From #32, Sec. 2.4, we first note that $4 - 4x - x^2 + x^3 = 4(1-x) - x^2(1-x)$

$= (4-x^2)(1-x)$. Thus $\lim\limits_{x \to 1} f(x) = \lim\limits_{x \to 1} \dfrac{(4-x^2)(1-x)}{1-x} = \lim\limits_{x \to 1} 4-x^2 = 3$ which is

$\neq f(1) = 4$. Thus f is discontinuous at x = 1, but is continuous at all other
real numbers by the quotient theorem.

31. f is continuous on (-3,3) by the quotient theorem since the denominator is
non-zero there. (It is 0 only at $x = \pm3$.) For continuity of f at x = 3, we
must have $\lim\limits_{x \to 3^-} f(x) = f(3)$. Since f(3) = d, we find d by computing this

limit. $\lim\limits_{x \to 3^-} f(x) = \lim\limits_{x \to 3^-} \dfrac{9-x^2}{4-\sqrt{x^2+7}} = \lim\limits_{x \to 3^-} \dfrac{9-x^2}{4-\sqrt{x^2+7}} \cdot \dfrac{4+\sqrt{x^2+7}}{4+\sqrt{x^2+7}} =$

$\lim\limits_{x \to 3^-} \dfrac{(9-x^2)(4+\sqrt{x^2+7})}{16-(x^2+7)} = \lim\limits_{x \to 3^-} (4 + \sqrt{x^2+7}) = (4 + \sqrt{9+7}) = 8$. Hence, d = 8.

For continuity at x = -3, we need $\lim_{x \to -3^+} f(x) = f(-3) = c$. As above, $\lim_{x \to -3^+}$

$f(x) = 8$ and, thus, $c = 8$ also.

34. (a) $x \in [n, n+1) \Rightarrow [x] = n \Rightarrow f(x) = (x-[x])^2 = (x-n)^2$. As a polynomial, f is continuous on the open interval $(n, n+1)$. Since $\lim_{x \to n^+} f(x) = \lim_{x \to n^+} (x-n)^2$

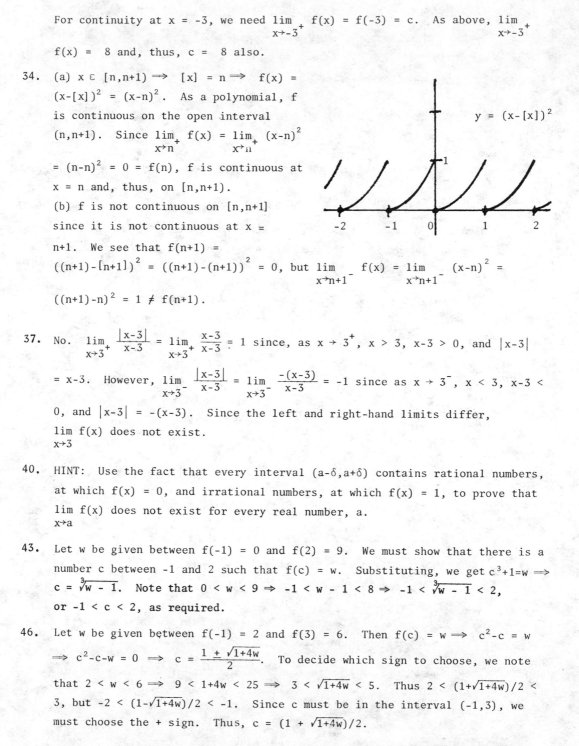

$y = (x-[x])^2$

$= (n-n)^2 = 0 = f(n)$, f is continuous at

$x = n$ and, thus, on $[n, n+1)$.

(b) f is not continuous on $[n, n+1]$

since it is not continuous at x =

n+1. We see that $f(n+1) =$

$((n+1)-[n+1])^2 = ((n+1)-(n+1))^2 = 0$, but $\lim_{x \to n+1^-} f(x) = \lim_{x \to n+1^-} (x-n)^2 =$

$((n+1)-n)^2 = 1 \neq f(n+1)$.

37. No. $\lim_{x \to 3^+} \frac{|x-3|}{x-3} = \lim_{x \to 3^+} \frac{x-3}{x-3} = 1$ since, as $x \to 3^+$, $x > 3$, $x-3 > 0$, and $|x-3|$

$= x-3$. However, $\lim_{x \to 3^-} \frac{|x-3|}{x-3} = \lim_{x \to 3^-} \frac{-(x-3)}{x-3} = -1$ since as $x \to 3^-$, $x < 3$, $x-3 <$

0, and $|x-3| = -(x-3)$. Since the left and right-hand limits differ,

$\lim_{x \to 3} f(x)$ does not exist.

40. HINT: Use the fact that every interval $(a-\delta, a+\delta)$ contains rational numbers, at which $f(x) = 0$, and irrational numbers, at which $f(x) = 1$, to prove that $\lim_{x \to a} f(x)$ does not exist for every real number, a.

43. Let w be given between $f(-1) = 0$ and $f(2) = 9$. We must show that there is a number c between -1 and 2 such that $f(c) = w$. Substituting, we get $c^3+1=w \Rightarrow$ $c = \sqrt[3]{w - 1}$. Note that $0 < w < 9 \Rightarrow -1 < w - 1 < 8 \Rightarrow -1 < \sqrt[3]{w - 1} < 2$, or $-1 < c < 2$, as required.

46. Let w be given between $f(-1) = 2$ and $f(3) = 6$. Then $f(c) = w \Rightarrow c^2-c = w$ $\Rightarrow c^2-c-w = 0 \Rightarrow c = \frac{1 \pm \sqrt{1+4w}}{2}$. To decide which sign to choose, we note that $2 < w < 6 \Rightarrow 9 < 1+4w < 25 \Rightarrow 3 < \sqrt{1+4w} < 5$. Thus $2 < (1+\sqrt{1+4w})/2 <$ 3, but $-2 < (1-\sqrt{1+4w})/2 < -1$. Since c must be in the interval $(-1,3)$, we must choose the + sign. Thus, $c = (1 + \sqrt{1+4w})/2$.

48. Let $f(x) = x^5 - 3x^4 - 2x^3 - x + 1$. Then $f(0) = 1$, $f(1) = -4$ and f is continuous on $[0,1]$. If we choose $w = 0$, w lies between $f(0)$ and $f(1)$, and, by

the intermediate value theorem, there exists a number c ε (0,1) such that f(c) = 0. This number, c, is a solution of the given equation.

EXERCISES 2.6, page 74

1. $\lim\limits_{x\to 3} \dfrac{5x+11}{\sqrt{x+1}} = \dfrac{5(3)+11}{\sqrt{3+1}} = \dfrac{26}{2} = 13.$

4. $\lim\limits_{x\to 4^-} (x - \sqrt{16-x^2}) = 4 - \sqrt{16-4^2} = 4.$ (The right-hand limit, however, does not exist.)

7. $\lim\limits_{x\to 2} \dfrac{x^4-16}{x^2-x-2} = \lim\limits_{x\to 2} \dfrac{(x+2)(x-2)(x^2+4)}{(x-2)(x+1)} = \lim\limits_{x\to 2} \dfrac{(x+2)(x^2+4)}{x+1} = \dfrac{(4)(8)}{3} = \dfrac{32}{3}.$

10. $\lim\limits_{x\to 5} \dfrac{(1/x)-(1/5)}{x-5} = \lim\limits_{x\to 5} \dfrac{(5-x)/5x}{x-5} = \lim\limits_{x\to 5} \dfrac{-1}{5x} = -\dfrac{1}{25}.$

13. $\lim\limits_{x\to 3^+} \dfrac{3-x}{|3-x|} = \lim\limits_{x\to 3^+} \dfrac{3-x}{-(3-x)} = -1$ since $x > 3 \Rightarrow 3-x < 0 \Rightarrow |3-x| = -(3-x).$

16. $\lim\limits_{x\to -3} \sqrt[3]{\dfrac{x+3}{x^3+27}} = \lim\limits_{x\to -3} \sqrt[3]{\dfrac{x+3}{(x+3)(x^2-3x+9)}} = \lim\limits_{x\to -3} \sqrt[3]{\dfrac{1}{x^2-3x+9}} = \sqrt[3]{\dfrac{1}{9+9+9}} = \sqrt[3]{\dfrac{1}{27}} = \dfrac{1}{3}.$

19. $\lim\limits_{x\to 2^+} \dfrac{\sqrt{(x-2)^2}}{2-x} = \lim\limits_{x\to 2^+} \dfrac{|x-2|}{2-x} = \lim\limits_{x\to 2^+} \dfrac{x-2}{2-x} = \lim\limits_{x\to 2^+} (-1) = -1$ since as $x \to 2^+$, $x > 2$, $x-2 > 0$ and $|x-2| = x-2.$

22. If $2 < x < 3$, then [x] = 2. Thus $\lim\limits_{x\to 3^-} [x] = 2$ and $\lim\limits_{x\to 3^-} [x] - x^2 = 2-9 = -7.$

(However, in #27, $\lim\limits_{x\to 3^+} [x] = 3$ and $\lim\limits_{x\to 3^+} [x] - x^2 = 3-9 = -6.$)

25. If c is any real number, $\lim\limits_{x\to c} f(x) = \lim\limits_{x\to c} (2x^4 - \sqrt[3]{x} + 1) = 2c^4 - \sqrt[3]{c} + 1 = f(c)$ by limit theorems of Section 3. Thus f is continuous.

28. $\sqrt{x}$ requires $x \geq 0$, and x^2-1 in the denominator means $x = 1$ must be excluded. Thus the domain of f is $[0,1) \cup (1,\infty)$ where f is continuous by the theorems of Sections 3 and 5.

31. f is a rational function which is continuous everywhere except at the points where the denominator is 0. Here $x^2-2x = x(x-2) = 0$ at $x = 0$ and $x = 2$ where f is discontinuous.

34. Let $f(x) = x^5 + 7x^2 - 3x - 5$. Then $f(-2) = -32 + 28 + 6 - 5 = -3$, $f(-1) =$
     $-1 + 7 + 3 - 5 = 4$, and f is continuous on $[-2,-1]$. Choosing $w = 0$ and
     noting that $f(-2) < 0 < f(-1)$, by the intermediate value theorem there
     exists a number c between -2 and -1 such that $f(c) = 0$. Thus, c is the
     desired solution of the given equation.

EXERCISES 3.1, page 79

1. By (3.1) the slope at $P(a,f(a) = P(a,2-a^3)$ is

$$m = \lim_{h \to 0} \frac{f(a+h)-f(a)}{h} = \lim_{h \to 0} \frac{(2-(a+h)^3)-(2-a^3)}{h}$$

$$= \lim_{h \to 0} \frac{-a^3 - 3a^2h - 3ah^2 - h^3 + a^3}{h}$$

$$= \lim_{h \to 0} \frac{-h(3a^2 + 3ah + h^2)}{h} = \lim_{h \to 0} -(3a^2 + 3ah + h^2)$$

$$= -3a^2.$$

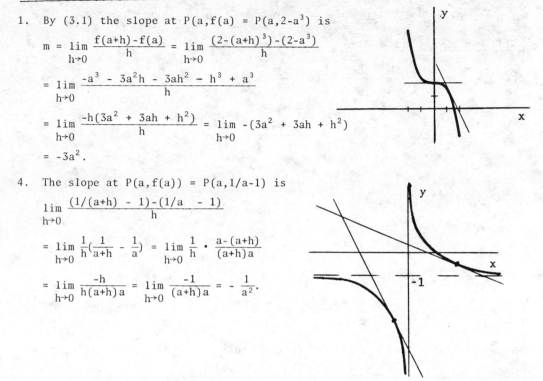

4. The slope at $P(a,f(a)) = P(a,1/a-1)$ is

$$\lim_{h \to 0} \frac{(1/(a+h) - 1)-(1/a - 1)}{h}$$

$$= \lim_{h \to 0} \frac{1}{h}(\frac{1}{a+h} - \frac{1}{a}) = \lim_{h \to 0} \frac{1}{h} \cdot \frac{a-(a+h)}{(a+h)a}$$

$$= \lim_{h \to 0} \frac{-h}{h(a+h)a} = \lim_{h \to 0} \frac{-1}{(a+h)a} = - \frac{1}{a^2}.$$

7. The velocity at $t = a$ is $\lim_{h \to 0} \frac{f(a+h)-f(a)}{h}$ where $f(t)$ is the distance function.

If $v(a)$ is the velocity at $t = a$, we have, with $f(t) = 112t - 16t^2$,

$$v(a) = \lim_{h \to 0} \frac{[112(a+h) - 16(a+h)^2] - [112a - 16a^2]}{h}$$

$$= \lim_{h \to 0} \frac{112h - 32ah - 16h^2}{h} = \lim_{h \to 0} 112 - 32a - 16h$$

$$= 112 - 32a \text{ ft/sec.}$$

Thus $v(2) = 112-64 = 48$, $v(3) = 112-96 = 16$, $v(4) = 112-128 = -16$ ft/sec. (i.e. downward motion at $t = 4$). The maximum height occurs when $v(a) = 0 \iff$ $112-32a = 0 \iff a = 112/32 = 7/2$ sec. The object hits the ground when the distance above it is 0, i.e. when $f(t) = 0$. Solving: $112t - 16t^2 = 0 \iff$ $16t(7-t) = 0 \iff t = 0$ or $t = 7$. So, it leaves the ground at $t = 0$ and re- turns to strike it at $t = 7$. Impact velocity is $v(7)=112-32(7) = -112$ ft/sec.

10. If $f(t) = c$, then the velocity at any time $t = a$ is $\lim_{h \to 0} \frac{f(a+h) - f(a)}{h} =$

$\lim\limits_{h\to 0} \dfrac{c-c}{h} = \lim\limits_{h\to 0} 0 = 0$. The "motion" of the particle is to remain motionless

at the point corresponding to the number c on the number line.

EXERCISES 3.2, page 85

1. $f'(x) = \lim\limits_{h\to 0} \dfrac{f(x+h)-f(x)}{h} = \lim\limits_{h\to 0} \dfrac{37-37}{h} = \lim\limits_{h\to 0} 0 = 0$ for all x.

4. $f'(x) = \lim\limits_{h\to 0} \dfrac{(7(x+h)^2-5)-(7x^2-5)}{h} = \lim\limits_{h\to 0} \dfrac{7(x^2+2xh+h^2)-7x^2}{h} = \lim\limits_{h\to 0} \dfrac{14xh+7h^2}{h}$

    $= \lim\limits_{h\to 0} 14x + 7h = 14x$ for all x.

7. $f'(x) = \lim\limits_{h\to 0} \dfrac{1}{h}\left[\dfrac{1}{x+h-2} - \dfrac{1}{x-2}\right] = \lim\limits_{h\to 0} \dfrac{1}{h}\left[\dfrac{(x-2)-(x+h-2)}{(x+h-2)(x-2)}\right] = \lim\limits_{h\to 0} \dfrac{1}{h}\dfrac{-h}{(x+h-2)(x-2)}$

    $= \lim\limits_{h\to 0} \dfrac{-1}{(x+h-2)(x-2)} = \dfrac{-1}{(x-2)^2}$, for $x \neq 2$.

10. $f'(x) = \lim\limits_{h\to 0} \dfrac{1}{h}\left[\dfrac{1}{2(x+h)} - \dfrac{1}{2x}\right] = \dfrac{1}{2}\lim\limits_{h\to 0} \dfrac{1}{h}\left[\dfrac{x-(x+h)}{(x+h)x}\right] = \dfrac{1}{2}\lim\limits_{h\to 0} \dfrac{1}{h}\dfrac{-h}{(x+h)x}$

    $= \dfrac{1}{2}\lim\limits_{h\to 0} \dfrac{-1}{(x+h)x} = -\dfrac{1}{2x^2}$, for $x \neq 0$.

13. If $y = f(x)$, then $D_x y$ is just $f'(x)$. Thus,

$$D_x y = \lim\limits_{h\to 0} \frac{[2(x+h)^3 - 4(x+h) + 1] - [2x^3 - 4x + 1]}{h}$$

$$= \lim\limits_{h\to 0} \frac{[(2x^3 + 6x^2h + 6xh^2 + 2h^3) - (4x + 4h) + 1] - [2x^3 - 4x + 1]}{h}$$

$$= \lim\limits_{h\to 0} \frac{6x^2h + 6xh^2 + 2h^3 - 4h}{h} = \lim\limits_{h\to 0} 6x^2 + 6xh + 2h^2 - 4 = 6x^2 - 4.$$

16. $f'(a) = \lim\limits_{x\to a} \dfrac{f(x)-f(a)}{x-a} = \lim\limits_{x\to a} \dfrac{\sqrt{2}\,x - \sqrt{2}\,a}{x-a} = \lim\limits_{x\to a} \dfrac{\sqrt{2}(x-a)}{x-a} = \lim\limits_{x\to a} \sqrt{2} = \sqrt{2}.$

19. $f'(a) = \lim\limits_{x\to a} \dfrac{[1/(x+5) - 1/(a+5)]}{x-a} = \lim\limits_{x\to a} \dfrac{(a+5) - (x+5)}{(x-a)(x+5)(a+5)} = \lim\limits_{x\to a} \dfrac{a-x}{(x-a)(x+5)(a+5)}$

    $= \lim\limits_{x\to a} \dfrac{-1}{(x+5)(a+5)} = -\dfrac{1}{(a+5)^2}$.

22. First note that $\lim\limits_{h\to 0^+} [5+h] = 5$ and $\lim\limits_{h\to 0^-} [5+h] = 4$. Then, $\lim\limits_{h\to 0^+} \dfrac{f(5+h)-f(5)}{h}$

$= \lim\limits_{h\to 0^+} \dfrac{[5+h] - [5]}{h} = \lim\limits_{h\to 0^+} \dfrac{5-5}{h} = 0$, but $\lim\limits_{h\to 0^-} \dfrac{[5+h]-[5]}{h} = \lim\limits_{h\to 0^-} \dfrac{4-5}{h} = \lim\limits_{h\to 0^-} \dfrac{-1}{h}$

which does not exist. Both limits must exist and be equal in order for f to

be differentiable at 5. Thus f is not differentiable there.

28. The graph of f is the line $y = 2x - 1$ for $x \leq 1$, and the parabola $y = x^2$ for $x > 1$. These meet continuously at the point $(1,1)$. $x < 1 \Rightarrow f'(x) =$

$$\lim_{h \to 0} \frac{f(x+h) - f(x)}{h}$$

$$= \lim_{h \to 0} \frac{[2(x+h) - 1] - [2x-1]}{h}$$

$$= \lim_{h \to 0} \frac{2h}{h} = 2. \quad x > 1 \Rightarrow f'(x) = 2x.$$

(See Exercise 15.) To see if f is differentiable at $x = 1$, we must compute
the right-hand and left-hand derivatives
there since f is defined by different
formulas on either side of $x = 1$. Note that $f(1) = 2(1) - 1 = 1$, $f(1+h) = 2(1+h) - 1 = 1 + 2h$ if $h < 0$, and $f(1+h) = (1+h)^2 = 1 + 2h + h^2$ if $h > 0$.

The left-hand derivative is $\displaystyle\lim_{h \to 0^-} \frac{f(1+h) - f(1)}{h} = \lim_{h \to 0^-} \frac{(1+2h) - 1}{h} =$

$\displaystyle\lim_{h \to 0^-} \frac{2h}{h} = 2.$ The right-hand derivative is $\displaystyle\lim_{h \to 0^+} \frac{f(1+h) - f(1)}{h} =$

$\displaystyle\lim_{h \to 0^+} \frac{(1+2h+h^2) - 1}{h} = \lim_{h \to 0^+} \frac{2h+h^2}{h} = \lim_{h \to 0^+} (2+h) = 2.$ Since both exist and

are equal, $f'(1)$ exists and $f'(1) = 2$. Hence the domain of f' is $\mathbb{R}$.

31. Hint: $x > 0 \Rightarrow |x| = x$, and $x < 0 \Rightarrow |x| = -x$.

EXERCISES 3.3, page 93

1. $f'(x) = D_x(10x^2 + 9x - 4) = D_x(10x^2) + D_x(9x) - D_x(4) = 10\,D_x(x^2) + 9\,D_x(x)$

   $- D_x(4) = 10(2x) + 9(1) - 0 = 20x + 9.$

4. $f'(t) = D_t(12 - 3t^4 + 4t^6) = D_t(12) - D_t(3t^4) + D_t(4t^6) = D_t(12) - 3\,D_t(t^4)$

   $+ 4\,D_t(t^6) = 0 - 3(4t^3) + 4(6t^5) = -12t^3 + 24t^5.$

7. $h'(r) = D_r(r^2(3r^4 - 7r + 2)) = D_r(3r^6 - 7r^3 + 2r^2) = 3(6r^5) - 7(3r^2) + 2(2r)$

   $= 18r^5 - 21r^2 + 4r.$

10. $h'(x) = D_x\left(\dfrac{8x^2 - 6x + 11}{x-1}\right) = \dfrac{(x-1)D_x(8x^2 - 6x + 11) - (8x^2 - 6x + 11)D_x(x-1)}{(x-1)^2}$

    $= [(x-1)(16x-6) - (8x^2 - 6x + 11)(1)]/(x-1)^2$

    $= (16x^2 - 6x - 16x + 6 - 8x^2 + 6x - 11)/(x-1)^2$

    $= (8x^2 - 16x - 5)/(x-1)^2$

13. $D_x(3x^3 - 2x^2 + 4x - 7) = D_x(3x^3) + D_x(-2x^2) + D_x(4x) + D_x(-7) = 3(3x^2) +$

$(-2)(2x) + 4(1) + 0 = 9x^2 - 4x + 4$.

16. $D_x(2x + 1/2x) = D_x(2x) + D_x((1/2)x^{-1}) = 2 + (1/2)(-1)x^{-2} = 2 - \dfrac{1}{2x^2}$.

19. $D_v\dfrac{(v^3-1)}{(v^3+1)} = \dfrac{(v^3+1)D_v(v^3-1) - (v^3-1)D_v(v^3+1)}{(v^3+1)^2} = \dfrac{(v^3+1)(3v^2) - (v^3-1)(3v^2)}{(v^3+1)^2}$

   $= \dfrac{6v^2}{(v^3+1)^2}$.

22. $D_x(1 + 1/x + 1/x^2 + 1/x^3) = D_x(1) + D_x(x^{-1}) + D_x(x^{-2}) + D_x(x^{-3})$

   $= 0 - x^{-2} - 2x^{-3} - 3x^{-4} = -(1/x^2 + 2/x^3 + 3/x^4)$.

25. $D_s((3s)^{-4}) = D_s(3^{-4}s^{-4}) = 3^{-4}D_s(s^{-4}) = 3^{-4}(-4)s^{-5} = -4/(81s^5) = -(4/81)s^{-5}$.

28. First note that if $f = g$ in the product rule we get $(f^2)' = 2ff'$. Here

   $f(r) = (5r-4)^{-1} = \dfrac{1}{5r-4}$ and $f'(r) = \dfrac{(5r-4)D_r(1) - 1 \cdot D_r(5r-4)}{(5r-4)^2} = \dfrac{-5}{(5r-4)^2}$.

   Combining these calculations gives us $D_r(5r-4)^{-2} = 2(5r-4)^{-1}(-5(5r-4)^{-2})$

   $= -10(5r-4)^{-3}$.

31. $D_x(\dfrac{2x^3 - 7x^2 + 4x + 3}{x^2}) = D_x(2x - 7 + 4x^{-1} + 3x^{-2}) = 2 - 4x^{-2} - 6x^{-3}$.

34. (a) $D_x(\dfrac{x^2+1}{x^4}) = \dfrac{x^4(2x) - (x^2+1)(4x^3)}{x^8} = -\dfrac{2x^2 + 4}{x^5}$.

   (b) $D_x((x^2+1)x^{-4}) = (x^2+1)(-4x^{-5}) + x^{-4}(2x) = -2x^{-3} - 4x^{-5} = -(2x^2 + 4)x^{-5}$,

   the same as (a).

37. Grouping fgh as (fg)h we have by the product rule for 2 functions: $D_x(fgh)$

   $= D_x((fg)h) = (fg)h' + h(fg)' = fgh' + h(fg' + g'f) = fgh' + fhg' + hgf'$.

40. Using #37 with $f(x) = 3x^4 - 10x^2 + 8$, $g(x) = 2x^2 - 10$, $h(x) = 6x + 7$, we

   obtain $y' = (3x^4 - 10x^2 + 8)(2x^2 - 10)(6) + (3x^4 - 10x^2 + 8)(6x + 7)(4x) +$

   $(6x + 7)(2x^2 - 10)(12x^3 - 20x)$.

43. Here $y' = 3x^2 + 4x - 4$. (a) The tangent line is horizontal when $y' = 0$.

   $3x^2 + 4x - 4 = (3x-2)(x+2) = 0$ if $x = 2/3$ and $x = -2$. (b) The given line,

   $2y + 8x - 5 = 0$ has slope -4. The tangent line is parallel to it when $y' =$

   -4. $3x^2 + 4x - 4 = -4 \iff 3x^2 + 4x = x(3x+4) = 0 \implies x = 0$ and $x = -4/3$.

46. The velocity $v(t) = D_t f(t) = D_t(3t^5 - 5t^3) = 15t^4 - 15t^2 = 15t^2(t^2-1)$.

   (a) Motion is in the positive direction when $v(t) > 0$. Since $15t^2 \geq 0$, this

   reduces to the condition $t^2 - 1 > 0$ or $t^2 > 1$, which has solution $t > 1$ or

   $t < -1$.

   (b) Motion is in the negative direction when $v(t) < 0$ or $-1 < t < 1$.

   (c) $v(t) = 0$ at $t = -1, 0, 1$.

49. $f(x) = x^3 - x^2 + x + 1 \implies f'(x) = 3x^2 - 2x + 1$. To find where the graphs of

$f(x)$ and $f'(x)$ cross (intersect), we set $f(x) = f'(x)$ and solve for x.
$f(x) = f'(x) \iff x^3 - x^2 + x + 1 = 3x^2 - 2x + 1 \iff x^3 - 4x^2 + 3x = 0 \iff$
$x(x^2 - 4x + 3) = x(x-1)(x-3) = 0$. The solutions are $x = 0,1,3$.

52. Here, $y' = 3x^2$. The given line has slope 16/3. A tangent line to $y = x^3$ is
parallel to the given line when $y' = 16/3 \iff 3x^2 = 16/3 \iff x^2 = 16/9 \iff$
$x = \pm 4/3$. With $x = 4/3$, $y = x^3 = 64/27$, and, since the slope is 16/3, the
tangent line here is: $y - \frac{64}{27} = \frac{16}{3}(x - \frac{4}{3})$, or $144x - 27y = 128$. With
$x = -4/3$, $y = -64/27$ and the other tangent line is $y + \frac{64}{27} = \frac{16}{3}(x + \frac{4}{3})$ or
$144x - 27y = -128$.

55. The velocity $v(t) = s'(t) = 2 + 2t$.   (a) $v(1) = 4$, $v(4) = 10$, $v(8) = 18$
(ft/sec).   (b) $s(t) = 50 \iff 6 + 2t + t^2 = 50 \iff t^2 + 2t - 44 = 0$. By
the quadratic formula, $t = (-2 \pm \sqrt{4 - 4(-44)})/2 = (-2 \pm \sqrt{180})/2 = (-2 \pm 6\sqrt{5})/2$
$= -1 \pm 3\sqrt{5}$ sec. Since $0 \le t \le 10$, we must choose only the "+" sign. Thus
$t = -1 + 3\sqrt{5}$ and $v(-1 + 3\sqrt{5}) = 2 + 2(-1 + 3\sqrt{5}) = 6\sqrt{5}$.

EXERCISES 3.4, page 101

1. (a) $\Delta y = f(x+\Delta x) - f(x) = [2(x+\Delta x)^2 - 4(x+\Delta x) + 5] - [2x^2-4x+5]$
$= [2x^2+4x\Delta x + 2(\Delta x)^2 - 4x - 4\Delta x + 5] - [2x^2-4x+5]$
$= 4x\Delta x + 2(\Delta x)^2 - 4\Delta x$.
(b) $x = 2$, $\Delta x = -0.2 \implies \Delta y = 4(2)(-0.2) + 2(-0.2)^2 - 4(-0.2) = -1.6 + 0.08$
$+ 0.8 = -0.72$.

4. (a) $\Delta y = f(x+\Delta x) - f(x) = \frac{1}{2+x+\Delta x} - \frac{1}{2+x} = \frac{(2+x) - (2+x+\Delta x)}{(2+x+\Delta x)(2+x)} = \frac{-\Delta x}{(2+x+\Delta x)(2+x)}$.
(b) $x = 0$, $\Delta x = -0.03 \implies \Delta y = \frac{-(-0.03)}{(2+0-0.03)(2+0)} = \frac{0.03}{(1.97)(2)} = \frac{0.03}{3.94} \approx 0.0076$.

7. (a) $\Delta y = \frac{1}{x+\Delta x} - \frac{1}{x} = \frac{x-(x+\Delta x)}{x(x+\Delta x)} = -\frac{\Delta x}{x(x+\Delta x)}$.
(b) $dy = D_x y \, \Delta x = -\frac{1}{x^2} \Delta x$.
(c) $dy - \Delta y = -\frac{\Delta x}{x^2} + \frac{\Delta x}{x(x+\Delta x)} = \frac{\Delta x}{x}\left(\frac{1}{x+\Delta x} - \frac{1}{x}\right) = \frac{\Delta x}{x}\left(\frac{-\Delta x}{x(x+\Delta x)}\right) = -\frac{\Delta x^2}{x^2(x+\Delta x)}$.

10. (a) $\Delta y = f(x+\Delta x) - f(x) = 8 - 8 = 0$.   (b) $D_x y = D_x 8 = 0 \implies dy = D_x y \, \Delta x =$
$0(\Delta x) = 0$.   (c) $\Delta y - dy = 0 - 0 = 0$.

13. Let $y = f(x)$. The change $\Delta y = f(1.03) - f(1)$ is to be estimated. Here
$x = 1$, $x+\Delta x = 1.03$, so $\Delta x = .03$. **Therefore**, $\Delta y \approx dy = f'(x)\Delta x = f'(1)(.03)$.
$f'(x) = 20x^4 - 24x^3 + 6x \implies f'(1) = 2$. Thus $\Delta y \approx 2(.03) = .06$.

16. $dS = F'(t)\Delta t = D_t(\frac{1}{2-t^2})\Delta t = \frac{2t}{(2-t^2)^2} \Delta t$. If t changes from 1 to 1.02, we
take $t = 1$, $\Delta t = .02$. Thus $\Delta S \approx dS = F'(1)\Delta t = \frac{2}{(2-1^2)^2}(.02) = 2(.02) = .04$.

18. If A is the area of the square of side x, then $A = x^2$ where $x = 1'$ with

error Δx where $|\Delta x| \leq \frac{1}{16}{}'' = \frac{1}{192}{}'$. The actual error $\Delta A \approx dA = 2x\Delta x$ so that

$|\Delta A| \approx |dA| = 2|\Delta x| \leq \frac{2}{192} = \frac{1}{96}$ sq. ft. The last figure is the maximum pos-

sible error. The average error is $\approx dA/A \approx (1/96)/1^2 = 1/96$. The % error

is $\approx \frac{1}{96} \cdot 100 \approx 1.04\%$.

19. If V is the volume of a cube of edge x, then $V = x^3$. Here $x = 10$, $\Delta x = .1$.

Thus $\Delta V \approx dV = 3x^2\Delta x = 300(.1) = 30$ in^3. Exactly, $\Delta V = 10.1^3 - 10^3 =$

$1030.301 - 1000 = 30.301$ in^3.

22. If r is the radius of the cylinder and hemisphere, the silo volume is the

volume of the cylinder + the volume of the hemisphere $= \pi r^2 h + \frac{2}{3}\pi r^3$. If C

is the circumference of the cylinder then $C = 2\pi r$, or $r = C/2\pi$, and $C =$

$30 \pm .5$ ft. So, in terms of C, using $h = 50$, the silo volume is $V(C) =$

$50\pi(\frac{C}{2\pi})^2 + \frac{2}{3}\pi(\frac{C}{2\pi})^3 = \frac{25}{2\pi}C^2 + \frac{1}{12\pi^2}C^3$ and $V(30) =$

$\frac{25}{2\pi}(30)^2 + \frac{1}{12\pi^2}(30)^3 = \frac{900}{2\pi}(25\pi + 5) \approx 3808.96$ ft^3.

The error in this calculation is $\Delta V \approx dV = V'(C)\Delta C$.
To get the maximum error we can proceed as in #18
above, or, alternately, take $C = 30$, the measured
value, and $\Delta C = 0.5$, the maximum error in C. $V'(C)$

$= \frac{25C}{\pi} + \frac{C^2}{4\pi^2} \Longrightarrow$ the maximum error in V is $V'(30)(.5)$

$= [\frac{25(30)}{\pi} + \frac{900}{4\pi^2}](.5) = \frac{150}{4\pi^2}(10\pi + 3) \approx 130.8$. The

average error is $\approx \frac{dV}{V} = \frac{(10\pi + 3)}{60(5\pi + 1)} \approx 0.0343$, and the % error is $\approx 3.43\%$.

25. Here, we are given the % change in F and are to find the Δs that produces it.

Recall: % change $= \frac{\Delta F}{F}(100) \approx \frac{dF}{F}(100) = \frac{F'(s)\Delta s}{F}(100)$. Let $K = gm_1m_2$, a con-

stant. Then $F(s) = Ks^{-2}$, and $F'(s) = -2Ks^{-3}$, so that $\frac{F'(s)}{F} = \frac{-2Ks^{-3}}{Ks^{-2}} = -\frac{2}{s}$.

Using this above, setting $s = 20$ and setting the result equal to 10 (the de-

sired % change) we obtain: $\frac{-2\Delta s}{20}(100) = 10 \iff -10\Delta s = 10 \iff \Delta s = -1$.

28. Let $f(x) = x^4 - 3x^3 + 4x^2 - 5$ so that $f(2.01)$ is desired. Taking $x = 2$,

$\Delta x = .01$, we know $\Delta y = f(2.01) - f(2) \approx dy = f'(2)(.01)$ or $N = f(2.01) \approx$

$f'(2)(.01) + f(2)$. Now, $f'(x) = 4x^3 - 9x^2 + 8x$, $f'(2) = 4(8) - 9(4) +$

$8(2) = 12$ and $f(2) = 16 - 3(8) + 4(4) - 5 = 3$. Thus $N \approx 12(.01) + 3 = 3.12$.

The exact value of N works out to be 3.12100501.

31. Let P = pressure difference, and r = radius. Then $P = K/r^4 = Kr^{-4}$, where K
     is a constant. A 10% reduction in r means that $\Delta r = dr = -0.1\ r$. Then
     $dP = -4Kr^{-5}dr = -4Kr^{-5}(-0.1\ r) = 0.4Kr^{-4}$. The % change in P is
     $\approx \dfrac{dP}{P}(100) = \dfrac{0.4Kr^{-4}}{Kr^{-4}}(100) = 40\%$.

EXERCISES 3.5, page 108

 1. By (3.29), $f'(x) = 3(x^2 - 3x + 8)^2 \cdot D_x(x^2 - 3x + 8) = 3(x^2 - 3x + 8)^2(2x - 3)$.

 4. $k'(x) = -3(5x^2 - 2x + 1)^{-4} \cdot D_x(5x^2 - 2x + 1) = -3(5x^2 - 2x + 1)^{-4}(10x - 2)$.

 7. $D_x(8x^3 - 2x^2 + x - 7)^5 = 5(8x^3 - 2x^2 + x - 7)^4 \cdot D_x(8x^3 - 2x^2 + x - 7) =$
     $5(8x^3 - 2x^2 + x - 7)^4(24x^2 - 4x + 1)$.

10. $K'(x) = (-1)(3x^2 - 5x + 7)^{-2}\ D_x(3x^2 - 5x + 7) = -(3x^2 - 5x + 7)^{-2}(6x - 5)$.

13. $N'(x) = (6x - 7)^3\ D_x(8x^2 + 9)^2 + (8x^2 + 9)^2\ D_x(6x-7)^3$
     $\quad = (6x - 7)^3 \cdot 2(8x^2 + 9)\ D_x(8x^2 + 9) + (8x^2 + 9)^2 \cdot 3(6x - 7)^2\ D_x(6x-7)$
     $\quad = (6x - 7)^3 \cdot 2(8x^2 + 9)(16x) + (8x^2 + 9)^2 \cdot 3(6x - 7)^2 \cdot 6$
     $\quad = (6x - 7)^2(8x^2 + 9)[32x(6x - 7) + 18(8x^2 + 9)]$
     $\quad = (6x - 7)^2(8x^2 + 9)(336x^2 - 224x + 162)$.

16. $S'(t) = 3\left(\dfrac{3t+4}{6t-7}\right)^2\ D_t\left(\dfrac{3t+4}{6t-7}\right) = 3\left(\dfrac{3t+4}{6t-7}\right)^2\left[\dfrac{(6t-7)(3)-(3t+4)(6)}{(6t-7)^2}\right]$
     $\quad = 3\left(\dfrac{3t+4}{6t-7}\right)^2\ \dfrac{-45}{(6t-7)^2} = \dfrac{-135(3t+4)^2}{(6t-7)^4}$.

19. $f'(x) = 2\left(\dfrac{3x^2-5}{2x^2+7}\right)D_x\left(\dfrac{3x^2-5}{2x^2+7}\right) = 2\left(\dfrac{3x^2-5}{2x^2+7}\right)\left[\dfrac{(2x^2+7)(6x)-(3x^2-5)(4x)}{(2x^2+7)^2}\right]$
     $\quad = 2\left(\dfrac{3x^2-5}{2x^2+7}\right)\dfrac{62x}{(2x^2+7)^2} = \dfrac{124x(3x^2-5)}{(2x^2+7)^3}$.

22. $F'(v) = (-3)(v^{-1}-2v^{-2})^{-4}D_v(v^{-1}-2v^{-2}) = -3(v^{-1}-2v^{-2})^{-4}(-v^{-2}+4v^{-3})$.

25. $F'(t) = [2t(2t+1)^2]D_t(2t+3)^3 + (2t+3)^3 D_t[2t(2t+1)^2]$
     $\quad = [2t(2t+1)^2]3(2t+3)^2 \cdot 2 + (2t+3)^3[2t \cdot 2(2t+1) \cdot 2 + (2t+1)^2 \cdot 2]$
     $\qquad$ (by the product and chain rules)
     $\quad = 2(2t+1)(2t+3)^2(24t^2 + 26t + 3)$.

28. $y' = 5(x + 1/x)^4 D_x(x + 1/x) = 5(x + 1/x)^4(1 - 1/x^2)$

     (a) $x = 1 \implies y' = 5(2)^4(1-1) = 0$. Thus the tangent line is $y = 32$.
     (b) The tangent line is horizontal if $y'(x) = 0$. Thus the equation
     $5(x + 1/x)^4(1 - 1/x^2) = 0$ or, after multiplying by $x^6/5$, $(x^2+1)^4(x^2-1) = 0$
     with solution $x = \pm1$. The points are: $(1,32)$, $(-1,-32)$.

31. $dy = 10(x^4 - 3x^2 + 1)^9 D_x(x^4 - 3x^2 + 1)dx = 10(x^4 - 3x^2 + 1)^9(4x^3 - 6x)dx$.
     Now, $x = 1$, $x + \Delta x = 1.01 \implies \Delta x = dx = .01$ and $\Delta y \approx dy =$
     $10(-1)^9(-2)(.01) = 0.2$.

34. If $v = F(u)$ and $u = G(t)$, then $v = F(G(t))$ and $\frac{dv}{dt} = F'(G(t))G'(t) = \frac{dv}{du} \cdot \frac{du}{dt}$.

Therefore with $v = (u^4 + 2u^2 + 1)^3$, $u = 4t^2$, we get $\frac{dv}{dt} = 3(u^4 + 2u^2 + 1)^2 \cdot$

$(4u^3 + 4u) \cdot 8t$.

37. Let $y = f(g(x))$. Here, $x = 1$, $x+\Delta x = 0.99$ so that $\Delta x = -.01$. $\Delta y \approx dy =$
$f'(g(x))g'(x)\Delta x = f'(g(1))g'(1)\Delta x$. Now, $g(1) = 1$, and $g'(x) = 3x^2 - 6x + 2$
$\Rightarrow g'(1) = -1$. Next, $f'(x) = 4x^3 - 9x^2 + 3 \Rightarrow f'(g(1)) = f'(1) = -2$.
Substituting: $\Delta y \approx (-2)(-1)(-.01) = -.02$.

40. $r(x) = s(t(x)) \Rightarrow r'(x) = s'(t(x))t'(x) \Rightarrow r'(0) = s'(t(0))t'(0) =$
$s'(0)t'(0)$ since $t(0) = 0$. Using $r'(0) = 2$ and $s'(0) = -3$, we get $2 =$
$-3t'(0)$ so that $t'(0) = -2/3$.

43. $f'(x_1)$ is the slope of the tangent line at $P \Rightarrow -1/f'(x_1)$ is the slope of
the normal line, perpendicular to the tangent.

46. $f'(x) = -3x^2 \Rightarrow f'(1) = -3 \Rightarrow -1/f'(1) = 1/3$, the slope of the normal.
The equation is $y - 7 = (1/3)(x-1)$ or $x - 3y + 20 = 0$.

49. Let (x_1,y_1) be the point of intersection of the graph and the normal line of
slope 4. Then the tangent line has slope $-1/4$ there. $y = (8x+3)^{-2} \Rightarrow y'$
$= -2(8x+3)^{-3}(8)$. Now, $y'(x_1) = -1/4 \Leftrightarrow -16(8x_1+3)^{-3} = -1/4 \Leftrightarrow (8x_1+3)^3$
$= 64 \Leftrightarrow 8x_1 + 3 = 4 \Leftrightarrow x_1 = 1/8$. Thus $y_1 = (8(1/8)+3)^{-2} = 4^{-2} = 1/16$.
Now using $m = 4$, the equation is: $y - 1/16 = 4(x - 1/8)$.

52. $D_x f(g(x)) = f'(g(x))g'(x) = f(g(x))g'(x)$ for this special function.

EXERCISES 3.6, page 113

1. The object in #1-8 is to solve the given equation for y in terms of x. Thus
$3x - 2y + 4 = 2x^2 + 3y - 7x \Rightarrow -2x^2 + 10x + 4 = 5y$ and $y = (-2/5)x^2 + 2x + (4/5)$ is one implicit function defined by the equation. Its domain is $\mathbb{R}$.

4. $3x^2 - 4y^2 = 12 \Leftrightarrow y^2 = (3x^2 - 12)/4$. So, $y = (1/2)\sqrt{3x^2 - 12}$ is one
function defined by the equation. The domain is $\{x: 3x^2 - 12 \geq 0\} = (-\infty,2] \cup [2,\infty)$.

7. $\sqrt{x} + \sqrt{y} = 1 \Leftrightarrow \sqrt{y} = 1 - \sqrt{x} \Rightarrow y = 1 - 2\sqrt{x} + x$. The domain is tricky. Obviously $x \geq 0$. But from the 2nd equation $\sqrt{y} = 1 - \sqrt{x} \geq 0$ or $\sqrt{x} \leq 1$, which
gives $0 \leq x \leq 1$ as the domain.

10. $4x^3 - 2y^3 = x \Rightarrow 12x^2 - 6y^2y' = 1 \Rightarrow y' = (12x^2-1)/6y^2$.

13. $5x^2 - xy - 4y^2 = 0 \Rightarrow 10x - (xy'+y) - 8yy' = 0$ (The middle term is $D_x(xy)$)
$\Rightarrow (-x-8y)y' = y - 10x \Rightarrow y' = (10x-y)/(x+8y)$.

16. $x = \sin xy \Rightarrow 1 = (\cos xy) D_x(xy) = (\cos xy)(xy' + y) = (x \cos xy)y'$
$+ y \cos xy \Rightarrow (x \cos xy)y' = 1 - y \cos xy \Rightarrow y' = (1 - y \cos xy)/(x \cos xy)$.

19. $(y^2 - 9)^4 = (4x^2 + 3x - 1)^2 \Rightarrow 4(y^2 - 9)^3(2yy') = 2(4x^2 + 3x - 1)(8x + 3)$
    $\Rightarrow y' = (4x^2 + 3x - 1)(8x + 3)/4y(y^2 - 9)^3$.

22. $y^2 - 4x^2 = 5 \Rightarrow 2yy' - 8x = 0 \Rightarrow y' = 4x/y$. At $P(-1,3)$, $y' = -4/3 \Rightarrow$
    $y - 3 = (-4/3)(x+1)$ is the tangent line equation.

28. $x^2 + y^2 = a^2 \Rightarrow 2x + 2yy' = 0 \Rightarrow y' = -x/y$. If $P(x_1,y_1)$ is on the circle
    and $y_1 \neq 0$, the tangent line has slope $y' = -x_1/y_1$ and $m_{OP} = y_1/x_1 = -1/y' \Rightarrow$
    $OP \perp$ tangent. If $y_1 = 0$, then $x_1 = \pm a$ and the tangent is vertical while OP
    is on the x-axis, horizontal.

EXERCISES 3.7, page 115

1. $f(x) = \sqrt[3]{x^2} + 4\sqrt{x^3} = x^{2/3} + 4x^{3/2} \Rightarrow f'(x) = \frac{2}{3}x^{-1/3} + 4(\frac{3}{2})x^{1/2} = \frac{2}{3\sqrt[3]{x}} + 6\sqrt{x}$.

4. $D_z[(2z^2 - 9z + 8)^{-2/3}] = (-2/3)(2z^2 - 9z + 8)^{-5/3} D_z(2z^2 - 9z + 8) =$
   $(-2/3)(2z^2 - 9z + 8)^{-5/3}(4z - 9)$.

7. $D_x(\sqrt{2x}) = \sqrt{2}D_x(x^{1/2}) = (\sqrt{2}/2)x^{-1/2} = 1/\sqrt{2x}$.

10. $f(t) = \sqrt[3]{t^2} - 1/\sqrt{t^3} = t^{2/3} - t^{-3/2} \Rightarrow f'(t) = \frac{2}{3}t^{-1/3} + \frac{3}{2}t^{-5/2} = 2/3\sqrt[3]{t} + 3/2\sqrt{t^5}$.

13. $D_x(\sqrt{4x^2 - 7x + 4}) = D_x(4x^2 - 7x + 4)^{1/2} = \frac{1}{2}(4x^2 - 7x + 4)^{-1/2}D_x(4x^2 - 7x + 4)$
    $= (8x - 7)/2\sqrt{4x^2 - 7x + 4}$.

16. $D_v(1/\sqrt{v^4 + 7v^2})^3 = D_v(v^4 + 7v^2)^{-3/2} = -\frac{3}{2}(v^4 + 7v^2)^{-5/2}(4v^3 + 14v)$.

19. $D_s((s^2+9)^{1/4}(4s+5)^4) = (s^2+9)^{1/4}D_s(4s+5)^4 + (4s+5)^4D_s(s^2+9)^{1/4}$
    $= (s^2+9)^{1/4} 4(4s+5)^3(4) + (4s+5)^4(1/4)(s^2+9)^{-3/4}(2s)$
    $= 16\sqrt[4]{s^2+9}(4s+5)^3 + s(4s+5)^4/2\sqrt[4]{(s^2+9)^3}$.

22. $f'(w) = D_w(w^3(9w + 1)^5)^{1/2} = \frac{1}{2}(w^3(9w + 1)^5)^{-1/2}D_w(w^3(9w + 1)^5) =$
    $\dfrac{w^3 \cdot 5(9w + 1)^4 9 + 3w^2(9w + 1)^5}{2(w^3(9w + 1)^5)^{1/2}} = \dfrac{3w^2(9w + 1)^4[15w + (9w + 1)]}{2w^{3/2}(9w + 1)^{5/2}} =$
    $(3/2)w^{1/2}(9w + 1)^{3/2}(24w + 1)$.

25. $D_x(7x+(x^2+3)^{1/2})^6 = 6(7x+\sqrt{x^2+3})^5 D_x(7x+(x^2+3)^{1/2}) = 6(7x+\sqrt{x^2+3})^5(7+x/\sqrt{x^2+3})$.

28. $y = (5x-8)^{1/3} \Rightarrow y' = (1/3)(5x-8)^{-2/3} \cdot 5$. At $P(7,3)$, $y' = (1/3)(35-8)^{-2/3}$
    $\cdot 5 = (5/3)/27^{2/3} = 5/27$. Thus the tangent line is: $y - 3 = (5/27)(x-7)$.

31. $y = (2x-4)^{1/2} \Rightarrow y' = (1/2)(2x-4)^{-1/2}(2) = 1/\sqrt{2x-4}$. Thus the slope of the
    tangent line at $(a,\sqrt{2a-4})$ is $1/\sqrt{2a-4}$ and the equation is $y - \sqrt{2a-4} =$
    $(1/\sqrt{2a-4})(x-a)$. Since the desired line is to pass through the origin,

x = y = 0 must satisfy this equation. Thus $-\sqrt{2a-4} = -a/\sqrt{2a-4} \implies 2a-4 = a$
$\iff a = 4$. Thus the point is $(4, \sqrt{8-4}) = (4,2)$.

34. $x^{2/3} + y^{2/3} = 4 \iff \frac{2}{3}x^{-1/3} + \frac{2}{3}y^{-1/3}y' = 0 \implies y^{-1/3}y' = -x^{-1/3} \implies y'$

$= -\frac{x^{-1/3}}{y^{-1/3}} = -(\frac{y}{x})^{1/3}$.

37. First, $D_x(xy)^{1/3} = \frac{1}{3}(xy)^{-2/3}D_x(xy) = \frac{1}{3}(xy)^{-2/3}(xy' + y)$. Then $3x^2 + (xy)^{1/3}$

$= 2y^2 + 20 \implies 6x + \frac{1}{3}(xy)^{-2/3}(xy' + y) = 4yy'$. Multiply by $3(xy)^{2/3}$ to

obtain: $18x^{5/3}y^{2/3} + xy' + y = 12x^{2/3}y^{5/3}y' \implies (12x^{2/3}y^{5/3} - x)y' = 18x^{5/3}y^{2/3} + y$.

40. $dy = D_xy\Delta x = D_x[(x^2+1)^{-1/2}]\Delta x = (-1/2)(x^2+1)^{-3/2}D_x(x^2+1)\Delta x = -\frac{x}{\sqrt{x^2+1}^3}\Delta x$.

43. $dy = D_x(4x^2+9)^{3/2}\Delta x = (3/2)(4x^2+9)^{1/2}D_x(4x^2+9)\Delta x = (3/2)\sqrt{4x^2+9}\,8x\Delta x$. With
$x = 2$, $x+\Delta x = 1.998$. $\Delta x = -.002$. $\Delta y \approx dy = (3/2)\sqrt{16+9}\,(16)(-.002) = -120(.002) = -.24$.

46. Write $T = K\ell^{1/2}$ where $K = 2\pi/\sqrt{g}$. We seek $\Delta\ell$ so that $\frac{\Delta T}{T}(100) = 1$ (i.e., a
1% increase in T) or $\frac{\Delta T}{T} = .01$. Now, $\frac{\Delta T}{T} \approx \frac{dT}{T} = \frac{(1/2)K\ell^{-1/2}\Delta\ell}{K\ell^{1/2}} = \frac{\Delta\ell}{2\ell} = .01$ if
$\frac{\Delta\ell}{\ell} = .02$ or $\Delta\ell = .02\ell = \frac{\ell}{50}$. (i.e., ℓ must increase by 2%.)

49. $f(x) = |1-x^2| = \sqrt{(1-x^2)^2} = [(1-x^2)^2]^{1/2} \implies f'(x) = \frac{1}{2}[(1-x^2)^2]^{-1/2}D_x(1-x^2)^2$

$= \frac{1}{2|1-x^2|} \cdot 2(1-x^2)(-2x) = -2x\frac{(1-x^2)}{|1-x^2|}$. Now, if $|x| < 1$, then $x^2 < 1$,
$0 < 1-x^2$ and $|1-x^2| = (1-x^2)$. So, if $|x| < 1$, $f'(x) = -2x$. Similarly, if
$|x| > 1$ then $0 > 1-x^2$, and $|1-x^2| = -(1-x^2)$. Thus if $|x| > 1$, $f'(x) = -2x(-1) = +2x$. f is not differentiable if $|x| = 1$, i.e. at $x = \pm1$. At
$x = 1$, for example, the right-hand derivative of f is 2, whereas the left-hand derivative is -2. These are reversed at $x = -1$. Thus the domain of
f' is $\{x: x \neq \pm1\}$.

EXERCISES 3.8, page 118

1. See Example 1.

2. $g'(x) = 24x^7 - 10x^4$, $g''(x) = 168x^6 - 40x^3$.

4. $F'(t) = (3/2)t^{1/2} - t^{-1/2} - 2t^{-3/2}$, $F''(t) = (3/4)t^{-1/2} + (1/2)t^{-3/2} + 3t^{-5/2}$.

7. $k'(r) = 5(4r+7)^4D_r(4r+7) = 20(4r+7)^4$, $k''(r) = 20(4)(4r+7)^3D_r(4r+7) = 80(4r+7)^3 \cdot 4$.

10. $h(x) = 1 \implies h'(x) = 0 \implies h''(x) = 0.$

13. $D_x y = \dfrac{(3x+1)D_x(2x-3)-(2x-3)D_x(3x+1)}{(3x+1)^2} = \dfrac{(3x+1)(2)-(2x-3)(3)}{(3x+1)^2} = 11(3x+1)^{-2}.$

$D_x^2 y = -2(11)(3x+1)^{-3}D_x(3x+1) = -66(3x+1)^{-3}.$

$D_x^3 y = (-3)(-66)(3x+1)^{-4}D_x(3x+1) = 198(3)(3x+1)^{-4}.$

16. $D_x y = 4(3x+1)^3 D_x(3x+1) = 12(3x+1)^3.$ $D_x^2 y = 36(3x+1)^2 D_x(3x+1) = 108(3x+1)^2.$
$D_x^3 y = 216(3x+1) \cdot D_x(3x+1) = 648(3x+1).$

19. $x^2 - 3xy + y^2 = 4 \implies 2x - 3xy' - 3y + 2yy' = 0 \implies y' = (3y-2x)/(2y-3x) \implies y'' =$
$\dfrac{(2y-3x)(3y'-2) - (3y-2x)(2y'-3)}{(2y-3x)^2}$. Substituting for y' (from the 1st line),
the numerator of y'' becomes: $3(3y-2x)-2(2y-3x) - 2\dfrac{(3y-2x)^2}{(2y-3x)} + 3(3y-2x)$
$= (14y-6x) - 2(3y-2x)^2/(2y-3x) = [(14y-6x)(2y-3x) - 2(3y-2x)^2]/(2y-3x)$
$= [10y^2 - 30xy + 10x^2]/(2y-3x)$, which when substituted into the y'' equation
yields the answer given in the text.

22. $f(x) = (x^2-1)^3 = x^6 - 3x^4 + 3x^2 - 1 \implies f'(x) = 6x^5 - 12x^3 + 6x \implies f''(x) =$
$30x^4 - 36x^2 + 6 \implies f'''(x) = 120x^3 - 72x \implies f^{(4)}(x) = 360x^2 - 72 \implies$
$f^{(5)}(x) = 720x \implies f^{(6)}(x) = 720.$

28. Let $g(x) = f'(x) = 4x^3 - 3x^2 - 12x + 7.$ A tangent line to the graph of g
has slope $g'(x)$ or $f''(x) = 12x^2 - 6x - 12.$ At $x = 2$, $g'(2) = f''(2) =$
$12(4) - 6(2) - 12 = 24$, and the equation of the tangent line at $(2,3)$ is
$y-3 = 24(x-2).$

31. $y = f(g(x)) \implies D_x y = f'(g(x))g'(x).$ Using the product rule: $D_x^2 y =$
$f'(g(x))D_x g'(x) + [D_x f'(g(x))]g'(x) = f'(g(x))g''(x) + [f''(g(x))g'(x)]g'(x).$

EXERCISES 3.9 , page 121

1. To find $\sqrt[3]{2}$, we must solve $f(x) = x^3 - 2 = 0.$ Since $f(1) = -1$ and $f(2) = 6$, the
root lies between 1 and 2. With the initial guess of $x_1 = 1$ and using $x_{n+1} =$
$x_n - \dfrac{f(x_n)}{f'(x_n)} = x_n - \dfrac{(x_n^3 - 2)}{3x_n^2}$, we obtain the following results as tabulated,
after rounding off to 4 places.

n	x_n	$f(x_n)$
1	1.0000	-1.0000
2	1.3333	0.3704
3	1.2639	0.0190
4	1.2599	0.0001
5	1.2599	0.0000

Thus $\sqrt[3]{2}$ = 1.2599 to 4 decimal places.

4. Preliminary analysis: To find the interval in which the largest root of
   $f(x) = 2x^3 - 4x^2 - 3x + 1 = 0$ lies, we begin by evaluating f at convenient x
   values. We get $f(0) = 1$, $f(1) = -4$, $f(2) = -5$, $f(3) = 10$, $f(4) = 53$. From
   this point on, the values of f become increasingly large. Thus, the largest
   root lies between 2 and 3. Our initial guess will be $x_1 = 2$, and the for-

   mula to be used is: $x_{n+1} = x_n - \dfrac{2x_n^3 - 4x_n^2 - 3x_n + 1}{6x_n^2 - 8x_n - 3}$.

n	x_n	$f(x_n)$
1	2.0000	-5.0000
2	3.0000	10.0000
3	2.6296	1.8188
4	2.5254	0.1256
5	2.5171	0.0008
6	2.5170	0.0000
7	2.5170	0.0000

Thus the largest root is 2.5170 to 4 places.

7. Preliminary analysis: With $f(x) = x^5 + x^2 - 9x - 3$, we have $f(-2) = -13$ and
   $f(-1) = 6$ and, thus, there is a root between -2 and -1. Our initial guess

   will be $x_1 = -2$, and the formula is: $x_{n+1} = x_n - \dfrac{x_n^5 + x_n^2 - 9x_n - 3}{5x_n^4 + 2x_n - 9}$

n	x_n	$f(x_n)$
1	-2.0000	-13.0000
2	-1.8060	-2.6959
3	-1.7395	-0.2462
4	-1.7321	-0.0016
5	-1.7321	-0.0016

Thus, the desired root is -1.7321 to 4 places. (It is interesting to note
that if x_1 had been chosen to be -1, the root obtained would have been
-0.3222.)

10. Preliminary analysis: To find the interval in which the largest zero of
     $f(x) = x^3 - 36x - 84$ lies, we begin by evaluating f at convenient x's. We
     find that $f(0) = -84$, $f(2) = -148$, $f(4) = -164$, $f(6) = -84$, $f(7) = 7$,
     $f(8) = 140$, and, from this point on, the values of f become increasingly
     larger. Thus the largest zero of f lies in [6,7]. Our initial guess will
     be $x_1 = 7$ and the formula is $x_{n+1} = x_n - \dfrac{x_n^3 - 36x_n - 84}{3x_n^2 - 36}$.

n	x_n	$f(x_n)$
1	7.00000	-7.00000
2	6.93694	0.08327
3	6.93617	0.00001
4	6.93617	0.00000

Thus, the desired root is 6.93617 to 5 places.

13. Preliminary analysis: $x = -1$ is one root of $f(x) = x^4-x-2 = 0$ obtained by
     checking the four possible rational roots ± 1, ± 2. Thus, there is a factor
     of $(x+1)$, and by long division we find that $x^4-x-2 = (x+1)(x^3-x^2+x-2)$. The
     cubic factor, $c(x) = x^3-x^2+x-2$, has only one real root. This can be deter-
     mined by noting that $c(x) < 0$ if $x < 0$, $c(0) = -2$, $c(1) = -1$, $c(2) = 4$, $c(3)$
     = 19, and the values of $c(x)$ get increasingly positive from that point on.
     Since $c(1) < 0$ and $c(2) > 0$, $c(x)$ has its root between 1 and 2, and the 2nd
     root of $f(x)$ lies there also. Our initial guess will be $x_1 = 1$, and the
     formula is: $x_{n+1} = x_n - \dfrac{x_n^4 - x_n - 2}{4x_n^3 - 1}$.

n	x_n	$f(x_n)$
1	1.00	-2.00
2	1.67	4.05
3	1.44	0.81
4	1.36	0.07
5	1.35	0.00
6	1.35	0.00

Thus, the roots are -1 and 1.35 to 2 places.

16. Preliminary analysis: We begin by making a table of values of $f(x) = x^3 +$
     $2x^2 - 8x - 3$ to determine the intervals in which the roots lie.

x	-5	-4	-3	-2	-1	0	1	2	3	4
f(x)	-38	-3	12	13	6	-3	-8	-3	18	61

From the table (and the intermediate value theorem) the roots of f are in the intervals $[-4,-3]$, $[-1,0]$, and $[2,3]$. Our initial guesses will be -4, -1, and 2, respectively, and the formula is

$$x_{n+1} = x_n - \frac{x_n^3 + 2x_n^2 - 8x_n - 3}{3x_n^2 + 4x_n - 8} \ .$$

Root in $[-4,-3]$			Root in $[-1,0]$			Root in $[2,3]$		
n	x_n	$f(x_n)$	n	x_n	$f(x_n)$	n	x_n	$f(x_n)$
1	-4.00	-3.00	1	-1.00	6.00	1	2.00	-3.00
2	-3.88	-0.15	2	-0.33	-0.15	2	2.25	0.52
3	-3.87	0.00	3	-0.35	0.00	3	2.22	0.00
4	-3.87	0.00	4	-0.35	0.00	4	2.22	0.00

Thus, the three roots are -3.87, -0.35, and 2.22 to 2 places.

EXERCISES 3.10, page 122

1. $f'(x) = \lim_{h \to 0} \frac{1}{h}(\frac{4}{3(x+h)^2+2} - \frac{4}{3x^2+2}) = \lim_{h \to 0} \frac{4}{h} \frac{-(6xh-3h^2)}{(3(x+h)^2+2)(3x^2+2)} = \frac{-24x}{(3x^2+2)^2}$.

4. $D_x(x^4-x^2+1)^{-1} = (-1)(x^4-x^2+1)^{-2}D_x(x^4-x^2+1) = -(4x^3-2x)/(x^4-x^2+1)^2$.

7. $D_z(7z^2-4z+3)^{1/3} = (1/3)(7z^2-4z+3)^{-2/3}D_z(7z^2-4z+3) = (14z-4)/3\sqrt[3]{(7z^2-4z+3)^2}$.

10. $D_x((1/6)(3x^2-1)^4) = (4/6)(3x^2-1)^3(6x) = 4x(3x^2-1)^3$.

13. $D_x(\sqrt[5]{(3x+2)^4}) = D_x(3x+2)^{4/5} = (4/5)(3x+2)^{-1/5}(3)$.

16. Multiply out to get $g(w) = (w^2-4w+3)/(w^2+4w+3)$. Then

$g'(w) = \frac{(w^2+4w+3)(2w-4) - (w^2-4w+3)(2w+4)}{(w+1)^2(w+3)^2} = (8w^2-24)/(w+1)^2(w+3)^2$.

19. $g'(y) = (7y - 2)^{-2}D_y(2y + 1)^{2/3} + (D_y(7y - 2)^{-2})(2y + 1)^{2/3} =$

$(7y - 2)^{-2} \frac{2}{3}(2y + 1)^{-1/3}(2) + (-2)(7y - 2)^{-3}(7)(2y + 1)^{2/3}$.

22. $H'(t) = 6(t^6 + t^{-6})^5 D_t(t^6 + t^{-6}) = 6(t^6 + t^{-6})^5(6t^5 - 6t^{-7})$.

25. $f'(x) = [(3x+2)^{1/2}D_x(2x+3)^{1/3} - (2x+3)^{1/3}D_x(3x+2)^{1/2}]/(3x+2)$

$= \frac{(3x+2)^{1/2}(\frac{1}{3})(2x+3)^{-2/3}(2)-(2x+3)^{1/3}(\frac{1}{2})(3x+2)^{-1/2}(3)}{3x+2}$

$= (3x+2)^{-1/2}(2x+3)^{-2/3}[(2/3)(3x+2)-(3/2)(2x+3)]/(3x+2)$

which may be reduced to $-(x + 19/6)/(3x+2)^{3/2}(2x+3)^{2/3}$.

28. $F'(t) = [(t^2+2)(10t) - (5t^2-7)(2t)]/(t^2+2)^2 = 34t/(t^2+2)^2$.

31. $5x^3 - 2x^2y^2 + 4y^3 - 7 = 0 \implies 15x^2 - 2x^2 \cdot 2yy' - 4xy^2 + 12y^2y' = 0 \implies$
    $(15x^2 - 4xy^2) + (12y^2 - 4x^2y)y' = 0.$

34. $y^2 - x^{1/2}y^{1/2} + 3x = 2 \implies 2yy' - (1/2)x^{1/2}y^{-1/2}y' - (1/2)y^{1/2}x^{-1/2} + 3 = 0$
    $\implies (2y - (1/2)\sqrt{x/y})y' - ((1/2)\sqrt{y/x} - 3) = 0$
    $\implies y' = ((1/2)\sqrt{y/x} - 3)/(2y - (1/2)\sqrt{x/y}).$

37. $x^2y - y^3 = 8 \implies x^2y' + 2xy - 3y^2y' = 0 \implies y' = -2xy/(x^2 - 3y^2)$. At
    $P(-3,1)$, $y' = 6/6 = 1$. Thus the tangent line is $y-1 = (1)(x-3)$.

40. $y = 2x^3 - x^2 - 3x \implies y' = 6x^2 - 2x - 3$. (a) $y' = 0 \implies 6x^2 - 2x - 3 = 0$
    $\implies x = \dfrac{2 \pm \sqrt{4 - 4(6)(-3)}}{12} = \dfrac{2 \pm \sqrt{76}}{12} = \dfrac{1 \pm \sqrt{19}}{6}$. (b) $y = 0 \implies 2x^3 - x^2$
    $- 3x = 0 \implies x(2x^2 - x - 3) = x(x + 1)(2x - 3) = 0 \implies x = -1, 0, 3/2.$
    $y'(-1) = 6 + 2 - 3 = 5$, $y'(0) = -3$ and $y'(3/2) = 15/2.$

43. $x^2 + 4xy - y^2 = 8 \implies 2x + 4xy' + 4y - 2yy' = 0 \implies y' = (2x+4y)/(2y-4x)$
    $= (x+2y)/(y-2x) \implies y'' = [(y-2x)(1+2y')-(x+2y)(y'-2)]/(y-2x)^2$
    $= 5(y - xy')/(y - 2x)^2$. Substituting for y' from the 2nd line and simplify-
    ing yields the given answer.

46. $y' = [(x^2+1)(5) - 5x(2x)]/(x^2+1)^2 = 5(1-x^2)/(x^2+1)^2$. Thus $dy =$
    $[5(1-x^2)/(x^2+1)^2]\Delta x$. If x changes from 2 to 1.98, we select $x = 2$, $\Delta x =$
    $-.02$ and $\Delta y \approx dy = (5(1-4)/5^2)(-.02) = (-3/5)(-.02) = (.6)(.02) = 0.012.$
    Exactly, $\Delta y = f(1.98)-f(2) = \dfrac{9.9}{4.9204} - \dfrac{10}{5} \approx 0.0120315.$

49. Let $h(x) = g(f(x))$. If x changes from -1 to -1.01, then select $x = -1$,
    $\Delta x = -.01$ and $\Delta y \approx dy = h'(x)\Delta x = g'(f(x))f'(x)\Delta x = g'(f(-1))f'(-1)\Delta x$. Now,
    $f'(x) = 6x^2 + 2x - 1$, $f'(-1) = 6-2-1 = 3$, $g'(x) = 5x^4 + 12x^2 + 2$, $f(-1) =$
    $-2+1+1+1 = 1$, $g'(f(-1)) = g'(1) = 5+12+2 = 19$. Thus $\Delta y \approx (19)(3)(-.01) =$
    $-0.57.$

52. First we get S in terms of V. $V = \dfrac{4}{3}\pi r^3 \implies r^2 = (\dfrac{3}{4\pi})^{2/3}V^{2/3} \implies$
    $S = 4\pi r^2 = (4\pi)^{1/3}3^{2/3}V^{2/3} = (36\pi)^{1/3}V^{2/3} \implies dS = \dfrac{2}{3}(36\pi)^{1/3}V^{-1/3}dV.$
    When $r = 4$, $V = \dfrac{4}{3}\pi 4^3 = \dfrac{256\pi}{3}$. This, with $dV = 12$, gives $\Delta S \approx dS =$
    $\dfrac{2}{3}(36\pi)^{1/3}(\dfrac{3}{256\pi})^{1/3} \cdot 12 = 8(\dfrac{108}{256})^{1/3} = 8(\dfrac{27}{64})^{1/3} = 8 \cdot \dfrac{3}{4} = 6$ cm^2.
    Alternately: $V = \dfrac{4}{3}\pi r^3 \implies dV = 4\pi r^2 dr \implies 12 = 4\pi 4^2 dr \implies dr = 12/64\pi$
    $= 3/16\pi$. Then $S = 4\pi r^2 \implies dS = 8\pi r\, dr = 32\pi \cdot \dfrac{3}{16\pi} = 6$ cm^2.

55. Since $f(-1) = 4$ and $f(0) = -5$, there is a root between -1 and 0. Our
     initial guess will be $x_1 = 0$.

n	x_n	$f(x_n)$
1	0.0000	-5.0000
2	-0.7143	-0.4373
3	-0.7586	0.0294
4	-0.7560	0.0001
5	-0.7560	0.0000

CHAPTER 4

APPLICATIONS OF THE DERIVATIVE

<u>EXERCISES 4.1, page 131</u>

1. $f'(x) = -12x - 6x^2 = -6x(x+2)$. Since $f'(x)$ exists for all x, the only crit-
    ical numbers are solutions of $f'(x) = 0$, or $-6x(x+2) = 0 \Rightarrow x = 0$, $x = -2$,
    both of which are in the given interval $[-3,1]$. Now we calculate the values
    of $f(x)$ at $x = 0$ and $x = -2$, the critical numbers, and at $x = -3$ and $x = 1$,
    the end points of the interval. The absolute maximum of f on $[-3,1]$ is the
    largest of these values, and the absolute minimum of f is the smallest. $f(x)$
    $= 5 - 6x^2 - 2x^3 \Rightarrow f(0) = 5$, $f(-2) = 5 - 6(4) - 2(-8) = -3$, $f(-3) = 5 -$
    $6(9) - 2(-27) = 5$, $f(1) = 5 - 6 - 2 = -3$. Thus the maximum is 5 attained at
    $x = 0$ and -3; the minimum is -3 attained at $x = 1$ and -2.

4. $f'(x) = 4x^3 - 10x = 2x(2x^2-5)$, which exists for all x. Thus the only crit-
    ical numbers are solutions of $f'(x) = 0$, or $2x(2x^2 - 5) = 0 \Rightarrow x = 0$ and x
    $= \pm\sqrt{5/2}$. Of these, $-\sqrt{5/2}$ is not in the given interval, $[0,2]$, but 0 and
    $\sqrt{5/2} \approx 1.6$ are. Again, we calculate $f(x)$ at the critical numbers in the in-
    terval and at the end points. $(x = 0$ is both, but we consider it only an
    end point since, strictly speaking, $f'(0)$ does not exist--only the right-
    hand derivative does exist.) $f(0) = 4$, $f(2) = 16 - 5(4) + 4 = 0$, $f(\sqrt{5/2}) =$
    $(\sqrt{5/2})^4 - 5(\sqrt{5/2})^2 + 4 = 25/4 - 25/2 + 4 = -9/4$. Thus the maximum is $f(0)$
    $= 4$, and the minimum is $f(\sqrt{5/2}) = -9/4$.

6. For $f(x) = |x|$, $f'(0)$ does not exist by Example 3, Sec. 3.2, but $f'(x) = 1$ if
    $x > 0$, $f'(x) = -1$ if $x < 0$. Thus $x = 0$ is the only critical point, and the
    graph has no tangent line at $(0,0)$. Since $f(0) = 0$, f has a local minimum
    at $x = 0$ because $f(x) = |x| \geq 0 = f(0)$ for all x in any interval (a,b) con-
    taining 0.

10. $g'(x) = 2$, exists for all x and is never 0. Thus, no critical numbers.

13. $F'(w) = 4w^3 - 32 = 4(w^3-8) = 0$ only if $w = 2$, the only critical number.

16. $M'(x) = (2x-1)/3(x^2-x-2)^{2/3} = (2x-1)/3\sqrt[3]{(x-2)(x+1)^2}$. Thus $M'(x) = 0$ if $x =$
    $1/2$, and $M'(x)$ fails to exist at $x = -1$ and $x = 2$.

19. $G'(x) = (-2x^2 + 6x - 18)/(x^2-9)^2$ fails to exist at $x = \pm3$, but neither of
    these are in the domain of G. Setting $G'(x) = 0$, we obtain no real solutions
    since $b^2 - 4ac = 36 - 144 < 0$. Thus, no critical numbers.

22. $g'(x) = 3x^2 - 6/x^2$ fails to exist at $x = 0$, but 0 is not in the domain of g
    and is not a critical number. $g'(x) = 0 \Rightarrow 3x^4 - 6 = 0 \Rightarrow x^4 = 2 \Rightarrow$
    $x = \pm\sqrt[4]{2}$, the only critical numbers.

25. $f'(x) = (x + 5)^4 \cdot 3(2x - 3)^2 \cdot 2 + 4(x + 5)^3(2x - 3)^3 =$
    $(x + 5)^3(2x - 3)^2[6(x + 5) + 4(2x - 3)] = (x + 5)^3(2x - 3)^2(14x + 18) = 0$
    if $x = -5$, $3/2$, and $-18/14 = -9/7$.

28. If $f(x) = k$ for all x in (a,b) and if $c \in (a,b)$, then $f(x) = f(c)$ for all x
     there, and so $f(x) \geq f(c)$ and $f(x) \leq f(c)$ are both true.

34. If $f(x)$ is a polynomial of degree n, then $f'(x)$ has degree n-1 and can have
     at most n-1 distinct zeros. Since $f'(x)$, as a polynomial, exists everywhere,
     these are the only possible critical points.

EXERCISES 4.2, page 135

1. $f'(0)$ doesn't exist by Example 3, Section 3.2.

4. If $[a] = n$ and $b-a \geq 1$, then $b \geq a+1$ and $[b] \geq n+1$. Thus $f(b) - f(a) = [b] -$
    $[a] \geq 1$. Trying to solve $f(b) - f(a) = f'(c)(b-a)$ we get $f'(c) =$
    $\frac{f(b)-f(a)}{b-a} \geq \frac{1}{b-a}$. This equation has no solutions since $f'(x) = 0$ if x is not
    an integer and $f'(x)$ does not exist if x is an integer. (See #22, Section
    3.2.) There is no contradiction since $b-a \geq 1 \Longrightarrow [a,b]$ contains at least
    one integer at which f is neither continuous nor differentiable.

7. As a polynomial function, f is continuous and differentiable everywhere.
    Rolle's Theorem applies since $f(3) = f(-3) = 118$. $f'(x) = 4x^3 + 8x =$
    $4x(x^2+2) = 0$ only at $x = c = 0$, the desired solution.

10. As a polynomial function, f is continuous and differentiable everywhere.
    With $a = 1$, $b = 3$ we obtain: $f(3) - f(1) = f'(c)(3-1) \iff 37 - 3 =$
    $(10c-3) \cdot 2 \iff 17 = 10c - 3 \iff c = 2$.

13. $f(x) = x^{2/3}$ is continuous on $[-8,8]$, but $f'(0)$ does not exist.
    $(f'(0) = \lim_{h \to 0} \frac{f(h) - f(0)}{h} = \lim_{h \to 0} \frac{h^{2/3} - 0}{h} = \lim_{h \to 0} \frac{1}{h^{1/3}}$ which does not exist.)
    Thus f does not satisfy the hypotheses of the Mean Value Theorem.

16. $f(x) = 1 - 3x^{1/3}$ is continuous on $[-8,-1]$ and differentiable on $(-8,-1)$.
    ($f'(0)$ does not exist, but $0 \notin (-8,-1)$.) $f(-1) - f(-8) = f'(c)(-1-(-8)) \iff$
    $4-7 = (-c^{-2/3})(7) \iff c^{-2/3} = 3/7 \iff c^{2/3} = 7/3 \iff c^2 = (7/3)^3 \iff$
    $c = \pm \sqrt{(7/3)^3}$. The negative root must be chosen for c to be in $(-8,-1)$.
    Thus $c = -\sqrt{(7/3)^3} \approx -3.6$.

20. $f'(x)$ is a linear polynomial (i.e. of degree one). Thus $f(b) - f(a) =$
    $f'(c)(b-a)$ is a linear equation in the unknown c.

25. Hint: Let $f(x)$ be the number of miles travelled from A to B t hours after
    the start of the trip. To make the trip in one hour means $f(1) - f(0) = 50$.
    Now, recall that, since f is a distance, f' is the velocity, or speedometer
    reading.

EXERCISES 4.3, page 141

1. $f'(x) = -7-8x = 0 \implies x = -7/8$ is the only critical
    point, and the intervals to be considered are $(-\infty, -7/8)$
    and $(-7/8, \infty)$. Choosing $k = -1$ in the 1st, we have
    $f'(k) = f'(-1) = -7+8 = 1 > 0$; hence $f'(x) > 0$ on
    $(-\infty, -7/8)$ and f is increasing on $(-\infty, -7/8]$. Choosing
    $k = 0$ in the 2nd interval, $f'(k) = f'(0) = -7 < 0$; hence
    $f'(x) < 0$ on $(-7/8, \infty)$ and f is increasing on $[-7/8, \infty)$.
    Thus $f(-7/8)$ is a local maximum.

4. (Graph)

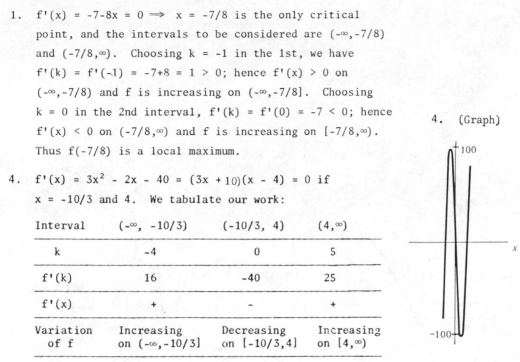

4. $f'(x) = 3x^2 - 2x - 40 = (3x + 10)(x - 4) = 0$ if
    $x = -10/3$ and 4. We tabulate our work:

Interval	$(-\infty, -10/3)$	$(-10/3, 4)$	$(4, \infty)$
k	-4	0	5
$f'(k)$	16	-40	25
$f'(x)$	+	-	+
Variation of f	Increasing on $(-\infty, -10/3]$	Decreasing on $[-10/3, 4]$	Increasing on $[4, \infty)$

Thus $f(-10/3) = 2516/27 \approx 93.2$ is a local maximum, and $f(4) = -104$
is a local minimum. (See graph above.)

7. $f'(x) = \frac{4}{3}(x^{1/3} + x^{-2/3}) = \frac{4}{3}x^{-2/3}(x + 1) = 4(x + 1)/3x^{2/3}$. Thus, the
    critical numbers are $x = -1$ and 0.

Interval	$(-\infty, -1)$	$(-1, 0)$	$(0, \infty)$
k	-8	-1/8	1
$f'(k)$	-7/3	14/3	8/3
$f'(x)$	-	+	+
Variation of f	Decreasing on $(-\infty, -1]$	Increasing on $[-1, 0]$	Increasing on $[0, \infty)$

Thus $f(-1) = -3$ is a local minimum. There is no extremum at $x = 0$, only a
vertical tangent.

10. $f'(x) = \dfrac{x(-2x)}{2\sqrt{4-x^2}} + \sqrt{4-x^2} = \dfrac{-x^2 + (4-x^2)}{\sqrt{4-x^2}} = \dfrac{2(2-x^2)}{\sqrt{4-x^2}} = 0$ at $x = \pm\sqrt{2}$.

Interval	$(-2, -\sqrt{2})$	$(-\sqrt{2}, \sqrt{2})$	$(\sqrt{2}, 2)$
k	$-\sqrt{3}$	0	$\sqrt{3}$
f'(k)	-2	2	-2
f'(x)	-	+	-
Variation of f	Decreasing on $[-2, -\sqrt{2}]$	Increasing on $[-\sqrt{2}, \sqrt{2}]$	Decreasing on $[\sqrt{2}, 2]$

Thus $f(\sqrt{2}) = 2$ is a local maximum, and $f(-\sqrt{2}) = -2$ is a local minimum.

10. (Graph)   16. (Graph)

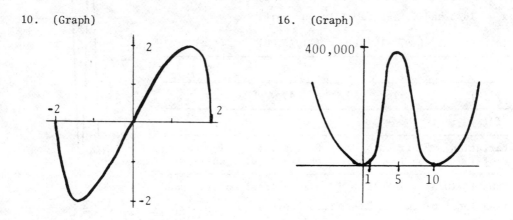

13. $f'(x) = 3x^2 - 3/x^2 = 3(x^4 - 1)/x^2 = 3(x^2 + 1)(x^2 - 1)/x^2 = 0$ at $x = \pm 1$.
     ($x = 0$, although not a critical number, is not in the domain of f and must
     be used to form the intervals below.)

Interval	$(-\infty, -1)$	$(-1, 0)$	$(0, 1)$	$(1, \infty)$
k	-2	-1/2	1/2	2
f'(k)	45/4	-45/4	-45/4	45/4
f'(x)	+	-	-	+
Variation of f	Increasing on $(-\infty, -1]$	Decreasing on $[-1, 0)$	Decreasing on $(0, 1]$	Increasing on $[1, \infty)$

Thus $f(-1) = -4$ is a local maximum, and $f(1) = 4$ is a local minimum.

16. $f'(x) = 4(x^2 - 10x)^3(2x - 10) = 8[x(x-10)]^3(x-5) = 8x^3(x-10)^3(x-5) = 0$
     at $x = 0, 5, 10$.

Interval	$(-\infty, 0)$	$(0,5)$	$(5,10)$	$(10,\infty)$
k	-1	1	6	11
f'(k)	$-48 \cdot 11^3$	$32 \cdot 9^3$	$8 \cdot 6^3 \cdot (-4)^3$	$48 \cdot 11^3$
f'(x)	−	+	−	+
Variation of f	Decreasing on $(-\infty, 0]$	Increasing on $[0,5]$	Decreasing on $[5,10]$	Increasing on $[10,\infty)$

Thus $f(0) = 0$ and $f(10) = 0$ are local minima, and $f(5) = 25^4$ is a local maximum. (See graph above, before #13.)

19. $f'(x) = (x-2)^3 4(x+1)^3 + 3(x-2)^2(x+1)^4 = (x-2)^2(x+1)^3[4(x-2) + 3(x+1)] = (x-2)^2(x+1)^3 (7x-5) = 0$ at $x = -1$, $5/7$ and 2.

Interval	$(-\infty,-1)$	$(-1,5/7)$	$(5/7,2)$	$(2,\infty)$
k	-2	0	1	3
f'(k)	$64 \cdot 19$	-20	16	$64 \cdot 16$
f'(x)	+	−	+	+
Variation of f	Increasing on $(-\infty,-1]$	Decreasing on $[-1,5/7]$	Increasing on $[5/7,2]$	Increasing on $[2,\infty)$

Thus $f(-1) = 0$ is a local maximum, and $f(5/7) = (-9/7)^3(12/7)^4 \approx -18.4$ is a local minimum. (No extremum at $x = 2$--only a horizontal tangent line.)

22. $f'(x) = \dfrac{(x-1)2x - (x^2+3)}{(x-1)^2} = \dfrac{x^2 - 2x - 3}{(x-1)^2} = \dfrac{(x+1)(x-3)}{(x-1)^2} = 0$ at $x = -1$ and 3, the only critical numbers. (However, the discontinuity of f at $x = 1$ must be used to form the intervals below.)

Interval	$(-\infty,-1)$	$(-1,1)$	$(1,3)$	$(3,\infty)$
k	-2	0	2	4
f'(k)	5/9	-3	-3	5/9
f'(x)	+	−	−	+
Variation of f	Increasing on $(-\infty,-1]$	Decreasing on $[-1,1)$	Decreasing on $(1,3]$	Increasing on $[3,\infty)$

Thus $f(-1) = -2$ is a local maximum, and $f(3) = 6$ is a local minimum.

NOTE: Solutions to #23 and #26, which refer to #1 and #4 above, will be included rather than #25.

23. Since f has only one local maximum, $f(-7/8) = 8\frac{1}{16}$ this will be the absolute maximum on any interval containing -7/8. The absolute minimum will be at an

end point.   (a) On [-1,1], f(-1) = 8, f(1) = -6. Thus, absolute maximum
f(-7/8) and absolute minimum f(1).   (b) On [-4,2], f(-4) = -31, f(2) = -25.
Thus, absolute maximum f(-7/8) and absolute minimum f(-4).   (c) On [0,5],
f is decreasing. Thus, absolute maximum f(0) and absolute minimum f(5).

26. f here has a local maximum f(-10/3) and a local minimum f(4).

(a) On [-1,1] f is decreasing. Thus, absolute maximum f(-1) = 46 and absolute minimum f(1) = -32.

(b) [-4,2] contains x = -10/3, and the local maximum of f there will be the absolute maximum on this interval. Since f(-4) = 88 and f(2) = -68, the absolute minimum is f(2).

(c) [0,5] contains x = 4, and the local minimum of f there will be the absolute minimum on this interval. Since f(0) = 8 and f(5) = -92, the absolute maximum if f(0).

28.

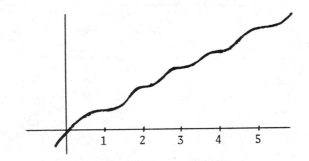

31. $f(x) = ax^3 + bx^2 + cx + d \implies f'(x) = 3ax^2 + 2bx + c$. The given conditions
on f mean $f(-1) = 2$, $f(1) = -1$, $f'(-1) = f'(1) = 0$. Substituting these into
the f and f' formulas, we get the system of equations:

$$\begin{cases} a + b + c + d = -1 \\ -a + b - c + d = 2 \\ 3a + 2b + c = 0 \\ 3a - 2b + c = 0 \end{cases}$$ Subtract to get 4b = 0 or b = 0.

Using b = 0, we get

$$\begin{cases} a + c + d = -1 \\ -a - c + d = 2 \\ 3a + c = 0 \end{cases}$$ Add to get 2d = 1 or d = 1/2.

Using d = 1/2 in the 1st and 3rd equations, we get

$$\begin{cases} a + c = -3/2 \\ \\ 3a + c = 0 \end{cases}$$ with solution a = 3/4, c = -9/4.

EXERCISES 4.4, page 149

1. $f'(x) = 3x^2 - 4x + 1 = (3x-1)(x-1)$, $f''(x) = 6x-4 = 6(x - 2/3)$. The critical
    numbers are $x = 1/3$, 1 and $f''(1/3) = -2$. $\therefore$ local maximum $f(1/3) = 31/27$;
    $f''(1) = 2$ $\therefore$ local minimum $f(1) = 1$. Since $f''(x) > 0$ if $x > 2/3$ and $f''(x)$
    < 0 if $x < 2/3$, the graph is CU on $(-\infty, 2/3)$, CD on $(2/3, \infty)$, and has a point
    of inflection at $x = 2/3$.

4. $f'(x) = 16x - 8x^3 = 8x(2-x^2)$, $f''(x) = 16-24x^2 = $
    $8(2-3x^2)$. The critical numbers are $x = 0$, $\pm\sqrt{2}$ and
    $f''(0) = 16$ $\therefore$ local minimum $f(0) = 0$; $f''(\pm\sqrt{2}) = $
    -32, $\therefore$ local maxima $f(\pm\sqrt{2}) = 8$. Next, $f''(x) > 0$
    $\Longleftrightarrow 2 - 3x^2 > 0 \Longleftrightarrow x^2 < 2/3 \Longleftrightarrow |x| < \sqrt{2/3}$.
    Thus the graph is CU on $(-\sqrt{2/3}, \sqrt{2/3})$, CD on
    $(-\infty, -\sqrt{2/3})$, and $(\sqrt{2/3}, \infty)$ with points of inflection
    at $x = \pm\sqrt{2/3}$.

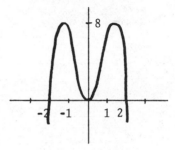

7. $f(x) = (x^2-1)^2 = x^4 - 2x^2 + 1 \Longrightarrow f'(x) = 4x^3 - 4x = 4x(x^2-1) \Longrightarrow f''(x) = $
    $12x^2 - 4 = 4(3x^2 - 1)$. From $f'(x) = 0$, the critical numbers are $x = 0$, ± 1.
    $f''(0) = -4$. $\therefore$ local maximum $f(0) = 1$. $f''(\pm 1) = 8$. $\therefore$ local minima $f(\pm 1)$
    $= 0$. Next, $f''(x) < 0 \Longleftrightarrow 3x^2 - 1 < 0 \Longleftrightarrow x^2 < 1/3 \Longleftrightarrow |x| < 1/\sqrt{3}$. Thus
    the graph is CU on $(-\infty, -1/\sqrt{3})$ and $(1/\sqrt{3}, \infty)$, CD on $(-1\sqrt{3}, 1/\sqrt{3})$ with points of
    inflection at $x = \pm 1/\sqrt{3}$.

10. $f(x) = (x+4)/\sqrt{x} = x^{1/2} + 4x^{-1/2} \Longrightarrow f'(x) = \frac{1}{2}x^{-1/2} - 2x^{-3/2} = (x-4)/2x^{3/2} \Longrightarrow$
    $f''(x) = (x^{3/2} - \frac{3}{2}(x-4)x^{1/2})/2x^3 = \sqrt{x}(12-x)/4x^3$. The only critical number is
    $x = 4$ (not $x = 0$ since 0 is not in the domain of f), and $f''(4) = 1/8$. $\therefore$
    local minimum $f(4) = 4$. Noting that $f''(x) > 0$ if $0 < x < 12$, and $f''(x) < 0$
    if $x > 12$, the graph is CU on $(0,12)$, CD on $(12, \infty)$, with a point of inflec-
    tion at $x = 12$.

10. (Graph)   16. (Graph)

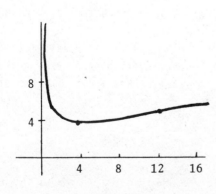

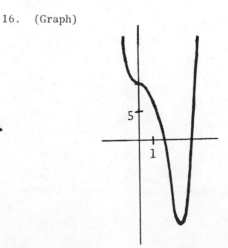

13. $f'(x) = \dfrac{(x^2+1)-2x^2}{(x^2+1)^2} = \dfrac{1-x^2}{(x^2+1)^2}$ • $f''(x) = \dfrac{(x^2+1)^2(-2x)-(1-x^2)2(x^2+1)2x}{(x^2+1)^4}$

$= \dfrac{2x^3-6x}{(x^2+1)^3} = \dfrac{2x(x^2-3)}{(x^2+1)^3}$. From $f'(x) = 0$, $x = \pm 1$ are the only critical numbers. $f''(1) = -4/8$. ∴ a local maximum $f(1) = 1/2$. $f''(-1) = 4/8$. ∴ a local minimum $f(-1) = -1/2$. Now, $f''(x) = 0$ if $x = 0, \pm\sqrt{3}$. We tabulate our work as follows:

Interval	$(-\infty, -\sqrt{3})$	$(-\sqrt{3},0)$	$(0,\sqrt{3})$	$(\sqrt{3},\infty)$
k	-2	-1	1	2
f''(k)	-4/125	1/2	-1/2	4/125
f''(x)	-	+	-	+
Concavity	CD	CU	CD	CU

Thus the graph has PI's at $x = -\sqrt{3}$, 0 and $\sqrt{3}$.

16. $f'(x) = 4x^3 - 12x^2 = 4x^2(x-3) = 0$ at $x = 0,3$. $f''(x) = 12x^2 - 24x = 12x(x-2)$. $f''(3) = 36 \Rightarrow f(3) = -17$ is a local minimum. $f''(0) = 0$ means that the 2nd derivative test is not applicable. Trying the 1st derivative test, if $x < 0$ then $f'(x) < 0$, and if $0 < x < 3$ then $f'(x) < 0$ also. Thus f is decreasing on $(-\infty,3)$ and has no local extremum at $x = 0$, only a horizontal tangent. Now, $f''(x) = 0$ at $x = 0,2$. We tabulate:

Interval	$(-\infty,0)$	$(0,2)$	$(2,\infty)$
k	-1	1	3
f''(k)	36	-12	36
f''(x)	+	-	+
Concavity	CU	CD	CU

Thus, PI's at $x = 0$ and $x = 2$. (The graph is next to that of #10 above.)

22.

28. HINT. $f''(x)$ is a linear polynomial. Thus $f''(x) = 0$ has only one solution. Show $f''(x)$ changes sign there.

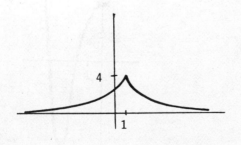

EXERCISES 4.5, page 161

1. $\lim\limits_{x\to\infty} \dfrac{5x^2 - 3x + 1}{2x^2 + 4x - 7} = \lim\limits_{x\to\infty} \dfrac{5 - 3/x + 1/x^2}{2 + 4/x - 7/x^2} = \dfrac{5 - 0 + 0}{2 + 0 - 0} = \dfrac{5}{2}.$

4. $\lim\limits_{x\to-\infty} \dfrac{(3x+4)(x-1)}{(2x+7)(x+2)} = \lim\limits_{x\to-\infty} \dfrac{3x^2 + x - 4}{2x^2 + 11x + 14} = \lim\limits_{x\to-\infty} \dfrac{3 + (1/x)-(4/x^2)}{2 + (11/x)+(14/x^2)} = \dfrac{3}{2}.$

7. $\lim\limits_{x\to\infty} \dfrac{\sqrt{4x+1}}{10-3x} = \lim\limits_{x\to\infty} \dfrac{\sqrt{(4/x) + (1/x^2)}}{10/x-3} = \dfrac{0}{-3} = 0.$ (Since $x\to\infty$, we may assume $x > 0$.

    Thus $x = \sqrt{x^2}$ when dividing numerator and denominator by x.)

10. The procedure here (as in 9 and 12) is to multiply and divide by an expression which will clear the radical from the numerator. Recalling that $(a-b)(a+b) = a^2 - b^2$ we have

    $\lim\limits_{x\to\infty} (x -\sqrt{x^2-3x}) = \lim\limits_{x\to\infty} \dfrac{(x -\sqrt{x^2-3x})(x + \sqrt{x^2-3x})}{(x + \sqrt{x^2-3x})} = \lim\limits_{x\to\infty} \dfrac{x^2 - (x^2-3x)}{x + \sqrt{x^2-3x}}$

    $= \lim\limits_{x\to\infty} \dfrac{3x}{x + \sqrt{x^2-3x}} = \lim\limits_{x\to\infty} \dfrac{3}{1 + \sqrt{1 - (3/x)}} = \dfrac{3}{1 + \sqrt{1}} = 3/2.$

13. Since $\lim\limits_{x\to\infty} f(x) = \lim\limits_{x\to-\infty} f(x) = \lim\limits_{x\to+\infty} \dfrac{4x^2}{1+x^2} = \lim\limits_{x\to+\infty} \dfrac{4}{1/x^2 + 1} = 4$, the line $y = 4$ is

    a horizontal asymptote. For the graph we need $f'(x) = 8x/(1+x^2)^2$ which is < 0 if $x < 0$ and > 0 if $x > 0$. Thus f is decreasing on $(-\infty,0]$, increasing on $[0,\infty)$, and has a local minimum $f(0) = 0$. Also, $f''(x) = 8(1-3x^2)/(1+x^2)^3 > 0$ if $|x| < 1/\sqrt{3}$ and < 0 if $|x| > 1/\sqrt{3}$. Thus the graph is CU on $(-1/\sqrt{3},1/\sqrt{3})$, CD on $(-\infty,-1/\sqrt{3})$ and $(1/\sqrt{3},\infty)$, with PI's at $x = \pm 1/\sqrt{3}$.

16. If $f(x) = a_n x^n + \ldots + a_0$, $a_n \neq 0$, $n \geq 1$, then $\dfrac{1}{f(x)} = \dfrac{1}{a_n x^n + \ldots + a_0}$

    $= \dfrac{(1/x^n)}{a_n + (a_{n-1}/x) + \ldots + (a_0/x^n)}$, which approaches $0/a_n = 0$ as $x \to \infty$.

19. Given any $\varepsilon > 0$, pick N so that $|g(x) - 0| < \varepsilon$ for $x \geq N$. Since $g(x) > 0$ this becomes $0 < g(x) < \varepsilon$ for such x. For the same x, $0 < f(x) = |f(x) - 0| < g(x) < \varepsilon$. Thus $\lim\limits_{x\to\infty} f(x) = 0.$

22. $\lim\limits_{x\to4^+} \dfrac{5}{4-x} = -\infty$ since, as $x \to 4^+$, $x > 4$, $4-x < 0$, whereas the numerator, 5,

    is > 0. $\lim\limits_{x\to4^-} \dfrac{5}{4-x} = \infty$ since, now, $x \to 4^- \implies x < 4$, $4-x > 0$. Thus,

    $x = 4$ is a vertical asymptote. $\lim\limits_{x\to\pm\infty} \dfrac{5}{4-x} = 0 \implies y = 0$ is a horizontal

    asymptote. For the graph we also need: $f'(x) = 5/(4-x)^2 > 0 \implies$ f is

increasing on $(-\infty,4)$ and $(4,\infty)$. $f''(x) =$
$10/(4-x)^3$ is > 0 if $x < 4$ and < 0 if $x > 4$.
Thus the graph is CU on $(-\infty,4)$, CD on $(4,\infty)$ with
no PI's.

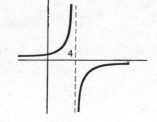

25. If x is nearly -8, then the numerator, $3x$, is nearly $-24 < 0$ whereas the de-
nominator is always positive. Thus $\lim\limits_{x \to -8^+} \dfrac{3x}{(x+8)^2} = \lim\limits_{x \to -8^-} \dfrac{3x}{(x+8)^2} = -\infty$. Thus,

$x = -8$ is a vertical asymptote. $y = 0$ is a horizontal asymptote since

$\lim\limits_{x \to +\infty} \dfrac{3x}{(x+8)^2} = 0$. For the details of the graph, we need $f'(x)$ and $f''(x)$

analyzed. $f'(x) = (24-3x)/(x+8)^3$, after simplification, so that $x = 24/3 =$
8 is the only critical number. As in Sec. 4.3, we find that f is decreasing
on $(-\infty,-8)$ and on $[8,\infty)$, increasing on $(-8,8]$ so that $f(8) = 3/32$ is a local
maximum. $f''(x)$ simplifies to $6(x-16)/(x+8)^4 < 0$ if $x < 16$ and > 0 if $x > 16$.
Hence, the graph is CD on $(-\infty,-8)$ and $(-8,16)$, and is CU on $(16,\infty)$ with a PI
at $x = 16$.

28. $f(x) = 4x/(x^2 - 4x + 3) = 4x/(x-1)(x-3)$.
For x near 1 or 3, $4x > 0$, and the sign of
$f(x)$ is that of $(x-1)(x-3)$. As $x \to 1^-$,
$x-1 < 0$, $x-3 < 0 \implies f(x) > 0$ and the limit
is ∞. As $x \to 1^+$ or $x \to 3^-$, $x-1 > 0$, $x-3 <$
$0 \implies f(x) < 0$, and both limits are $-\infty$.
As $x \to 3^+$, $x-1 > 0$, $x-3 > 0 \implies f(x) > 0$
and the limit is ∞. Thus $x = 1$ and $x = 3$
are vertical asymptotes. $y = 0$ is a hori-
zontal asymptote since $\lim\limits_{x \to +\infty} f(x) = 0$.

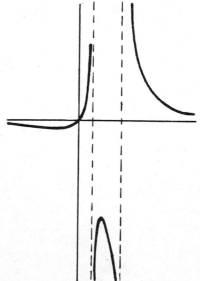

Also $f'(x) = 4(3-x^2)/(x^2-4x+3)^2 = 0$ at
$x = \pm\sqrt{3}$, and $f''(x) = 8(x^3-9x+12)/(x^2-4x+3)^3$
$\implies f(\sqrt{3}) \approx -7.5$ is a local maximum,
$f(-\sqrt{3}) \approx -0.53$ is a local minimum and
there is a PI between $x = -4$ and $x = -3$.

31. The denominator, x^2-4, is zero at $x = \pm2$ which are the vertical asymptotes
since $\lim\limits_{x \to -2^+} f(x) = \lim\limits_{x \to 2^-} f(x) = -\infty$ and $\lim\limits_{x \to -2^-} f(x) = \lim\limits_{x \to 2^+} f(x) = \infty$.

$\lim\limits_{x \to +\infty} \dfrac{1}{x^2-4} = 0 \implies y = 0$ is a horizontal asymptote.

34. Since the denominator, x^2+1, is never 0, $f(x)$ is defined and continuous for all x. Thus there are no vertical asymptotes. $y = 0$ is a horozontal asymptote since $\lim\limits_{x\to+\infty} \dfrac{3x}{x^2+1}$

$= \lim\limits_{x\to\infty} \dfrac{3/x}{1+1/x^2} = \dfrac{0}{1} = 0.$

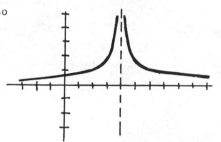

37. $f(x) = (x+2)(x+1)/(x+3)(x-1) \to \pm\infty$ as $x \to -3$ and as $x \to 1$, and these are vertical asymptotes. $y = 1$ is a horizontal asymptote since $f(x) = (1+3/x+2/x^2)/(1+2/x-3/x^2) \to 1$ as $x \to \pm\infty$.

39. HINT. $f(x) = (x+4)/(x^2-16) = 1/(x-4)$ if $x \neq -4$. Thus $x = -4$ is not a vertical asymptote since a finite limit exists as $x \to -4$.

40. $f(x) = \dfrac{\sqrt[3]{(4-x)(4+x)}}{4-x} = \sqrt[3]{\dfrac{(4+x)}{(4-x)^2}} \to \infty$ as $x \to 4$ so that $x = 4$ is a vertical asymptote. Dividing numerator and denominator of the original $f(x)$ formula by x

$f(x) = \dfrac{\sqrt[3]{16/x^2 - 1/x}}{4/x - 1} \to \dfrac{0}{-1}$ as $x \to \pm\infty$.

Thus $y = 0$ is a horizontal asymptote.

43. Since $f(x) = (8-x^3)/2x^2 \to \infty$ as $x \to 0$, $x = 0$ is a vertical asymptote. Next, we may write $f(x) = \dfrac{8}{2x^2} - \dfrac{x^3}{2x^2} = -\dfrac{1}{2}x + \dfrac{4}{x^2}$. Thus $y = -\dfrac{1}{2}x$ is an oblique asymptote since $4/x^2 \to 0$ as $x \to \pm\infty$.

46. The denominator of $f(x)$ is $2x^3 - 8x = 2x(x^2-4) = 0$ at $x = 0$, $x = -2$ and $x = 2$, which are the three vertical asymptotes since $f(x) = (1-x^4)/(2x^3 - 8x) \to \pm\infty$ as x approaches these values from left or right. Next, by long division, we obtain $f(x) = -\dfrac{1}{2}x + \dfrac{1-4x^2}{2x^3-8x}$. Thus $y = -\dfrac{1}{2}x$ is an oblique asymptote since $(1-4x^2)/(2x^3-8x) \to 0$ as $x \to \pm\infty$.

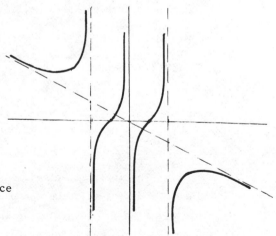

49. $f'(x) = (3/5)x(x+2)^{-2/5} + (x+2)^{3/5}$. As $x \to -2$ the first term becomes in-
     finite and the second term approaches 0. Thus $|f'(x)| \to \infty$ as $x \to -2$. Thus
     there is a vertical tangent line when $x = -2$ at the point $(-2,0)$.

52. $f'(x) = (1/3)x^{-2/3} = 1/3x^{2/3} \to \infty$ as $x \to 0$. Thus there is a vertical tan-
     gent when $x = 0$ at the point $(0,-5)$.

55. HINT. $g(x)$ can have no more than n distinct roots. These zeroes of the de-
     nominator are the only candidates for the locations of the vertical
     asymptotes.

EXERCISES 4.6, page 169

1. Let x and y be the 2 desired numbers with $x > y$, $x-y = 40$, and $P = xy$ is to
    be minimized. Since $y = x-40$, $P = x(x-40) = x^2 - 40x$ and $P' = 2x-40 = 0$
    when $x = 20$. This value minimizes P since $P'' = 2 > 0$. Thus $x = 20$, $y = -20$.

4. Let x be the length of the side of the square base, and y the height. Then
    $x^2y = 4$ so that $y = 4/x^2$. If S is the total surface area, then

    $\quad$ S = 4 · (Area of one side) + 2 · (Area of base)

    $\quad\quad$ = 4·xy $\quad\quad\quad\quad\quad\quad$ + 2·x^2

    $\quad\quad$ = 4x(4/x²) + 2x² = 16/x + 2x².

    Thus $S' = -16/x^2 + 4x = 0$ if $-16 + 4x^3 = 0$ or $x^3 = 4$. Thus $x = \sqrt[3]{4}$ and y =
    $4/4^{2/3} = \sqrt[3]{4}$ and the box of least surface area (since $S''(\sqrt[3]{4}) > 0$) is a cube
    $\sqrt[3]{4}$ on a side.

7. Placing the circle as shown (with equation $x^2 + y^2 = a^2$)
    and the rectangle in the upper half, if (x,y) is the
    point shown, then the area, A, is $A = 2xy$.

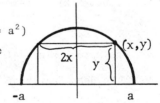

METHOD 1 The Explicit Method. From the equation of the circle, y =
$(a^2-x^2)^{1/2}$ and $A = 2x(a^2-x^2)^{1/2}$, $0 \le x \le a$. $A' = 2x(a^2-2x^2)/\sqrt{a^2-x^2} = 0$
when $x = a/\sqrt{2}$ and thus $y = a/\sqrt{2}$ also. This produces a maximum for A since
$A = 0$ when $x = 0$ or $x = a$ and $A > 0$ otherwise. The dimensions of the rectangle of maximum area are $x = a/\sqrt{2}$ by $2y = \sqrt{2}a$.

METHOD 2 The Implicit Method. As above, $A = 2xy$ and $A' = 2xy' + 2y$. We obtain y' by differentiating the equation of the circle implicity: $2x + 2yy'$
$= 0$ or $y' = -x/y$. Substituting into A' we get $A' = -2x^2/y + 2y = 2(y^2-x^2)/y$
$= 0$ when $x = y$. Substituting this into the equation of the circle we get
$2x^2 = a^2$ or $x = y = a/\sqrt{2}$ as in Method 1.

10. Let r and h be the base radius and height of the
     cylinder. Then $r^2 = a^2 - h^2/4$. If V is the
     volume of the cylinder, then $V = \pi r^2 h =$
     $\pi(a^2 h - h^3/4)$, for $0 \le h \le a$. $V' = \pi(a^2 - 3h^2/4)$
     $= 0$ if $3h^2 = 4a^2$ or $h = 2a/\sqrt{3}$. The corresponding
     r is $\sqrt{2/3}\,a$. This value of h produces a maximum
     for V on physical grounds or by an analysis as
     in #7 above.

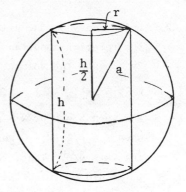

13. Let x and y denote the length and width, respectively, of the base and z the
     height of the shed (in feet). We are given that $y = \frac{3}{4}x$ and that the volume,
     V, is to be 900 ft^3. Since $V = xyz$, these yield $x(\frac{3}{4}x)z = 900$, or $z =$
     $1200/x^2$. Now, the total cost, C, of the shed is $C = 4(\text{floor area}) +$
     $6(\text{total area of the 4 sides}) + 3(\text{root area}) = 4(xy) + 6(2xz + 2yz) + 3(xy)$
     $= 7xy + 12xz + 12yz$. Substituting for y and z, we obtain:
     $$C = 7x \cdot \frac{3}{4}x + 12x \cdot \frac{1200}{x^2} + 12 \cdot \frac{3}{4}x \cdot \frac{1200}{x^2} = \frac{21}{4}x^2 + \frac{21(1200)}{x}, \text{ for } x > 0.$$
     Note that $C \to \infty$ as $x \to 0^+$ or $x \to \infty$. Thus any local minimum of C will be the
     absolute minimum. Next, $\frac{dC}{dx} = \frac{21}{2}x - \frac{21(1200)}{x^2} = 0$ if $x^3 = 2400$ or $x = \sqrt[3]{2400}$
     $= 2\sqrt[3]{300} \approx 13.4$ ft. $(\frac{d^2C}{dx^2} > 0 \implies$ this minimizes C.)

16. Let the field dimensions be x and y as shown. If b is
     the barn length, then x-b ft of fencing is required on
     the side next to the barn. Then the total amount of
     fencing, L, required is $L = 2y + x + (x-b) = 2y + 2x - b$.
     Since $xy = A$, $y = A/x$ and $L = \frac{2A}{x} + 2x - b \implies L' = \frac{-2A}{x^2}$
     $+ 2 = 0$ if $x = \sqrt{A}$. Then $y = A/\sqrt{A} = \sqrt{A} = x$.

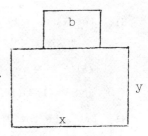

19. The capacity of the trough will be maximized when
     the cross-sectional area, A, is maximized. Let
     y be the amount turned up and x the base. Then
     $x + 2y = 12$ and $A = xy = (12-2y)y$, $0 \le y \le 6$.
     $A' = 12-4y = 0$ when $y = 3$, which maximizes A
     since $A'' = -4 < 0$.

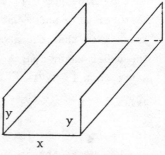

22. Let x and y be the dimensions of the rectangle with
     the rotation about an edge of length y. Then 2x +
     2y = p and the volume, V, of the cylinder is V =

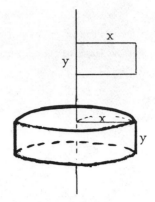

$\pi x^2 y = \pi x^2 (\frac{p}{2} - x) = \pi(\frac{px^2}{2} - x^3)$. $V' = \pi(px - 3x^2)$

= 0 when x = 0 or x = p/3. The maximum of V occurs
when x = p/3 (V = 0 when x = 0) and the corresponding y is p/6. Thus, for maximum volume, the base,
x, should be twice the height y.

25. If f(x) is the square of the distance of a point (x, x^2+1) on the parabola
     from (3,1), then $f(x) = (x-3)^2 + x^4$. $f'(x) = 2(x-3) + 4x^3 = 0$ only when
     x = 1 and the point is (1,2). Since f''(1) = 14 > 0, this is a minimum.
     (It's also obvious from a sketch.)

28. Referring to Example 5, the change to be made is that the time on the water
     is now $\sqrt{x^2+4}/15$ so that $T = \frac{\sqrt{x^2+4}}{15} + \frac{6-x}{5}$, $0 \le x \le 6$; $\therefore$ $T' = \frac{x}{15\sqrt{x^2+4}} - \frac{1}{5} =$

     $\frac{5x - 15\sqrt{x^2+4}}{75\sqrt{x^2+4}}$ which is always negative if $x \ge 0$, $(15\sqrt{x^2+4} > 15x \ge 5x)$. Thus

     the minimum of T occurs at the right end point x = 6, i.e., he should stay
     on the water the entire way.

31. Let x and y be the dimensions shown and A the area. Then
     7x + 2y = 100 $\implies$ y = (1/2)(100-7x). A = xy = (1/2)x(100-

     7x) = $50x - \frac{7}{2}x^2$ $\implies$ dA/dx = 50 - 7x = 0 when x = 50/7

     and y=(1/2)(100 - 7(50/7)) = 25.

34. Let x be the distance between C and the point op-
     posite A. Then $0 \le x \le \sqrt{8}$ for neither x < 0 nor
     $x > \sqrt{8}$ can produce a minimum cost. Let k be the
     cost of pipe per mile above ground. Then 4 k is the
     cost per mile under water. The above ground length
     is $\sqrt{8}-x$ so that the above ground cost is $k(\sqrt{8}-x)$.
     The under water length is $\sqrt{1+x^2}$ so that the under
     water cost is $4k\sqrt{1+x^2}$. If C(x) is the total cost then $C(x) = k(\sqrt{8}-x) +$

     $4k\sqrt{1+x^2}$, $0 \le x \le \sqrt{8}$. $C'(x) = -k + \frac{4kx}{\sqrt{1+x^2}} = 0$ if $\frac{4x}{\sqrt{1+x^2}} = 1 \implies 4x = \sqrt{1+x^2} \implies$

     $16x^2 = 1 + x^2 \implies 15x^2 = 1 \implies x = \sqrt{1/15}$ miles. That this minimizes C(x)
     can be checked by computing $C''(x) = 4k/(1+x^2)^{3/2} > 0$, or by evaluating C(0)
     = $(\sqrt{8}+4)k \approx 6.83k$, $C(\sqrt{8}) = 12k$, and $C(1/\sqrt{15}) = (\sqrt{15} + \sqrt{8})k \approx 6.70$ k.

37. Let the point on the ground be x ft. from the 6' pole
    and 10-x ft. from the 8' pole, and let L be the cable
    length. Then $L = \sqrt{x^2+36} + \sqrt{(10-x)^2+64}$, $0 \le x \le 10$.

$$\frac{dL}{dx} = \frac{x}{\sqrt{x^2+36}} + \frac{(10-x)(-1)}{\sqrt{(10-x)^2+64}}$$

$$= \frac{x\sqrt{(10-x)^2+64} - (10-x)\sqrt{x^2+36}}{\sqrt{x^2+36}\ \sqrt{(10-x)^2+64}} \cdot \frac{dL}{dx} = 0 \text{ if the}$$

numerator is 0, i.e. when $x\sqrt{(10-x)^2+64} = (10-x)\sqrt{x^2+36}$. Squaring:
$x^2[(10-x)^2+64] = (10-x)^2(x^2+36)$. Cancelling $x^2(10-x)^2$ from each side yields
$64x^2 = (10-x)^2 \cdot 36 \implies 16x^2 - 9(100 - 20x + x^2) = 0 \implies 7x^2 + 180x - 900$
$= 0$. Using the quadratic formula, or seeing the factorization $(7x-30)(x+30)$,
we obtain $x = 30/7$ as the only critical number in $[0,10]$. L is a minimum there
since $L(0) = 6 + \sqrt{164} \approx 18.8$, $L(10) = \sqrt{136} + 8 \approx 19.7$, whereas $L(30/7) \approx 17.2$.

40. For the fourth side to be parallel to one of the 8'
    sides, the trapezoid must be symmetric as shown. With
    x as shown, the fourth side has length $y = 8 + 2x$,
    $0 \le x \le 8$ (if $x > 8$, then the fourth side is longer
    than the sum of the other three sides), and the
    height is $h = \sqrt{64-x^2}$. The area, then, is

$$A = \frac{(8+y)}{2} h = (8+x)\sqrt{64-x^2}.$$

$$\frac{dA}{dx} = \frac{(8+x)(-x)}{\sqrt{64-x^2}} + \sqrt{64-x^2} = \frac{-8x - x^2 + (64-x^2)}{\sqrt{64-x^2}}$$

$= -(2x^2 + 8x - 64)/\sqrt{64-x^2} = 0$ if $2x^2 + 8x - 64 = 0 \implies x^2 + 4x - 32 =$
$(x-4)(x+8) = 0 \implies x = 4$ is the only critical number in $[0,8]$. By evaluating $A(0) = 64$, $A(4) = 12\sqrt{48} \approx 83.1$, $A(8) = 0$, $x = 4$ maximizes A. The
fourth side then has length $y = 8 + 2(4) = 16$.

43. Let x be the side of the square base, g the girth $(g = 4x)$,
    and ℓ the length in inches. Postal regulations require
    $ℓ + g \le 96$. Clearly, to maximize the volume, V, we must
    take $ℓ + g = 96$, or $ℓ + 4x = 96 \implies ℓ = 96 - 4x$. Then V
    $= x^2ℓ = 96x^2 - 4x^3$, $0 < x < 24$. $dV/dx = 192x - 12x^2 =$
    $12x(16-x) = 0$ when $x = 16$. $(V''(16) = -192 \implies V$ is maximized.) The cor-
    responding length is $ℓ = 96 - 4(16) = 32$.

46. First note that 8 wells producing 1600 barrels daily means that the average
    production is $1600/8 = 200$ bbl/well/day. Let x be the number of additional
    wells. Then the total number of wells is $8+x$ and the average daily produc-
    tion per well is $200-10x$. Then the total production, P, is (# of wells) ·
    (average production per well), or $P = (8+x)(200-10x) = 1600 + 120x - 10x^2$.
    Clearly $x \ge 0$ and $x \le 20$ for at $x = 20$, the average yield per well is 0. To

maximize P we compute P' = 120 - 20x = 0 at x = 6. P'' < 0 $\Longrightarrow$ 6 additional wells maximizes P.

49. Hint. If P(x,y) is any point on the line, then the distance from (x_1, y_1) to P is L = $\sqrt{(x-x_1)^2 + (y-y_1)^2}$. Now solve the equation of the line for y, substitute, compute L' and set L' = 0.

EXERCISES 4.7, page 177

1. (a) With r(t) = $3(t+8)^{1/3}$, r'(8) is sought. r'(t) = $(t+8)^{-2/3}$ = $1/\sqrt[3]{(t+8)^2}$ $\Longrightarrow$ r'(8) = $1/\sqrt[3]{16^2}$ = $1/4\sqrt[3]{4}$.

(b) Recall that the volume, V, of a sphere of radius r is V = $\frac{4}{3}\pi r^3$. As a function of t, V = $\frac{4}{3}\pi [3\sqrt[3]{t+8}]^3$ = $36\pi(t+8)$ $\Longrightarrow$ $D_t V$ = 36π for all t.

(c) Recall that the surface area, A, of a sphere of radius r is A = $4\pi r^2$ = $4\pi(3(t+8)^{1/3})^2$ = $36\pi(t+8)^{2/3}$ $\Longrightarrow$ $\frac{dA}{dt}$ = $\frac{2}{3} \cdot 36\pi \cdot (t+8)^{-1/3}$. At t = 8, this becomes $\frac{dA}{dt}$ = $24\pi \cdot \frac{1}{\sqrt[3]{16}}$ = $6\pi\sqrt[3]{4}$.

(NOTE: (b) and (c) could also be done using the chain rule, e.g. V = $\frac{4}{3}r\pi^3$ $\Longrightarrow$ $\frac{dV}{dt}$ = $4\pi r^2 \frac{dr}{dt}$ and substitute the values of r and $\frac{dr}{dt}$ when t = 8.)

4. By (4.26) we seek T'(t) at t = 2,5,9. T'(t) = $4 - 3/(t+1)^2$.   (a) T'(2) = 4 - 3/9 = 11/3.   (b) T'(5) = 4 - 3/36 = 47/12.   (c) T'(9) = 4 - 3/100 = 3.97.

7. v(t) = s'(t) = 6t-12 = 6(t-2), a(t) = v'(t) = 6, $0 \le t \le 5$. Since v(t) < 0 for $0 \le t < 2$ and > 0 for $2 < t \le 5$, the motion is to the left from s(0) = 1 to s(2) = -11 from t = 0 to t = 2, then to the right to s(5) = 16 from t = 2 to t = 5.

10. v(t) = $6-3t^2$ = $3(2-t^2)$, a(t) = -6t, $-2 \le t \le 3$. Since v(t) > 0 if $|t| < \sqrt{2}$ and < 0 if $|t| > \sqrt{2}$, we have the following motion: to the left from s(-2) = 20 to s($-\sqrt{2}$) = $24 - 4\sqrt{2} \approx 18.4$ as t goes from -2 to $-\sqrt{2}$; then to the right until t = $\sqrt{2}$ and s($\sqrt{2}$) = 24 + $4\sqrt{2} \approx 29.66$; finally to the left until t = 3 and s(3) = 15.

13. v(t) = $8t^3 - 12t$ = $4t(2t^2-3)$, a(t) = $24t^2 - 12$, $-2 \le t \le 2$. On the intervals $[-2, -\sqrt{3/2})$ and $(0, \sqrt{3/2})$, v(t) < 0 and the motion is to the left. On $(-\sqrt{3/2}, 0)$ and $(\sqrt{3/2}, 2]$, v(t) > 0 and the motion is to the right.

16. v(t) = $(1/3)t^{-2/3}$ = $1/3\sqrt[3]{t^2}$. a(t) = $-2/9\sqrt[3]{t^5}$. Since v(t) > 0 for all t, the motion is strictly to the right from s(-8) = -2 to s(0) as t goes from -8 to 0.

19. $v(t) = 6t^2 - 30t + 48$, $a(t) = 12t - 30$. $v(t) = 12 \iff 6t^2 - 30t + 48 = 12$
     $\iff 6(t^2 - 5t + 6) = 0 \implies t = 2$ and $t = 3$, $a(2) = 24 - 30 = -6$, $a(3) = 36 - 30 = 6$. For the next part, $a(t) = 10 \iff 12t - 40 = 0 \iff t = 10/3$.
     $v(10/3) = (600/9) - 100 + 48 = 44/3$.

22. $V = \frac{4}{3}\pi r^3 \implies \frac{dV}{dr} = 4\pi r^2 = A$.

25. We seek $\frac{dF}{dC}$ here. Solving $C = \frac{5}{9}(F-32)$ for F as a function of C we obtain
     $F = \frac{9}{5}C + 32 \implies \frac{dF}{dC} = \frac{9}{5}$ for all C.

28. If k is the constant of proportionality, then $R = \frac{k}{d^2}$ and $D_d R = \frac{-2k}{d^3}$. (Don't
     use the differential notation if d is the independent variable. $\frac{dR}{dd}$ would
     result, with 2 meanings for the d's.)

EXERCISES 4.8, page 182

1. Let x and y be the distances shown. Then $x^2 + y^2 = 20^2$;
    it is given that $dx/dt = 3$, and dy/dt is desired when
    $y = 8$ (and thus $x = \sqrt{400-64} = \sqrt{336}$). $x^2 + y^2 = 400 \implies$
    $2x\frac{dx}{dt} + 2y\frac{dy}{dt} = 0 \implies \frac{dy}{dt} = -\frac{x}{y}\frac{dx}{dt} = -\frac{\sqrt{336}}{8}(3) \approx -6.9$
    ft/sec. (Negative since it's falling and y is
    decreasing.)

4. Let x be the distance of the first girl east of A, y the distance of the
    second girl north of A, z the distance between them. Then $z^2 = x^2 + y^2$;
    $2z\frac{dz}{dt} = 2x\frac{dx}{dt} + 2y\frac{dy}{dt}$. When $t = 2$ min $= 120$ sec, $x = 1200$ since $\frac{dx}{dt} = 10$. The
    second girl has only been running for 60 seconds, and so $y = 480$ since $\frac{dy}{dt} = 8$.

    At that time $z = \sqrt{1200^2 + 480^2} = 120\sqrt{116}$ and substituting these values:
    $2(120)\sqrt{116}\frac{dz}{dt} = 2(1200)(10) + 2(480)(8) = 240(132) \implies \frac{dz}{dt} = \frac{132}{\sqrt{116}}$
    ≈ 12.3 ft/sec.

7. Let L = the thickness of the ice so that $\frac{dL}{dt} = -\frac{1}{4}$ in/hr. Let V = volume of
    the ice so that $\frac{dV}{dt}$ is desired when $L = 2$ in. Now, V = (volume of a hemis-
    phere of radius (120+L)" - volume of a hemisphere of radius 120") =
    $\frac{1}{2}(\frac{4}{3})\pi(120+L)^3 - \frac{1}{2}(\frac{4}{3})\pi(120)^3$. $\frac{dV}{dt} = \frac{dV}{dL}\frac{dL}{dt} = 2\pi(120+L)^2\frac{dL}{dt}$, which, when $L = 2$
    yields $\frac{dV}{dt} = 2\pi(122)^2(-\frac{1}{4}) \approx -23,380$ in^3/hr.

10. All distances will be in feet; thus the observer
     is 300 ft. (100 yds) from the point below the bal-
     loon. Let y be the altitude of the balloc in feet,
     and L the distance between it and the observer.
     Then $dy/dt = 2$ and we want dL/dt when $y = 500$.
     $L^2 = y^2 + 300^2 \implies 2L\ dL/dt = 2y\ dy/dt \implies$
     $dL/dt = (y/L)\,dy/dt$. When $y = 500$, $L =$
     $\sqrt{340,000} \doteq 100\sqrt{34}$. Thus $dL/dt = 10/\sqrt{34} \approx$
     1.7 ft/sec.

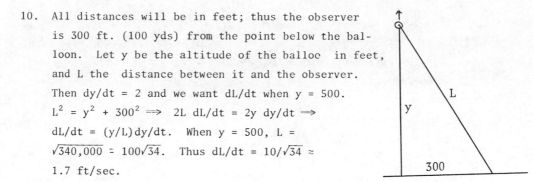

13. Let V be the volume and h the depth of the water. If A is
     the area of the wetted triangular region at the end of the
     trough as pictured, then $V = 8A$. The region is an equi-
     lateral triangle of side length s and altitude h. Then
     $s^2 = h^2 + s^2/4 \implies s = 2h/\sqrt{3}$. Also, $A = sh/2 = h^2/\sqrt{3}$ and
     $V = 8h^2/\sqrt{3}$. Thus $\dfrac{dV}{dt} = \dfrac{16h}{\sqrt{3}}\dfrac{dh}{dt}$. Using $\dfrac{dV}{dt} = 5$, $h = 8'' =$
     $\dfrac{2'}{3}$, we get $5 = \dfrac{32}{3\sqrt{3}}\dfrac{dh}{dt}$ or $\dfrac{dh}{dt} = \dfrac{15\sqrt{3}}{32} \approx .8$ ft/min ≈ 9.75 in/min.

16. $y^2 = x^2 - 9 \implies 2y\dfrac{dy}{dt} = 2x\dfrac{dx}{dt} = 2x(\dfrac{1}{x}) = 2$. Thus $\dfrac{dy}{dt} = \dfrac{1}{y}$ which at (5,4) is $\dfrac{1}{4}$.

19. Let C be the circumference and r the radius. Then $C = 2\pi r$. We are given
     that $\dfrac{dr}{dt} = 0.5$ m/sec, and we seek $\dfrac{dC}{dt}$ when $r = 4$. $\dfrac{dC}{dt} = 2\pi\dfrac{dr}{dt} = 2\pi(.5) =$
     π m/sec for all r.

22. At the given instant, it is given that $p = 40$, $\dfrac{dp}{dt} = 3$, $v = 60$, and we are to
     find $\dfrac{dv}{dt}$ then. Using the product rule, $pv^{1.4} = c \implies 1.4\ pv^{0.4}\dfrac{dv}{dt} + v^{1.4}\dfrac{dp}{dt}$
     $= 0$ so that $\dfrac{dv}{dt} = -\dfrac{v^{1.4}}{1.4pv^{0.4}}\dfrac{dp}{dt} = -\dfrac{v}{1.4p}\dfrac{dp}{dt}$. So: $\dfrac{dv}{dt} = -\dfrac{60}{1.4(40)}(3) = -\dfrac{45}{14} \approx$
     -3.2 cm^3/sec., negative since v decreases as p increases (at constant temp.).

25. Let $t = 0$ be the instant at which the first stone is dropped. Then the second
     is dropped 2 seconds later at $t = 2$. If $2 \le t \le 3$, the first stone has fallen
     $16t^2$ ft. However, the second stone has been falling for only $t-2$ seconds,
     and has fallen, therefore, $16(t-2)^2$ ft. The distance, L, between them is
     then $L = 16t^2 - 16(t-2)^2 = 64t - 64$ and $\dfrac{dL}{dt} = 64$ for all t (i.e. the distance
     between them steadily increases at the rate of 64 ft/sec.).

28. Let t = # of hours past 10 a.m.,

       y = # of miles car is north of P,

       x = # of miles plane is <u>west</u> of P,

       z = altitude of plane in miles, and

       L = distance between car and plane.

Then $L^2 = x^2 + y^2 + z^2$. We are given that $\frac{dy}{dt} = 50$,

$\frac{dx}{dt} = -200$ (negative since plane is moving east and x

is decreasing), $\frac{dz}{dt} = 0$ (altitude is constant). We have to find $\frac{dL}{dt}$ when $t = \frac{1}{4}$

(10:15 a.m. is $\frac{1}{4}$ hour past 10). At $t = \frac{1}{4}$, $y = 50(\frac{1}{4}) = 12.5$, $x = 100 - 200(\frac{1}{4})$

$= 50$ (it started 100 miles west of P when t = 0, then moved east for $\frac{1}{4}$ hour),

$z = 5$, and $L = \sqrt{12.5^2 + 50^2 + 5^2} = \sqrt{2681.25} \approx 51.78$. Now, $L^2 = x^2 + y^2 + z^2$

$\Longrightarrow 2L\frac{dL}{dt} = 2x\frac{dx}{dt} + 2y\frac{dy}{dt} + 2z\frac{dz}{dt} \Longrightarrow \frac{dL}{dt} = \frac{1}{L}(x\frac{dx}{dt} + y\frac{dy}{dt})$ since $\frac{dz}{dt} = 0$.

Substituting: $\frac{dL}{dt} = \frac{1}{\sqrt{2681.25}}(50(-200) + \frac{25}{2}(50)) = \frac{-9375}{\sqrt{2681.25}} \approx -181$ mph.

EXERCISES 4.9, page 189

NOTE: In Exercises 1-28, F will denote the most general antiderivative of the given function. (4.33)-(4.34) are the formulas used to find F. Remember: The answer F can always be checked by differentiating, F' should be f.

1. $f(x) = 9x^2 - 4x + 3 \Longrightarrow F(x) = \frac{9x^3}{3} - \frac{4x^2}{2} + 3x + C = 3x^3 - 2x^2 + 3x + C.$

4. $f(x) = 10x^4 - 6x^3 + 5 \Longrightarrow F(x) = \frac{10x^5}{5} - \frac{6x^4}{4} + 5x + C = 2x^5 - \frac{3}{2}x^4 + 5x + C.$

7. $f(x) = 3\sqrt{x} + 1/\sqrt{x} = 3x^{1/2} + x^{-1/2} \Longrightarrow F(x) = \frac{3x^{3/2}}{(3/2)} + \frac{x^{1/2}}{(1/2)} + C = 2x^{3/2} +$
$2x^{1/2} + C.$

10. $f(x) = 3x^5 - \sqrt[3]{x^5} = 3x^5 - x^{5/3} \Longrightarrow F(x) = \frac{3x^6}{6} - \frac{x^{8/3}}{(8/3)} + C = \frac{x^6}{2} - \frac{3}{8}x^{8/3} + C.$

13. $f(x) = \frac{(3x + 4)^2}{x^4} = \frac{9x^2 + 24x + 16}{x^4} = 9x^{-2} + 24x^{-3} + 16x^{-4} \Longrightarrow F(x) = \frac{9x^{-1}}{-1}$
$+ \frac{24x^{-2}}{-2} + \frac{16x^{-3}}{-3} + C = -\frac{9}{x} - \frac{12}{x^2} - \frac{16}{3x^3} + C = (-1/x^3)(9x^2 + 12x + 16/3) + C.$

16. $f(x) = (2x-5)(3x+1) = 6x^2 - 13x - 5 \Longrightarrow F(x) = \frac{6}{3}x^3 - \frac{13}{2}x^2 - 5x + C = 2x^3 -$
$\frac{13}{2}x^2 - 5x + C.$

19. $f(x) = \sqrt[5]{32x^4} = 2x^{4/5} \Longrightarrow F(x) = \frac{2x^{9/5}}{9/5} + C = \frac{10}{9}x^{9/5} + C.$

22. $f(x) = \dfrac{x^3 + 3x^2 - 9x - 2}{x - 2} = \dfrac{(x-2)(x^2 + 5x + 1)}{x - 2} = x^2 + 5x + 1 \ (\text{if } x \neq 2) \implies$

$F(x) = \dfrac{x^3}{3} + \dfrac{5}{2}x^2 + x + C \ (\text{if } x \neq 2).$

25. $f''(x) = 4x-1 \implies f'(x) = 2x^2 - x + C. \quad f'(2) = -2 \implies 8 - 2 + C = -2 \implies C$

$= -8. \text{ Thus, } f'(x) = 2x^2 - x - 8 \implies f(x) = \dfrac{2}{3}x^3 - \dfrac{x^2}{2} - 8x + D. \quad f(1) = 3$

$\implies \dfrac{2}{3} - \dfrac{1}{2} - 8 + D = 3 \implies D = 11 - 1/6 = 65/6.$

28. $f''(t) = t^{2/3} \implies f'(t) = \dfrac{3}{5} t^{5/3} + C. \quad f'(1) = 2 \implies \dfrac{3}{5} + C = 2, \text{ or } C = \dfrac{7}{5}.$

Thus $f'(t) = \dfrac{3}{5} t^{5/3} + \dfrac{7}{5} \implies f(t) = \dfrac{3}{5} \cdot \dfrac{3}{8} t^{8/3} + \dfrac{7}{5} t + D = \dfrac{9}{40} t^{8/3} + \dfrac{7}{5} t + D.$

$f(1) = 3 \implies \dfrac{9}{40} + \dfrac{7}{5} + D = 3 \implies D = \dfrac{120 - 9 - 56}{40} = \dfrac{55}{40} = \dfrac{11}{8}.$

31. $a(t) = v'(t) = -32 \implies v(t) = -32t + C. \quad v(0) = 80 \implies C = 80 \text{ and } v(t) =$
$s'(t) = -32t + 80 \implies s(t) = -16t^2 + 80t + D. \quad s(0) = 240 \implies D = 240.$

34. We represent the motion as in Example 6--origin at ground level, positive
direction upward. Then $v(0) = 0$, $s(0) = 1000$. $a(t) = -32 \implies v(t) = -32t +$
C. But C = 0 from $v(0) = 0$. So, $v(t) = -32t$ and $s(t) = -16t^2 + 1000$, where
s is the distance above ground. Thus the distance <u>fallen</u> in t seconds is
$16t^2$, and $v(3) = -96$. It strikes the ground when $s(t)$ becomes 0, i.e. when
$16t^2 = 1000$ or $t = \sqrt{250}/2 \approx 7.9$ sec. (Alternate method: place origin at
the 1000 ft. level. Then $s(0) = 0$, $s(t) = -16t^2$, and it hits the ground
when $s(t) = -1000$.)

37. The same setup as in #34 is needed so that $s(t)$ is the distance above ground.
The initial conditions are $v(0) = v_0$, $s(0) = s_0$. $a(t) = -g \implies v(t) = -gt +$
C. $v(0) = v_0 \implies C = v_0 \implies v(t) = -gt + v_0 \implies s(t) = -\dfrac{1}{2}gt^2 + v_0 t + D.$
$s(0) = s_0 \implies D = s_0.$

40. Let $a(t) = k$, unknown. The initial and final conditions are $v(0) = 60$ mph $=$
88 ft/sec and $v(9) = 0$. $a(t) = k \implies v(t) = kt + C. \quad v(0) = 88 \implies C = 88$
$\implies v(t) = kt + 88. \quad v(9) = 0 \implies 9k + 88 = 0 \implies k = -88/9$ ft/sec$^2 =$
-60/9 mph/sec.

43. $\dfrac{dV}{dt} = 3\sqrt{t} + \dfrac{t}{4} = 3t^{1/2} + \dfrac{t}{4} \implies V = \dfrac{3t^{3/2}}{(3/2)} + \dfrac{t^2}{8} + C = 2\sqrt{t^3} + \dfrac{t^2}{8} + C.$ Setting
$t = 4$ and $V = 20$: $20 = 2\sqrt{64} + \dfrac{16}{8} + C = 16 + 2 + C \implies C = 2.$

EXERCISES 4.10, page 196

1. (a) $C(100) = 800 + .04(100) + .0002(10,000) = 800 + 4 + 2 = 806.$
    (b) Average cost $= c(x) = C(x)/x = 800/x + .04 + .0002x$, $c(100) = 8 + .04 +$
    $.02 = 8.06.$ Marginal cost $= C'(x) = .04 + .0004x$, $C'(100) = .04 + .04 = .08.$

(c) $c(x)$ is minimized when $C'(x) = c(x)$ (see p. 209), or $xC'(x) = C(x) \Longrightarrow$
$.04x + .0004x^2 = 800 + .04x + .0002x^2 \Longrightarrow .0002x^2 = 800 \Longrightarrow x^2 = 800/.0002 =$
$4,000,000 \Longrightarrow x = 2,000$. The minimum average cost is $c(2,000) = 800/2000 +$
$.04 + .0002(2000) = .40 + .04 + .40 = .84$.

(d) $c'(x) > 0$ for all $x \geq 0$ from (b). Thus $C(x)$ is an increasing function
and the minimum of $C(x)$ is at $x = 0$.

4. (a) $C(100) = 200 + 100/\sqrt{100} + \sqrt{100}/1000 = 200 + 10 + .01 = 210.01$.

(b) $c(x) = C(x)/x = 200/x + 100/x\sqrt{x} + 1/1000\sqrt{x}$, $c(100) = 2 + 1/10 + 1/10,000$
$= 2.1001$. $C'(x) = -50x^{-3/2} + x^{-1/2}/2000$, $C'(100) = -50/(100)10 + 1/(2000)10$
$= -.05 + .00005 = -.04995$.

(c) Directly, $c'(x) = -200/x^2 - 150x^{-5/2} - x^{-3/2}/2000 < 0$ for all $x > 0$.
Thus $c(x)$ decreases and has no minimum.

(d) $C'(x) = 0 \iff -50x^{-3/2} + x^{-1/2}/2000 = 0 \iff -50 + x/2000 = 0 \iff x = 50(2000) = 100,000$.

7. $3S + 4x - 800 = 0 \Longrightarrow S = 800/3 - (4/3)x = p(x)$ and $p'(x) = -4/3$, the demand
and marginal demand functions. $R(x) = xp(x) = \frac{800}{3}x - \frac{4}{3}x^2$, $R'(x) = \frac{800}{3} - \frac{8}{3}x$,
the total revenue and marginal revenue functions. $R'(x) = 0 \Longrightarrow x = 100$ and
$R''(x) < 0 \Longrightarrow 100$ units for maximum revenue. $p(100) = 800/3 - 400/3 = 400/3$
$= 133.33$.

10. $Sx^2 - 1000x + 144S - 5000 = 0 \Longrightarrow S = 1000(x+5)/(x^2+144) = p(x)$ and $p'(x) =$
$1000(144 - 10x - x^2)/(x^2+144)^2$. $R(x) = xp(x) = 1000(x^2+5x)/(x^2+144)$ and
$R'(x) = 1000(720 + 288x - 5x^2)/(x^2+144)^2 = 1000(60-x)(12+5x)/(x^2+144)^2$.
$R'(x) = 0$ and $x > 0$ only if $x = 60$. (This maximizes $R(x)$ by the first derivative test.) So, 60 units for maximum revenue. Price per item is $p(60)$
$= 1000(65)/3744 \approx 17.36$.

13. (a) $R(x) = 300x - x^3 \Longrightarrow R'(x) = 300 - 3x^2 = 3(100-x^2)$.

(b) $R'(x) = 0$ and $x > 0$ only if $x = 10$. $R''(10) = -60 \Longrightarrow$ maximum total
revenue is $R(10) = 3000 - 1000 = 2000$.

(c) $R(x) = xp(x) \Longrightarrow p(x) = R(x)/x = 300 - x^2$.

16. $p(x) = 80 - \sqrt{x-1}$, $C(x) = 75x + 2\sqrt{x-1}$.

(a) $p'(x) = -1/2\sqrt{x-1}$.   (b) $R(x) = xp(x) = 80x - x\sqrt{x-1}$.

(c) $P(x) = R(x) - C(x) = 5x - (x+2)\sqrt{x-1}$.

(d) $P'(x) = 5 - \frac{(x+2)}{2\sqrt{x-1}} - \sqrt{x-1} = \frac{10\sqrt{x-1} - (x+2) - 2(x-1)}{2\sqrt{x-1}} = (10\sqrt{x-1}-3x)/2\sqrt{x-1}$.

(e) $P'(x) = 0$ when $10\sqrt{x-1} = 3x \iff 100(x-1) = 9x^2 \iff 9x^2 - 100x + 100 = 0$
$\iff (9x-10)(x-10) = 0 \Longrightarrow x = 10/9$ and $x = 10$. We calculate $P(1) = 5$,
$P(10/9) = 122/27 \approx 4.52$, $P(10) = 14$ and observe that for $x > 10$, $P'(x) < 0$
and $P(x)$ decreases, eventually becoming negative. Thus the maximum profit

is 14 when 10 items are produced.

(f) $C'(x) = 75 + 1/\sqrt{x-1} \implies C'(10) = 75 + 1/3$.

19. Here, $C(x) = 500 + .02x + .001x^2$ and $p(x) = 8$. Thus $R(x) = 8x$ and $P(x) =$
    $R(x) - C(x) = 7.98x - 500 - .001x^2$. $P'(x) = 7.98 - .002x = 0$ when $x =$
    $7.98/.002 = 3990$. $P''(x) < 0 \implies$ this produces a maximum of $P(x)$. The
    maximum profit is $P(3990) = 7.98(3990) - 500 - .001(3990)^2 = 31,840.20 -$
    $500 - 15,920.10 = 15,420.10$ dollars.

22. $p(x) = ax^2 + b \implies R(x) = xp(x) = ax^3 + bx$
    $R'(x) = 3ax^2 + b = 0$ and $x > 0$ only if $x = \sqrt{-b/3a}$ $(b > 0, a < 0 \implies -b/3a > 0)$
    $R''(\sqrt{-b/3a}) < 0 \implies$ maximum.

25. $C'(x) = 20 - .015x \implies C(x) = 20x - .0075x^2 + D$. $C(1) = 25 = 20 - .0075 + D$
    $\implies D = 5.0075$. $C(50) = 20(50) - .0075(2500) + 5.0075 = 1000 - 18.75 +$
    $5.0075 \approx 986.26$.

28. $R'(x) = 4(x+2)^{-3/2} \implies R(x) = -8(x+2)^{-1/2} + D$. The initial condition is $R(0)$
    $= 0$. (No items sold means no revenue.) Thus $-8/\sqrt{2} + D = 0 \implies D = +8/\sqrt{2} \implies$
    $R(x) = xp(x) = 8(1/\sqrt{2} - 1/\sqrt{x+2}) \implies p(x) = 8/x(1/\sqrt{2} - 1/\sqrt{x+2}) \implies p'(x) =$
    $\frac{8}{x}(\frac{1}{2(x+2)^{3/2}}) - \frac{8}{x^2}(\frac{1}{\sqrt{2}} - \frac{1}{\sqrt{x+2}})$.

EXERCISES 4.11, page 198

1. $6x^2 - 2xy + y^3 = 9 \implies 12x - 2xy' - 2y + 3y^2y' = 0 \implies y' = (2y-12x)/(3y^2-2x)$.
   At $(2,-3)$, $y' = (-6 - 24)/(27 - 4) = -30/23$. Thus
       Tangent: $y+3 = (-30/23)(x-2)$
       Normal: $y+3 = (23/30)(x-2)$.

4. $x^2 - 2xy + y^2 - 4 = 0 \implies 2x - 2xy' - 2y + 2yy' = 0 \implies y' = 1$. Thus, no
   horizontal or vertical tangents. (Writing the given equations as
   $(x-y)^2 - 2^2 = 0$, the graph is seen to consist of the 2 parallel lines
   $x-y = \pm 2$.)

7. $f'(x) = \dfrac{-2x}{(1+x^2)^2}$ $\begin{cases} > 0 \text{ if } x < 0 \\ \\ < 0 \text{ if } x > 0 \end{cases}$

   Thus f is increasing on $(-\infty,0]$, decreasing on $[0,\infty)$, and has a local maximum
   $f(0) = 1$.

10. (Continuation of #7)

    $f''(x) = \dfrac{2(3x^2-1)}{(1+x^2)^3}$ $\begin{cases} > 0 \text{ if } |x| > 1/\sqrt{3} \\ \\ < 0 \text{ if } |x| < 1\sqrt{3} \end{cases}$

    Thus the graph is CU on $(-\infty,-1/\sqrt{3})$ and $(1/\sqrt{3},\infty)$, CD on $(-1/\sqrt{3},1/\sqrt{3})$ with points of inflection at $x = \pm 1/\sqrt{3}$. $f''(0) = -2$ confirms that there is a local maximum at $x = 0$.

13. First note that $x^3 - 6x = x(x^2 - 6)$ is ≥ 0 if $-\sqrt{6} \leq x \leq 0$ or $\sqrt{6} \leq x$, and is ≤ 0 if $x \leq -\sqrt{6}$ or $0 \leq x \leq \sqrt{6}$. Next, $f(x) = |x^3 - 6x| = ((x^2 + 6x)^2)^{1/2} \implies$

$$f'(x) = \frac{1}{2}((x^3 - 6x)^2)^{-1/2}D_x[(x^3 - 6x)^2] = \frac{(x^3 - 6x)(3x^2 - 6)}{\sqrt{(x^3 - 6x)^2}} =$$

$\dfrac{3(x^3 - 6x)(x^2 - 2)}{|x^3 - 6x|}$. The critical numbers of f are 0, $\pm\sqrt{6}$ at which f' fails to exist (at each point the left and right derivatives differ) and $x = \pm\sqrt{2}$ at which f' is 0. From the sign analysis at the start of the problem, $f'(x) = 3(x^2 - 2)$, $f''(x) = 6x$ if $-\sqrt{6} < x < 0$ or $\sqrt{6} < x$ where $x^3 - 6 > 0$. Moreover, $f'(x) = -3(x^2 - 2)$, $f''(x) = -6x$ if $x < -\sqrt{6}$ or $0 < x < \sqrt{6}$, where $x^3 - 6x < 0$. The analysis is then tabulated.

Interval	$(-\infty,-\sqrt{6})$	$(-\sqrt{6},-\sqrt{2})$	$(-\sqrt{2},0)$	$(0,\sqrt{2})$	$(\sqrt{2},\sqrt{6})$	$(\sqrt{6},\infty)$
k	-3	-2	-1	1	2	3
f'(k)	-21	6	-3	3	-6	21
f'(x)	-	+	-	+	-	+
Variation of f	Dec'g	Inc'g	Dec'g	Inc'g	Dec'g	Inc'g

Thus f has local minima at $x = 0$, $\pm\sqrt{6}$ and local maxima at $x = \pm\sqrt{2}$. From the f''(x) formula above, the graph is CD on $(-\sqrt{6},0)$ and $(0,\sqrt{6})$ and is CU on $(-\infty,-\sqrt{6})$ and $(\sqrt{6},\infty)$.

16. With x and y as shown, we are given that $\frac{dx}{dt} = 3$, and we seek $\frac{d}{dt}(\frac{y}{x})$ when $x = 6$. Since this derivative will contain dy/dt, we must first evaluate this when $x = 6$.

$x^2 + y^2 = 12^2 \implies 2x\frac{dx}{dt} + 2y\frac{dy}{dt} = 0 \implies \frac{dy}{dt} = -\frac{x}{y}\frac{dx}{dt}$.

When $x = 6$, $y = \sqrt{144-36} = \sqrt{108} = 6\sqrt{3}$, and, thus,

$\frac{dy}{dt} = \frac{-6}{6\sqrt{3}}(3) = -\sqrt{3}$. Now, $\frac{d}{dt}(\frac{y}{x}) = \frac{x\,dy/dt - y\,dx/dy}{x^2}$.

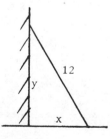

Substituting the values already computed we obtain

$\frac{6(-\sqrt{3}) - (6\sqrt{3})3}{36} = \frac{-24\sqrt{3}}{36} = -\frac{2\sqrt{3}}{3}$.

19. $f(x) = 3x^5 + 2x^3 - x \implies F(x) = \frac{3}{6}x^6 + \frac{2}{4}x^4 - \frac{1}{2}x^2 + C = (x^6 + x^4 - x^2)/2 + C$.

22. $f(x) = (2x+1)^3 = 8x^3 + 12x^2 + 6x + 1 \implies F(x) = \frac{8}{4}x^4 + \frac{12}{3}x^3 + \frac{6}{2}x^2 + x + C = 2x^4 + 4x^3 + 3x^2 + x + C$.

25. With x and y the field dimensions shown, $4x + 2y = 1000$
$\Rightarrow$ $y = (1000-4x)/2 = 500 - 2x \Rightarrow A = xy = x(500-2x) =$
$500x - 2x^2 \Rightarrow A' = 500 - 4x = 0$ if $x = 125$ yds.
$A'' = -4 < 0 \Rightarrow$ maximum. Thus the dimensions for
maximum area 125 yds by 250 yds.

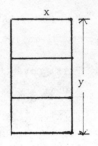

28. Let the lengths of the pieces be x and 5-x with the x length bent into a circle. The radius of this circle is $r = x/2\pi$ and the area is $\pi r^2 = x^2/4\pi$. The
perimeter of the square being 5-x gives us $(5-x)/4$ for the length of a side
and $(5-x)^2/16$ for the area. The sum of these areas, A, is thus $A =$
$x^2/4\pi + (5-x)^2/16$, $0 \le x \le 5$. We desire the maximum of A (for part (a)) and
the minimum of A (for part (b)) on [0,5]. First, we'll find the critical
numbers, if any, in [0,5]. $A' = \dfrac{x}{2\pi} - \dfrac{(5-x)}{8} = x(\dfrac{1}{2\pi} + \dfrac{1}{8}) - \dfrac{5}{8} = x(\dfrac{8+2\pi}{16\pi}) - \dfrac{5}{8} = 0$
if $x = \dfrac{5}{8}(\dfrac{16\pi}{8+2\pi}) = \dfrac{5\pi}{4+\pi} \approx 2.2$. A attains a local minimum there since $A'' > 0$.
Since $A(0) = 25/16 \approx 1.56$, and $A(5) = 25/4\pi \approx 2$, A is maximized when $x = 5$
(i.e. the entire wire is bent into a circle), and A is minimized when $x =$
$5\pi/(4+\pi)$.

31. From the figure, using similar triangles, $\dfrac{r}{h} = \dfrac{4}{12}$ or $r = \dfrac{h}{3}$.

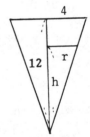

Thus $V = (1/3)\pi r^2 h = (\pi/27)h^3$ and $\dfrac{dV}{dt} = \dfrac{\pi}{9}h^2\dfrac{dh}{dt}$. We are given
that $\dfrac{dV}{dt} = -10$ ft^3/min., and we desire $\dfrac{dh}{dt}$ when $h = 5$. Substituting: $-10 = \dfrac{25\pi}{9}\dfrac{dh}{dt}$ or $\dfrac{dh}{dt} = -\dfrac{90}{25\pi} \approx -1.15$ ft/min.

34. $y^2 = 2x^3 \Rightarrow 2y\dfrac{dy}{dt} = 6x^2\dfrac{dx}{dt}$. At (2,4), $\dfrac{dy}{dt} = x = 2$ and thus $8(2) = 6(2)^2\dfrac{dx}{dt}$
$\Rightarrow \dfrac{dx}{dt} = \dfrac{16}{24} = \dfrac{2}{3}$.

37. $\lim\limits_{x \to -\infty} \dfrac{(2x-5)(3x+1)}{(x+7)(4x-9)} = \lim\limits_{x \to -\infty} \dfrac{(2-5/x)(3+1/x)}{(1+7/x)(4-9/x)} = \dfrac{(2)(3)}{(1)(4)} = \dfrac{3}{2}$.

40. $\lim\limits_{x \to -3} \sqrt[3]{\dfrac{x+3}{x^3+27}} = \lim\limits_{x \to -3} \sqrt[3]{\dfrac{x+3}{(x+3)(x^2-3x+9)}} = \lim\limits_{x \to -3} \sqrt[3]{\dfrac{1}{x^2-3x+9}} = \sqrt[3]{\dfrac{1}{9+9+9}} = \sqrt[3]{\dfrac{1}{27}} = \dfrac{1}{3}$.

43. As $x \to 0^+$, $\sqrt{x} \to 0$ and is positive. Thus $1/\sqrt{x} \to \infty$ and $\sqrt{x} - 1/\sqrt{x} \to -\infty$.

46. $\lim\limits_{x \to \pm\infty} \dfrac{x^2}{(x-1)^2} = \lim\limits_{x \to \pm\infty} \dfrac{1}{(1/x-1)^2} = 1 \Rightarrow y = 1$ is a horizontal asymptote.

$\lim\limits_{x \to 1} \dfrac{x^2}{(x-1)^2} = \infty \Rightarrow x = 1$ is a vertical asymptote. For the graph, $f'(x) =$

$-2x/(x-1)^3 = 0$ only at $x = 0$. $f''(x) = 2(2x+1)/(x-1)^4$. $f''(0) = 2 > 0 \Rightarrow$
$f(0) = 0$ is a local minimum.   There is a PI at $x = -1/2$.

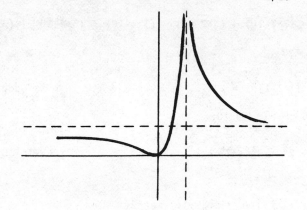

EXERCISES 5.1, page 208

1. $\displaystyle\sum_{k=1}^{5} (3k-10) = (3\cdot 1-10) + (3\cdot 2-10) + (3\cdot 3-10) + (3\cdot 4-10) + (3\cdot 5-10) =$

   $-7-4-1+2+5 = -5.$

4. Observe that $[1+(-1)^k] = 2$ if k is even and $= 0$ if k is odd. Thus $\displaystyle\sum_{k=1}^{10} [1+(-1)^k]$

   $= 0+2+0+2+0+2+0+2+0+2 = 10.$

7. $\displaystyle\sum_{i=1}^{8} 2^i = 2^1 + 2^2 + 2^3 + 2^4 + 2^5 + 2^6 + 2^7 + 2^8 = 2+4+8+16+32+64+128+256 = 510.$

10. $\displaystyle\sum_{k=1}^{1000} 2 = 2+2+...+2, 1000$ times yielding $2(1000) = 2000.$

13. $\displaystyle\sum_{k=1}^{n} (k^2+3k+5) = \sum_{k=1}^{n} k^2 + 3\sum_{k=1}^{n} k + \sum_{k=1}^{n} 5 = \frac{n(n+1)(2n+1)}{6} + \frac{3n(n+1)}{2} + 5n$

   $= \frac{n}{6}[(n+1)(2n+1) + 9(n+1) + 30] = n(n^2+6n+20)/3.$

16. $\displaystyle\sum_{k=1}^{n} (k^3+2k^2-k+4) = \sum_{k=1}^{n} k^3 + 2\sum_{k=1}^{n} k^2 - \sum_{k=1}^{n} k + \sum_{k=1}^{n} 4 = (\frac{n(n+1)}{2})^2 +$

   $\dfrac{2n(n+1)(2n+1)}{6} - \dfrac{n(n+1)}{2} + 4n = n[3n(n+1)^2 + 4(n+1)(2n+1) - 6(n+1) + 48]/12 =$

   $n(3n^3 + 14n^2 + 9n + 46)/12.$

19. $a = 0$, $b = 5 \Longrightarrow \Delta x = (b-a)/n = 5/n$, and the subdividing points are $x_o = 0$,

    $x_1 = a + \Delta x = 5/n$, $x_2 = a + 2\Delta x = 10/n$, ..., $x_i = a + i\Delta x = 5i/n$, ..., $x_n = 5$.

    Since $f(x) = x^2$ is increasing on $[0,5]$, the minimum value of f on $[x_{i-1},x_i]$

    occurs at the left end point, x_{i-1}, and the maximum value of f occurs at the

    right end point, x_i. Thus $u_i = x_{i-1} = 5(i-1)/n$ and $v_i = x_i = 5i/n$.

    (a) Here we need $f(u_i) = f(x_{i-1}) = f(\frac{5(i-1)}{n}) =$

    $[\frac{5(i-1)}{n}]^2 = \frac{25(i-1)^2}{n^2}$. Then

    $\displaystyle\sum_{i=1}^{n} f(u_i)\Delta x = \sum_{i=1}^{n} \frac{25(i-1)^2}{n^2} \cdot \frac{5}{n} = \frac{125}{n^3} \sum_{i=1}^{n} (i-1)^2.$

To evaluate the sum we write $\sum\limits_{i=1}^{n} (i-1)^2 =$

$$\sum_{i=1}^{n} (i^2 - 2i + 1) = \sum_{i=1}^{n} i^2 - 2 \sum_{i=1}^{n} i + \sum_{i=1}^{n} 1 =$$

$[\frac{n(n+1)(2n+1)}{6} - 2(\frac{n(n+1)}{2}) + n]$. We used (5.5ii) to evaluate the first sum,

(5.5i) for the second sum, and (5.2) (with c = 1) for the third. Substituting

the value for the sum into the previous expression, we obtain $\sum\limits_{i=1}^{n} f(u_i)\Delta x =$

$$\frac{125}{n^3}[\frac{n(n+1)(2n+1)}{6} - n(n+1) + n] = \frac{125(n+1)(2n+1)}{6n^2} - \frac{125(n+1)}{n^2} + \frac{125}{n^2} =$$

$\frac{125}{6}(1 + \frac{1}{n})(2 + \frac{1}{n}) - 125(\frac{1}{n} + \frac{1}{n^2}) + \frac{125}{n^2}$. As $\Delta x \to 0$, $\frac{5}{n} \to 0$, $n \to \infty$. Also $\frac{1}{n} \to 0$

and $\frac{1}{n^2} \to 0$ so that $(1 + \frac{1}{n}) \to 1$ and $(2 + \frac{1}{n}) \to 2$. Moreover, in the limit as

$n \to \infty$, the sums, $\sum\limits_{i=1}^{n} f(u_i)\Delta x$, approach the area. Thus, $\sum\limits_{i=1}^{n} f(u_i)\Delta x =$

$\frac{125}{6}(1+\frac{1}{n})(2+\frac{1}{n}) - 125(\frac{1}{n} + \frac{1}{n^2}) + \frac{125}{n^2} \to \frac{125}{6}(1)(2) - 125(0+0) - 125(0) = \frac{125}{3} = A.$

(b) Here we need $f(v_i) = f(x_i) = f(5i/n) = (5i/n)^2$

$= 25i^2/n^2$. Then $\sum\limits_{i=1}^{n} f(v_i)\Delta x = \sum\limits_{i=1}^{n} \frac{25i^2}{n^2} \cdot \frac{5}{n} =$

$\frac{125}{n^3} \sum\limits_{i=1}^{n} i^2 = \frac{125}{n^3} \cdot \frac{n(n+1)(2n+1)}{6} = \frac{125}{6}(1 + \frac{1}{n}) \cdot$

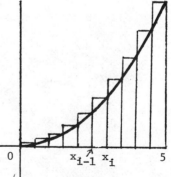

$(2 + \frac{1}{n})$, where we used (5.5ii) to evaluate the sum.

As above, these sums approach the area as $n \to \infty$

and we obtain $A = \frac{125}{6}(1)(2) = \frac{125}{3}$.

22. $a = -2$, $b = 6 \Rightarrow \Delta x = (6-(-2))/n = 8/n$, and the subdividing points are $x_o = a$

$= -2$, $x_1 = -2 + 8/n$, ..., $x_i = a + i\Delta x = -2 + 8i/n$, ..., $x_n = 6$. Since f is

constant, any point in $[x_{i-1}, x_i]$ can be used for u_i or v_i. $\sum\limits_{i=1}^{n} f(u_i)\Delta x =$

$$\sum_{i=1}^{n} f(v_i)\Delta x = \sum_{i=1}^{n} 7 \cdot \frac{8}{n} = \frac{56}{n} \sum_{i=1}^{n} 1 = \frac{56}{n}(n) = 56 \text{ for all } \Delta x \text{ and } n. \quad A = \lim_{n\to\infty} 56$$

= 56 as expected since the region is a rectangle with base 6-(-2) = 8 and height 7.

25. Here a = 1, b = 2, $\Delta x = 1/n$, and the subdividing points are $x_0 = 1$, $x_1 = 1 + 1/n$, ..., $x_i = 1 + i/n$, ..., $x_n = 2$. Since $f(x) = x^3 + 1$ is increasing, the minimum value of f on $[x_{i-1}, x_i]$ occurs at the left end point, x_{i-1}, and the maximum value of f occurs at the right end point, x_i. Thus $u_i = x_{i-1} = 1 + (i-1)/n$ and $v_i = x_i = 1 + i/n$.

(a) Here we need $f(u_i) = f(x_{i-1}) = f(1 + \frac{i-1}{n}) = (1 + \frac{i-1}{n})^3 + 1$. Recalling that $(c+d)^3 = c^3 + 3c^2d + 3cd^2 + d^3$ we obtain $f(u_i) =$

$$[1 + \frac{3(i-1)}{n} + \frac{3(i-1)^2}{n^2} + \frac{(i-1)^3}{n^3}] + 1. \quad \text{Then } \sum_{i=1}^{n} f(u_i)\Delta x = \sum_{i=1}^{n} [2 + \frac{3(i-1)}{n}$$

$$+ \frac{3(i-1)^2}{n^2} + \frac{(i-1)^3}{n^3}] \cdot \frac{1}{n} = \frac{1}{n} \sum_{i=1}^{n} 2 + \frac{1}{n} \sum_{i=1}^{n} [\frac{3(i-1)}{n} + \frac{3(i-1)^2}{n^2} + \frac{(i-1)^3}{n^3}].$$

We must now evaluate these sums. We could evaluate the second sum by expanding all the (i-1) expressions as in No. 19(a) above; however, there is an easier way. Observe that $\sum_{i=1}^{n} (i-1)^m = 0^m + 1^m + 2^m + \ldots + (n-1)^m = \sum_{j=1}^{n-1} j^m$ for any positive number m. Thus, (replacing the first sum by 2n using (5.2)),

$$\sum_{i=1}^{n} f(u_i)\Delta x = (\frac{1}{n}) 2n + \frac{1}{n} \sum_{i=1}^{n} [\frac{3(i-1)}{n} + \frac{3(i-1)^2}{n^2} + \frac{(i-1)^3}{n^3}] = 2 + \frac{1}{n} \sum_{j=1}^{n-1} (\frac{3j}{n}$$

$$+ \frac{3j^2}{n^2} + \frac{j^3}{n^3}) = 2 + \frac{3}{n^2} \sum_{j=1}^{n-1} j + \frac{3}{n^3} \sum_{j=1}^{n-1} j^2 + \frac{1}{n^4} \sum_{j=1}^{n-1} j^3. \quad \text{Now we use}$$

(5.5(i)-(iii)) with n replaced by n-1 (since the upper limit of summation is

now n-1) to obtain $\sum_{i=1}^{n} f(u_i)\Delta x = 2 + \frac{3}{n^2} \frac{(n-1)n}{2} + \frac{3}{n^3} \frac{(n-1)n(2n-1)}{6} +$

$\frac{1}{n^4}(\frac{(n-1)n}{2})^2 = 2 + \frac{3}{2} \frac{n-1}{n} + \frac{3}{6} \frac{n-1}{n} \frac{2n-1}{n} + \frac{1}{4}(\frac{n-1}{n})^2$. As $\Delta x \to 0$, $\frac{1}{n} \to 0$, and $n \to \infty$,

also $\frac{n-1}{n} = 1 - \frac{1}{n} \to 1$ and $\frac{2n-1}{n} = 2 - \frac{1}{n} \to 2$ and the sums $\sum_{i=1}^{n} f(u_i)\Delta x$ approach the area, A, as n approaches ∞. Thus, letting n approach ∞ in the above expression for $\sum\limits_{i=1}^{n} f(u_i)\Delta x$, we obtain $A = \lim\limits_{n\to\infty} \sum\limits_{i=1}^{n} f(u_i)\Delta x = \lim\limits_{n\to\infty} [2 + \frac{3}{2}\frac{n-1}{n} +$

$\frac{1}{2}\frac{n-1}{n}\frac{2n-1}{n} + \frac{1}{4}(\frac{n-1}{n})^2] = 2 + \frac{3}{2}(1) + \frac{1}{2}(1)(2) + \frac{1}{4}(1)^2 = 2 + \frac{3}{2} + 1 + \frac{1}{4} =$

$\frac{8+6+4+1}{4} = \frac{19}{4}$.

(b) $f(v_i) = f(x_i) = x_i^3 + 1 = (1 + \frac{i}{n})^3 + 1 = 2 + \frac{3}{n}i + \frac{3}{n^2}i^2 + \frac{i^3}{n^3}$. Then

recalling $\Delta x = 1/n$, $\sum\limits_{i=1}^{n} f(v_i)\Delta x = \sum\limits_{i=1}^{n} (2 + \frac{3}{n}i + \frac{3}{n^2}i^2 + \frac{i^3}{n^3}) \cdot \frac{1}{n} =$

$\frac{1}{n}\sum\limits_{i=1}^{n} 2 + \frac{3}{n^2}\sum\limits_{i=1}^{n} i + \frac{3}{n^3}\sum\limits_{i=1}^{n} i^2 + \frac{1}{n^4}\sum\limits_{i=1}^{n} i^3 = \frac{1}{n}(2n) + \frac{3}{n^2}\cdot\frac{n(n+1)}{2} + \frac{3}{n^3}\cdot$

$\frac{n(n+1)(2n+1)}{6} + \frac{1}{n^4}(\frac{n(n+1)}{2})^2 = 2 + \frac{3}{2}\frac{n+1}{n} + \frac{1}{2}\frac{(n+1)(2n+1)}{n^2} + \frac{1}{4}\frac{(n+1)^2}{n^2}$. As

$\Delta x \to 0$, $n \to \infty$, and, as above, $A = 2 + \frac{3}{2}(1) + \frac{1}{2}(1)(2) + \frac{1}{4}(1)^2 =$

$\frac{8+6+4+1}{4} = \frac{19}{4}$.

EXERCISES 5.2, page 215

1. $x_0 = 0$, $x_1 = 1.1$, $x_2 = 2.6$, $x_3 = 3.7$, $x_4 = 4.1$ and $x_5 = 5$. Thus $\Delta x_1 = x_1 - x_0$
= 1.1, $\Delta x_2 = x_2 - x_1 = 1.5$, $\Delta x_3 = x_3 - x_2 = 1.1$, $\Delta x_4 = x_4 - x_3 = 0.4$ and $\Delta x_5 =$
$x_5 - x_4 = 0.9$. The largest of the Δx_i's is $\Delta x_2 = 1.5 \implies \|P\| = 1.5$.

4. $x_0 = 1$, $x_1 = 1.6$, $x_2 = 2$, $x_3 = 3.5$, $x_4 = 4$. $\Delta x_1 = x_1 - x_0 = 0.6$, $\Delta x_2 = x_2 - x_1$
=0.4, $\Delta x_3 = x_3 - x_2 = 1.5$, $\Delta x_4 = x_4 - x_3 = 0.5$. $\|P\| = 1.5$ since the largest
Δx_i is $\Delta x_3 = 1.5$.

7. Since this is a regular partition, all Δx_i's are equal to $(b-a)/n = (6-0)/6$
= 1. With w_i as the midpoint of $[x_{i-1}, x_i] = [i-1, i]$, we have $R_p =$

$\sum\limits_{i=1}^{6} f(w_i)\Delta x_i = f(\frac{1}{2}) + f(\frac{3}{2}) + f(\frac{5}{2}) + f(\frac{7}{2}) + f(\frac{9}{2}) + f(\frac{11}{2}) = (8 - \frac{1}{2}(\frac{1}{4})) +$

$(8 - \frac{1}{2}(\frac{9}{4})) + (8 - \frac{1}{2}(\frac{25}{4})) + (8 - \frac{1}{2}(\frac{49}{4})) + (8 - \frac{1}{2}(\frac{81}{4})) + (8 - \frac{1}{2}(\frac{121}{4})) =$

$48 - \frac{1}{2} \frac{(1+9+25+49+81+121)}{4} = 48 - \frac{286}{8} = \frac{49}{4}$.

10. Here $\Delta x_1 = \Delta x_2 = \Delta x_3 = \Delta x_4 = 2$, $\Delta x_5 = 7$, and $R_p = f(1) \cdot 2 + f(4) \cdot 2 + f(5) \cdot 2 +$

 $f(9) \cdot 2 + f(9) \cdot 7 = 1 \cdot 2 + \sqrt{4} \cdot 2 + \sqrt{5} \cdot 2 + \sqrt{9} \cdot 2 + \sqrt{9} \cdot 7 = 2 + 4 + 2\sqrt{5} + 6 + 21 =$

 $33 + 2\sqrt{5} \approx 37.47.$

13. According to (5.8) , the expression involving w_i in the sum is $f(w_i)$. Here,

 $f(w_i) = 2\pi w_i (1+w_i^3)$ so that $f(x) = 2\pi x(1+x^3)$. The interval being partitioned

 is $[0,4]$. Thus, by (5.16) the limit is $\int_0^4 2\pi x(1+x^3)dx$.

16. By (5.10) , the value of the integral is 0.

19. $f(x) = 2x+6$ is continuous and ≥ 0 on $[-3,2]$. Thus, by (5.12) $\int_{-3}^2 2x+6 \ dx$ is

 the area under the graph of f from -3 to 2. The graph of $f(x) = 2x+6$ is a

 line from $(-3,0)$ to $(2,10)$, and the region is a triangle with base $2-(-3) =$

 5 and height 10. Thus the integral = area = $(1/2)5(10) = 25$.

22. $f(x) = \sqrt{a^2-x^2}$ is continuous and ≥ 0 on $[-a,a]$. By (5.12) the integral is the

 area under the graph of f from -a to a. The graph of f is the upper half of

 the circle of radius a centered at the origin. ($y = \sqrt{a^2-x^2} \implies y \geq 0$ and

 $y^2 = a^2 - x^2$, or $x^2 + y^2 = a^2$.) The region is, thus, a semi-circle of radius

 a and area $(1/2)\pi a^2$, which is the value of the integral.

EXERCISES 5.3, page 220

1. $\int_{-2}^4 5 \ dx = 5(4-(-2)) = 5(6) = 30.$

4. $\int_4^{-3} dx = -\int_{-3}^4 dx = -1(4-(-3)) = -7.$

7. By (5.15) $\int_1^4 (3x^2+5)dx = \int_1^4 3x^2 dx + \int_1^4 5 \ dx$. By (5.14) and (5.13) we get:

 $3\int_1^4 x^2 dx + 5(4-1) = 3(21) + 5(3) = 63 + 15 = 78.$

10. Using (5.15), (5.14) and (5.13), $\int_1^4 (3x+2)^2 \ dx = \int_1^4 (9x^2+12x+4)dx = \int_1^4 9x^2 dx$

 $+ \int_1^4 12x \ dx + \int_1^4 4 \ dx = 9\int_1^4 x^2 dx + 12\int_1^4 x \ dx + 4(4-1) = 9(21) + 12(15/2) + 12$

 $= 291.$

13. $\int_1^4 (\sqrt{x}-5)^2\,dx = \int_1^4 (x-10\sqrt{x}+25)\,dx = \int_1^4 x\,dx - 10\int_1^4 \sqrt{x}\,dx + \int_1^4 25\,dx = \frac{15}{2} -$

$10(\frac{14}{3}) + 25(3) = \frac{45}{6} - \frac{280}{6} + \frac{450}{6} = \frac{215}{6}$.

16. We can show that $f(x) = 5x^2 - 4\sqrt{x} + 2$ is positive for all x in [2,4]. For such x, $5x^2 + 2 \geq 22$ and $-4\sqrt{x} \geq -4\sqrt{4} = -8$. Adding these inequalities yields $5x^2 + 2 - 4\sqrt{x} \geq 22 - 8$, or $f(x) \geq 14$ on [2,4]. By (5.19),

$\int_2^4 f(x)\,dx \geq \int_2^4 14\,dx = 14(4-2) = 28 > 0$, as desired.

19. Rewriting the sum as $\int_{-3}^5 f(x)\,dx + \int_5^1 f(x)\,dx$, we use (5.17) to combine these

to get $\int_{-3}^1 f(x)\,dx$.

22. $\int_{-2}^6 f(x)\,dx - \int_{-2}^2 f(x)\,dx = \left[\int_{-2}^2 f(x)\,dx + \int_2^6 f(x)\,dx\right] - \int_{-2}^2 f(x)\,dx = \int_2^6 f(x)\,dx$,

where (5.17) was used to write the first integral as the sum in the brackets.

25. We write $\int_a^b$ as an abbreviation of $\int_a^b f(x)\,dx$. The first equation in each of

the four other cases follows from (5.16) for different a, b, c, of course.

(1) a < b < c. $\int_a^c = \int_a^b + \int_b^c \implies \int_a^b = \int_a^c - \int_b^c \implies \int_a^b = \int_a^c + \int_c^b$

(2) c < b < a. $\int_c^a = \int_c^b + \int_b^a \implies -\int_a^c = \int_c^b - \int_a^b \implies \int_a^b = \int_a^c + \int_c^b$

(3) b < a < c. $\int_b^c = \int_b^a + \int_a^c \implies -\int_c^b = -\int_a^b + \int_a^c \implies \int_a^b = \int_a^c + \int_c^b$

(4) b < c < a. $\int_b^a = \int_b^c + \int_c^a \implies -\int_a^b = -\int_a^c - \int_c^b \implies \int_a^b = \int_a^c + \int_c^b$

EXERCISES 5.4, page 223

1. We seek $z \in (0,3)$ so that $(3z^2)(3-0) = 27$ or $z^2 = 3$. Thus $z = \sqrt{3}$.

4. We seek $z \in (-2,-1)$ so that $8z^{-3}(-1-(-2)) = -3$ or $8z^{-3} = -3$. Thus $z = \sqrt[3]{-8/3} \approx -1.39$.

7. We seek $z \in (2,7)$ so that $\frac{1}{(z+3)^2}(7-2) = \frac{1}{10}$ or $\frac{1}{(z+3)^2} = \frac{1}{50}$. Thus $(z+3)^2 = 50$ $\implies z+3 = +\sqrt{50} = +5\sqrt{2} \implies z = -3 \pm 5\sqrt{2}$. For z to be in (2,7) the "+" sign must be chosen, and $z = -3 + 5\sqrt{2} \approx 4.07$.

10. We seek $z \in (1,3)$ so that $(z^2 + \frac{1}{z^2})(3-1) = \frac{28}{3}$ or $z^2 + \frac{1}{z^2} = \frac{14}{3}$. To solve,

    let $y = z^2$, and we obtain $y + \frac{1}{y} = \frac{14}{3}$ or $3y^2 - 14y + 3 = 0 \Rightarrow y =$

    $\frac{14 \pm \sqrt{14^2 - 4(3)(3)}}{6} = \frac{14 \pm \sqrt{196-36}}{6} = \frac{14 \pm \sqrt{160}}{6} = \frac{7 \pm \sqrt{40}}{3}$. If the "-"

    sign is used, then $y = z^2 = \frac{7 - \sqrt{40}}{3} \approx \frac{0.52}{3}$ and z is not in $(1,3)$. So we use

    the "+" sign and $y = z^2 = \frac{(7 + \sqrt{40})}{3} \Rightarrow z = \sqrt{(7 + \sqrt{40}/3} \approx 2.1$.

12. $\int_a^b x\, dx$ = area of the trapezoid shown = $\frac{(b+a)}{2}(b-a)$.

    Thus we seek $z \in (a,b)$ so that $z(b-a) = \frac{(b+a)}{2}(b-a)$.

    Thus $z = \frac{b+a}{2}$.

EXERCISES 5.5, page 229

1. $\int_1^4 (x^2-4x-3)\,dx = \frac{x^3}{3} - 2x^2 - 3x \Big]_1^4 = [\frac{64}{3} - 32 - 12] - [\frac{1}{3} - 2 - 3] = -18$.

4. $\int_0^2 (w^4-2w^3)\,dw = \frac{w^5}{5} - \frac{w^4}{2}\Big]_0^2 = [\frac{32}{5} - \frac{16}{2}] - [0-0] = -8/5$.

7. $\int_1^2 \frac{5}{8x^6}\,dx = \frac{5}{8}\int_1^2 x^{-6}\,dx = \frac{5}{8}[\frac{x^{-5}}{-5}]_1^2 = -\frac{1}{8}[2^{-5} - 1^{-5}] = -\frac{1}{8}[\frac{1}{32} - 1] = \frac{31}{256}$.

10. $\int_{-1}^{-2} \frac{2s-7}{s^3}\,ds = \int_{-1}^{-2} (2s^{-2} - 7s^{-3})\,ds = -2s^{-1} + \frac{7}{2}s^{-2}]_{-1}^{-2} = -\frac{2}{s} + \frac{7}{2s^2}]_{-1}^{-2} =$

    $[\frac{-2}{-2} + \frac{7}{2(4)}] - [\frac{-2}{-1} + \frac{7}{2}] = 1 + \frac{7}{8} - 2 - \frac{7}{2} = -\frac{29}{8}$.

13. $\int_0^1 (2x-3)(5x+1)\,dx = \int_0^1 (10x^2-13x-3)\,dx = \frac{10}{3}x^3 - \frac{13}{2}x^2 - 3x]_0^1 = \frac{10}{3} - \frac{13}{2} - 3$

    $= -\frac{37}{6}$.

16. The value is 0 since the upper and lower limits are the same. See (5.10).

17. HINT: $(x^2-1)/(x-1) = x+1$ if $x \neq 1$.

19. See #16.

22. $\displaystyle\int_{-2}^{-1} (r - \frac{1}{r})^2\,dr = \int_{-2}^{-1} (r^2 - 2r(\frac{1}{r}) + \frac{1}{r^2})\,dr = \int_{-2}^{-1} (r^2 - 2 + r^{-2})\,dr =$

$\displaystyle\frac{r^3}{3} - 2r - r^{-1}\Big]_{-2}^{-1} = [\frac{(-1)^3}{3} - 2(-1) - \frac{1}{(-1)}] - [\frac{(-2)^3}{3} - 2(-2) - \frac{1}{(-2)}] =$

$\displaystyle[-\frac{1}{3} + 2 + 1] - [-\frac{8}{3} + 4 + \frac{1}{2}] = \frac{7}{3} - \frac{3}{2} = \frac{5}{6}.$

25. $\displaystyle\int_0^4 \sqrt{3t}\,(\sqrt{t} + \sqrt{3})\,dt = \sqrt{3}\int_0^4 \sqrt{t}(\sqrt{t} + \sqrt{3})\,dt = \sqrt{3}\int_0^4 (t + \sqrt{3}\,t^{1/2})\,dt =$

$\displaystyle\sqrt{3}[\frac{t^2}{2} + \frac{\sqrt{3}}{3/2}\,t^{3/2}]_0^4 = \sqrt{3}\{[\frac{16}{2} + \frac{2\sqrt{3}}{3} \cdot 4^{3/2}] - [0-0]\} = \sqrt{3}(8 + \frac{2}{\sqrt{3}}(8)) = 8(\sqrt{3} + 2).$

28. $\displaystyle D_x\int_0^x (5t+3)^2\,dt = D_x\int_0^x (25t^2 + 30t + 9)\,dt = D_x[\frac{25}{3}t^3 + 15t^2 + 9t]_0^x =$

$\displaystyle D_x[\frac{25}{3}x^3 + 15x^2 + 9x] = 25x^2 + 30x + 9 = (5x+3)^2.$

31. Since $f(x) = x^2+1 > 0$, the area $= \displaystyle\int_{-1}^{2} (x^2+1)\,dx = \frac{x^3}{3} + x]_{-1}^{2} = (\frac{8}{3} + 2) -$

$(-\frac{1}{3} - 1) = 6.$

34. Verify by differentiating the function on the right to obtain the integrand.

37. $\displaystyle\int_0^4 (\sqrt{x}+1)\,dx = \int_0^4 (x^{1/2}+1)\,dx = \frac{2}{3}x^{3/2} + x]_0^4 = \frac{2}{3}(8) + 4 = \frac{28}{3}.$ Thus we seek

$z \varepsilon (0,4)$ such that $(\sqrt{z}+1)4 = \frac{28}{3}$ or $\sqrt{z} + 1 = \frac{7}{3} \implies \sqrt{z} = \frac{4}{3} \implies z = \frac{16}{9}.$

40. $\displaystyle\int_1^9 3x^{-2}\,dx = -3x^{-1}]_1^9 = -3(\frac{1}{9} - 1) = -3(-\frac{8}{9}) = \frac{8}{3}.$ $\frac{3}{z^2}(9-1) = \frac{8}{3} \iff 8z^2 = 72 \iff$

$z^2 = 9 \implies z = 3.$ $(z = -3$ is not in $(1,9))$.

43. $b-a = 2 - (-1) = 3$, and the average value is $\frac{1}{3}\displaystyle\int_{-1}^{2} (x^2 + 3x - 1)\,dx =$

$\displaystyle\frac{1}{3}[\frac{x^3}{3} + \frac{3x^2}{2} - x]_{-1}^{2} = \frac{1}{3}(\frac{20}{3} - \frac{13}{6}) = \frac{1}{3} \cdot \frac{27}{6} = \frac{3}{2}.$

46. Let F be an antiderivative of f. Then $F' = f$, and $D_x\displaystyle\int_{k(x)}^{g(x)} f(t)\,dt =$

$D_x[F(g(x)) - F(k(x))] = F'(g(x))g'(x) - F'(k(x))k'(x).$

49. $D_x\displaystyle\int_{3x}^{x^3} (t^3+1)^{10}\,dt = ((x^3)^3 + 1)^{10}D_x(x^3) - ((3x)^3 + 1)^{10}D_x(3x) =$

$(x^9 + 1)3x^2 - (27x^3 + 1) \cdot 3.$

EXERCISES 5.6, page 237

1. Let $u = 3x+1$ so that $du = 3\,dx$ or $dx = (1/3)du$. $\displaystyle\int (3x+1)^4\,dx = (1/3)\int u^4\,du =$

$u^5/15 + C = \frac{(3x+1)^5}{15} + C.$

4. Using the first method of Example 1, let $u = 9 - z^2$, so $du = -2z\,dz$. Then
$$\int \sqrt{9-z^2}\; z\,dz = (-1/2)\int (9-z^2)^{1/2}(-2z\,dz) = -\frac{1}{2}\int u^{1/2}du = -\frac{1}{2}(\frac{2}{3})\,u^{3/2} + C$$
$$= -\frac{1}{3}(9-z^2)^{3/2} + C.$$

7. Let $u = 1-2s^2$, $du = -4s\,ds$, $s\,ds = -\frac{1}{4}du$. $\int \frac{s}{\sqrt[3]{1-2s^2}}\,ds = -\frac{1}{4}\int u^{-1/3}du =$
$$-\frac{1}{4}(\frac{3}{2})u^{2/3} + C = -\frac{3}{8}(1-2s^2)^{2/3} + C.$$

10. Let $v = 1 + 1/u$, $dv = -1/u^2\,du$. Then $\int (1 + \frac{1}{u})^{-3}(\frac{1}{u^2})du = -\int v^{-3}\,dv = \frac{v^{-2}}{2} + C$
$$= \frac{1}{2}(1 + \frac{1}{u})^{-2} + C.$$

13. Let $u = t^2-1$, $du = 2t\,dt$. When $t = 1$ or -1, $u = 0$. Thus $\int_{-1}^{1} (t^2-1)^3 t\,dt =$
$$\frac{1}{2}\int_{0}^{0} u^3\,du = 0.$$

16. Let $u = x^2+9$. Then $du = 2x\,dx$, $x\,dx = (1/2)du$. $x = 0 \Rightarrow u = 9$. $x = 4 \Rightarrow$
$u = 25$. $\int_{0}^{4} \frac{x}{\sqrt{x^2+9}}\,dx = \int_{0}^{4} (x^2+9)^{-1/2} x\,dx = \int_{9}^{25} u^{-1/2}(1/2)du = u^{1/2}]_{9}^{25} =$
$\sqrt{25} - \sqrt{9} = 5 - 3 = 2$.

19. Let $u = 8x+5$, $du = 8\,dx$ so that $dx = \frac{1}{8}du$. Then $\int 5(8x+5)^{1/2}dx = \frac{5}{8}\int u^{1/2}\,du$
$$= \frac{5}{8}\frac{u^{3/2}}{(3/2)} + C = \frac{5}{8} \cdot \frac{2}{3}(8x+5)^{3/2} + C.$$

22. Let $u = 3-x^4$, $du = -4x^3dx$ so that $x^3dx = -\frac{1}{4}du$. Then $\int (3-x^4)^3 x^3dx =$
$$-\frac{1}{4}\int u^3du = -\frac{1}{4}\frac{u^4}{4} + C = -\frac{1}{16}(3-x^4)^4 + C.$$

25. Let I denote the given integral.
(a) Let $u = \sqrt{x} + 3$. Then $du = (1/2\sqrt{x})dx$ and $dx/\sqrt{x} = 2\,du$. Substituting we
obtain: $I = 2\int u^2du = \frac{2}{3}u^3 + C_a = \frac{2}{3}(x^{1/2} + 3)^3 + C_a = \frac{2}{3}(x^{3/2} + 9x + 27x^{1/2} + 27)$
$+ C_a = \frac{2}{3}x^{3/2} + 6x + 18x^{1/2} + 18 + C_a$.
(b) $I = \int \frac{x + 6\sqrt{x} + 9}{\sqrt{x}}\,dx = \int (\sqrt{x} + 6 + \frac{9}{\sqrt{x}})dx = \int (x^{1/2} + 6 + 9x^{-1/2})dx =$
$\frac{2}{3}x^{3/2} + 6x + 18x^{1/2} + C_b$. Comparing answers we see that $C_b = C_a + 18$.

28. Let $u = 3x+2$, $du = 3\,dx$ so that $dx = (1/3)du$. Then $D_x \int (3x+2)^7dx =$
$D_x \int \frac{u^7}{3}\,du = D_x(\frac{u^8}{24} + C) = D_x(\frac{(3x+2)^8}{24} + C) = \frac{8(3x+2)^7(3)}{24} = (3x+2)^7$.

31. An antiderivative of $D_x\sqrt{x^2+16}$ is $\sqrt{x^2+16}$ itself. Thus $\int_{0}^{3} D_x\sqrt{x^2+16}\,dx =$
$\sqrt{x^2+16}]_{0}^{3} = \sqrt{9+16} - \sqrt{16} = 5 - 4 = 1$.

34. Since $f(x)$ is ≥ 0 and continuous on $[1,2]$, the desired area is $A = \int_1^2 f(x)\,dx$

$= \int_1^2 (x^2+1)^{-2} x\,dx$. Let $u = x^2+1$, $du = 2x\,dx$, $x\,dx = (1/2)du$. $x = 1 \Rightarrow$

$u = 2$, $x = 2 \Rightarrow u = 5$. Thus $A = \frac{1}{2}\int_2^5 u^{-2}\,du = -\frac{1}{2} u^{-1}\big]_2^5 = -\frac{1}{2}(\frac{1}{5} - \frac{1}{2}) =$

$-\frac{1}{2}(-\frac{3}{10}) = \frac{3}{20}$.

37. Let $u = x+4$, $du = dx$. $x = 0 \Rightarrow u = 4$. $x = 5 \Rightarrow u = 9$. $\int_0^5 \sqrt{x+4}\,dx =$

$\int_4^9 u^{1/2}\,du = \frac{2}{3}u^{3/2}\big]_4^9 = \frac{2}{3}(9^{3/2} - 4^{3/2}) = \frac{2}{3}(3^3 - 2^3) = \frac{38}{3}$. Thus we seek

$z \in (0,5)$ (NOT $(4,9)$) such that $\sqrt{z+4}\,(5-0) = \frac{38}{3} \Rightarrow \sqrt{z+4} = \frac{38}{15} \Rightarrow z+4 =$

$(\frac{38}{15})^2 \Rightarrow z = (\frac{38}{15})^2 - 4 \approx 2.418$.

40. Verify by differentiating the expression on the right to obtain the integrand.

41, 42. HINT: $\int_{-a}^a f(x)\,dx = \int_{-a}^0 f(x)\,dx + \int_0^a f(x)\,dx$. In the 1st, let $u = -x$, du

$= -dx$ to obtain $-\int_a^0 f(-u)\,du$, or, replacing u by x, $\int_0^a f(-x)\,dx$. Now use the

definitions of even and odd functions, and combine with the 2nd integral.

EXERCISES 5.7, page 245

NOTE: T will denote the trapezoidal approximation and S the Simpson Rule approximation. In the tables, m and r denote the coefficients in T and S, respectively.

1. Here $f(x) = 1/x$, $b = 4$, $a = 1$, $n = 6$, $(b-a)/n = .5$. Our work is arranged in the following table.

i	x_i	$f(x_i)$	m	$mf(x_i)$	r	$rf(x_i)$
0	1.0	1.0000	1	1.0000	1	1.0000
1	1.5	0.6667	2	1.3334	4	2.6668
2	2.0	0.5000	2	1.0000	2	1.0000
3	2.5	0.4000	2	0.8000	4	1.6000
4	3.0	0.3333	2	0.6666	2	0.6666
5	3.5	0.2857	2	0.5714	4	1.1428
6	4.0	0.2500	1	0.2500	1	0.2500
				5.6214		8.3262

(a) $(b-a)/2n = 1/4 \Rightarrow T = 5.6214/4 = 1.40535 \approx 1.41$.

(b) $(b-a)/3n = 1/6 \Rightarrow S = 8.3262/6 = 1.3877 \approx 1.39$.

4. Tabulating as above, we have $f(x) = \sqrt{1+x^3}$, $(b-a)/n = .25$.

i	x_i	$f(x_i)$	m	$mf(x_i)$	r	$rf(x_i)$
0	2.00	3.0000	1	3.0000	1	3.0000
1	2.25	3.5200	2	7.0400	4	14.0800
2	2.50	4.0774	2	8.1548	2	8.1548
3	2.75	4.6687	2	9.3374	4	18.6748
4	3.00	5.2915	1	5.2915	1	5.2915
				32.8237		49.2011

Since $(b-a)/2n = 1/8$, $T = 32.8237/8 = 4.1030 \approx 4.10$.

Since $(b-a)/3n = 1/12$, $S = 49.2011/12 = 4.1001 \approx 4.10$.

7. We obtain with $f(x) = \sqrt[3]{x^2 + 8}$, $(b-a)/n = (3/2)/6 = 1/4$:

i	x_i	$f(x_i)$	m	$mf(x_i)$	r	$rf(x_i)$
0	1.0000	2.0801	1	2.0801	1	2.0801
1	1.2500	2.1225	2	4.2451	4	8.4902
2	1.5000	2.1722	2	4.3445	2	4.3445
3	1.7500	2.2282	2	4.4564	4	8.9127
4	2.0000	2.2894	2	4.5789	2	4.5789
5	2.2500	2.3551	2	4.7102	4	9.4204
6	2.5000	2.4244	1	2.4244	1	2.4224
				26.8395		40.2511

(a) Since $(b-a)/2n = 1/8$, $T = (1/8)(26.8395) = 3.3549 \approx 3.35$.

(b) Since $(b-a)/3n = 1/12$, $S = (1/12)(40.2511) = 3.3543 \approx 3.35$.

10. From #2, $f(x) = 1/(1+x)$, $b = 3$, $a = 0$, $n = 8$, $(b-a)/n = 3/8$. Thus, the partitioning points are: $x_0 = 0$, $x_1 = 3/8$, $x_2 = 6/8 = 3/4$, $x_3 = 9/8$, $x_4 = 3/2$, $x_5 = 15/8$, $x_6 = 9/4$, $x_7 = 21/8$ and $x_8 = 3$. The midpoints are: $\overline{x}_1 = 3/16$, $\overline{x}_2 = 9/16$, $\overline{x}_3 = 15/16$, $\overline{x}_4 = 21/16$, $\overline{x}_5 = 27/16$, $\overline{x}_6 = 33/16$, $\overline{x}_7 = 39/16$, and $\overline{x}_8 = 45/16$. By the Midpoint Rule, $\int_0^3 1/(x+1)dx \approx \frac{3}{8}[\frac{1}{1+3/16} + \frac{1}{1+9/16} + \frac{1}{1+15/16} + \frac{1}{1+21/16} + \frac{1}{1+27/16} + \frac{1}{1+33/16} + \frac{1}{1+39/16} + \frac{1}{1+45/16}] = \frac{3}{8}[\frac{16}{19} + \frac{16}{25} + \frac{16}{31} + \frac{16}{37} + \frac{16}{43} + \frac{16}{49} + \frac{16}{55} + \frac{16}{61}] \approx 1.38$

13. For notational convenience, let $A = \int_1^{2.7} \frac{1}{x}\, dx$ and $B = \int_1^{2.8} \frac{1}{x}\, dx$. The trape-

zoidal approximations to A and B are 0.9940 and 1.0304, respectively. (De-

tails omitted.) Since $f'(x) = -x^{-2}$ and $f''(x) = 2x^{-3}$, it follows that $|f''(x)|$

≤ 2 if $x \geq 1$. Thus, the error in this approximation to A, with M = 2 and

$(b-a)^3/n^2$ written as $(b-a)((b-a)/n)^2 = 1.7(.1)^2$, is $\leq \frac{2}{12}(1.7)(.1)^2 = \frac{.017}{6} \leq$

.003. Similarly, the error in the approximation to B is $\leq \frac{2}{12}(1.8)(.1)^2 =$

$\frac{.018}{6} = .003$. Thus, $0.9910 \leq A \leq 0.9970$, $1.0274 \leq B \leq 1.0334$, and $A < 1 < B$

as desired.

16. From the given data, b = 4, a = 2, n = 10, (b-a)/n = 0.2. We tabulate our
work as before.

i	x_i	$f(x_i)$	m	$mf(x_i)$	r	$rf(x_i)$
0	2.0	12.1	1	12.1	1	12.1
1	2.2	11.4	2	22.8	4	45.6
2	2.4	9.7	2	19.4	2	19.4
3	2.6	8.4	2	16.8	4	33.6
4	2.8	6.3	2	12.6	2	12.6
5	3.0	6.2	2	12.4	4	24.8
6	3.2	5.8	2	11.6	2	11.6
7	3.4	5.4	2	10.8	4	21.6
8	3.6	5.1	2	10.2	2	10.2
9	3.8	5.9	2	11.8	4	23.6
10	4.0	5.6	1	5.6	1	5.6
				146.1		220.7

Since $(b-a)/2n = .1$, $T = (.1)(146.1) \approx 14.61$.

Since $(b-a)/3n = .2/3$, $S = (.2/3)(220.7) \approx 14.71$.

19. Here, $f(x) = 1/x$, a = 1/2, b = 1 so that $1/2 \leq x \leq 1$, and $(b-a) = 1/2$.

(a) $f''(x) = 2/x^3$, $1/2 \leq x \implies |f''(x)| \leq 2/(1/2)^3 = 16$. Thus the error in

the trapezoidal approximation, E_T, satisfies, with M = 16, (b-a) = 1/2:

$E_T \leq \frac{M(b-a)^3}{12n^2} = \frac{16(1/2)^3}{12n^2} = \frac{1}{6n^2}$. We seek n such that $E_T < .0001$. This will

be true if $\frac{1}{6n^2} \leq .0001 \iff 6n^2 > 10,000 \implies n \geq 40.8$. The smallest in-

teger satisfying this is n = 41.

(b) $f^{(4)}(x) = 24/x^5 \leq 24/(1/2)^5 = 24 \cdot 2^5$ for $x \geq 1/2$. The error in

Simpson's Rule, E_S, satisfies, with $M = 24 \cdot 2^5$, (b-a) = 1/2:

$E_S \leq \frac{M(b-a)^5}{180n^4} = \frac{24 \cdot 2^5 \cdot (1/2)^5}{180n^4} = \frac{2}{15n^4}$. To make $E_S \leq .0001$, we seek n such that $\frac{2}{15n^4} \le .0001 \iff \frac{15n^4}{2} \ge 10,000 \iff n^4 \ge \frac{20,000}{15} \implies n \ge 6.05$. The smallest integer satisfying this is n = 7.

EXERCISES 5.8, page 247

1. $\sum\limits_{k=1}^{5} (k^2+3) = (1^2+3) + (2^2+3) + (3^2+3) + (4^2+3) + (5^2+3) = 4+7+12+19+28 = 70$.

4. Since [-2,3] is to be partitioned into 5 equal subintervals, each is of length 1 and $x_0 = -2$, $x_1 = -1$, $x_2 = 0$, $x_3 = 1$, $x_4 = 2$, $x_5 = 3$. Since w_i is the midpoint of $[x_{i-1},x_i]$, $w_1 = -3/2$, $w_2 = -1/2$, $w_3 = 1/2$, $w_4 = 3/2$, $w_5 = 5/2$. Since $\Delta x_i = 1$ for i = 1, ..., 5, we obtain

$$R_p = f(-3/2) + f(-1/2) + f(1/2) + f(3/2) + f(5/2)$$
$$= (1 - \frac{9}{4}) + (1 - \frac{1}{4}) + (1 - \frac{1}{4}) + (1 - \frac{9}{4}) + (1 - \frac{25}{4})$$
$$= 5 - (9+1+1+9+25)/4 = 5 - 45/4 = -25/4.$$

7. $\int_0^1 \sqrt[3]{8x^7}\, dx = \int_0^1 2x^{7/3}\, dx = 2(\frac{3}{10})\, [x^{10/3}]_0^1 = \frac{6}{10} = \frac{3}{5}$.

10. $\int (x^2+4)^2 dx = \int (x^4 + 8x^2 + 16) dx = \frac{x^5}{5} + \frac{8}{3}x^3 + 16x + C$.

13. Let $t = w^2 + 2w$, $dt = 2(w+1)dw$. When w = 1, t = 3 and when w = 2, t = 8. Thus $\int_1^2 \frac{w+1}{\sqrt{w^2+2w}}\, dw = \frac{1}{2} \int_3^8 \frac{1}{\sqrt{t}}\, dt = \frac{1}{2} \int_3^8 t^{-1/2} dt = t^{1/2}]_3^8 = \sqrt{8} - \sqrt{3} \approx 2.828 - 1.732 \approx 1.10$.

16. Noting that $(x^2-x-6)/(x+2) = x-3$ if $x \ne -2$, $\int_1^2 \frac{x^2-x-6}{x+2}\, dx = \int_1^2 (x-3)\, dx = \frac{x^2}{2} - 3x]_1^2 = -3/2$.

19. Let $u = x^3+1$, $du = 3x^2 dx$. When x = 0, u = 1, and when x = 2, u = 9. Then $\int_0^2 x^2\sqrt{x^3+1}\, dx = \frac{1}{3} \int_1^9 u^{1/2}\, du = \frac{2}{9}u^{3/2}]_1^9 = \frac{2}{9}[9^{3/2} - 1] = \frac{52}{9}$.

22. Let $u = 1 - v^{-1}$, $du = v^{-2} dv$ and $\int \frac{\sqrt[4]{1-v^{-1}}}{v^2}\, dv = \int \sqrt[4]{u}\, du = \frac{4}{5}u^{5/4} + C = \frac{4}{5}(1 - v^{-1})^{5/4} + C$.

25. Since an antiderivative of $D_x f(x)$ is $f(x)$ itself, $\int_{-1}^2 D_x \sqrt{\frac{x+1}{x+2}}\, dx = \sqrt{\frac{x+1}{x+2}}]_{-1}^2 = \sqrt{\frac{3}{4}} - \sqrt{\frac{0}{2}} = \frac{\sqrt{3}}{2}$.

28. $\int_0^7 D_x(\frac{x^2}{\sqrt{3x+4}}) dx = \frac{x^2}{\sqrt{3x+4}}]_0^7 = \frac{49}{\sqrt{25}} - 0 = \frac{49}{5}$.

31. (a) Tabulating our work as before with $f(x) = \sqrt{1+x^4}$ and $(b-a)/n = 10/5 = 2$, we have:

i	x_i	$f(x_i)$	m	$mf(x_i)$
0	0	1.0000	1	1.0000
1	2	4.1231	2	8.2462
2	4	16.0312	2	32.0624
3	6	36.0139	2	72.0278
4	8	64.0078	2	128.0156
5	10	100.0050	1	100.0050
				341.3570

Since $(b-a)/2n = 1$, $T = 341.36$.

(b) Now, $(b-a)/n = 10/8 = 1.25$.

i	x_i	$f(x_i)$	r	$rf(x_i)$
0	0.00	1.0000	1	1.0000
1	1.25	1.8551	4	7.4204
2	2.50	6.3295	2	12.6590
3	3.75	14.0980	4	56.3920
4	5.00	25.0200	2	50.0400
5	6.25	39.0753	4	156.3012
6	7.50	56.2589	2	112.5178
7	8.75	76.5690	4	306.2760
8	10.00	100.0050	1	100.0050
				802.6114

Since $(b-a)/3n = 10/24$, $S = 8026.114/24 \approx 334.42$.

CHAPTER 6

APPLICATIONS OF THE DEFINITE INTEGRAL

NOTE: In addition to presenting the solutions of #1, 4, 7, etc., I have included the integral forms of the answers to the remaining odd-numbered problems. In that wasy, you can determine if the reason for not getting the answer in the back of the text is due to incorrect set-up (i.e. the wrong integral) or to an arithmetic or algebraic mistake in evaluating the correct integral.

EXERCISES 6.1, page 256

1. The upper boundary of the region is $y = 1/x^2$; the lower is $y = -x^2$. (See sketches in the text for odd-numbered problems.) Thus $A = \int_1^2 [\frac{1}{x^2} - (-x^2)]\,dx$

   $= \int_1^2 (x^{-2} + x^2)\,dx = -x^{-1} + x^3/3 \,]_1^2 = 17/6.$

3. $A = \int_{-1}^2 ((4+y) - (-y^2))\,dy$.

4. Because of the shape and boundaries of the region, the easiest method is to use y as independent variable.

   $A = \int_{-2}^3 [y^2 - (y-2)]\,dy$

   $= \frac{y^3}{3} - \frac{y^2}{2} + 2y \,]_{-2}^3$

   $= \frac{21}{2} + \frac{26}{3} = \frac{115}{6}$.

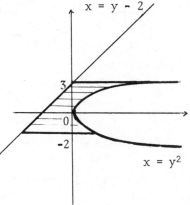

5. $A = \int_{-2}^2 (5 - (x^2+1))\,dx$.

7. For the points of intersection, we solve $x^2 = 4x \iff x^2 - 4x = x(x-4) = 0 \iff$

   $x = 0, 4$. Since $4x \geq x^2$ on $[0,4]$, $A = \int_0^4 (4x - x^2)\,dx = 2x^2 - \frac{x^3}{3} \,]_0^4 = 32 - \frac{64}{3} = \frac{32}{3}$

9. $A = \int_{-2}^1 ((1 - x^2) - (x-1))\,dx$.

10. The curves intersect when $3 - x^2 = -x+3 \iff x = 0, 1$.

    $A = \int_0^1 [(3-x^2) - (-x+3)]\,dx = \int_0^1 (-x^2 + x)\,dx =$

    $-\frac{x^3}{3} + \frac{x^2}{2} \,]_0^1 = \frac{1}{6}$.

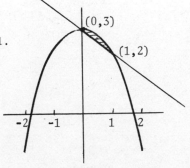

11. $A = \int_{-\sqrt{3}}^{\sqrt{3}} ((2 - y^2) - (y^2 - 4))\,dy.$

13. The lines $y = x$ and $y = 3x$ intersect at $(0,0)$; $y = x$ and $x+y = 4$ intersect at $(2,2)$; $y = 3x$ and $x+y = 4$ intersect at $(1,3)$. The region must be subdivided no matter which variable is chosen as independent. For $0 \leq x \leq 1$, the upper boundary is $y = 3x$; the lower is $y = x$. For $1 \leq x \leq 2$, the upper boundary is $x+y = 4$, the lower is $y = x$.

$A = \int_{0}^{1} (3x-x)\,dx + \int_{1}^{2} [(-x+4)-x]\,dx = \int_{0}^{1} 2x\,dx + \int_{1}^{2} (4-2x)\,dx = x^2]_{0}^{1} + 4x-x^2]_{1}^{2}$

$= 1 + [(8-4)-(4-1)] = 1 + 4 - 3 = 2.$

15. $A = \int_{-1}^{0} (x^3 - x)\,dx - \int_{0}^{1} (x^3 - x)\,dx.$

16. Writing $y = x(x^2-x-6) = x(x-3)(x+2)$, we see that $y \geq 0$ if $-2 \leq x \leq 0$ and $y \leq 0$ if $0 \leq x \leq 3$. Thus, using (6.1) on $[0,3]$, with $f(x) = 0$ and $g(x) = x^3 - x^2 - 6x$

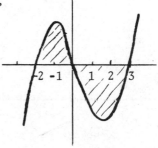

$A = \int_{-2}^{0} (x^3-x^2-6x)\,dx - \int_{0}^{3} (x^3-x^2-6x)\,dx$

$= [\frac{x^4}{4} - \frac{x^3}{3} - 3x^2]_{-2}^{0} + [-\frac{x^4}{4} + \frac{x^3}{3} + 3x^2]_{0}^{3}$

$= \frac{64}{12} + \frac{63}{4} = \frac{253}{12}.$

(Note that if you simply integrated y from -2 to 3 without the initial analysis, the "area" would have worked out to be $-125/12$, negative!)

17. $A = -\int_{-2}^{0} (4y - y^3)\,dy + \int_{0}^{2} (4y - y^3)\,dy.$

19. $y = x\sqrt{4-x^2}$ is ≤ 0 if $-2 \leq x \leq 0$ and is ≥ 0 if $0 \leq x \leq 2$. Thus

$A = \int_{-2}^{0} -x\sqrt{4-x^2}\,dx + \int_{0}^{2} x\sqrt{4-x^2}\,dx = \frac{1}{3}(4-x^2)^{3/2}]_{-2}^{0} - \frac{1}{3}(4-x^2)^{3/2}]_{0}^{2} = \frac{2}{3} \cdot 4^{3/2}$

$= \frac{16}{3}.$ (By symmetry, the area of the right have could have been computed and then doubled to get the answer.)

22. $x = \sqrt{1-y^2} \implies x \geq 0$ and $x^2+y^2 = 1 \implies R$ is semicircular with radius 1 $\implies A = \pi/2.$ If P is a partition of $[-1,1]$, $A = \lim_{\|P\| \to 0} \sum_{i=1}^{n} \sqrt{1-w_i^2}\,\Delta y_i$ where $w_i \in [y_{i-1}, y_i]$.

25. Δx_i in the sum tells us that x is the independent variable, and $f(w_i)$ = $4w_i + 1 \implies f(x) = 4x+1$. R is the trapezoidal region under the line y = $4x+1$, from x = 0 to x = 1. A = $\int_0^1 (4x+1)dx = 2x^2+x]_0^1 = 3$.

28. Δy_i in the sum $\implies$ y is the independent variable, and $f(w_i) = \sqrt{3w_i+1} \implies f(y)$ = $\sqrt{3y+1}$. R is the region to the right of the y axis and to the left of the graph of x = $\sqrt{3y+1}$ from y = 0 to y = 1. A = $\int_0^1 \sqrt{3y+1}\, dy$. Let u = 3y+1, du = 3 dy. y = 0 $\implies$ u = 1, y = 1 $\implies$ u = 4, and A = $\frac{1}{3}\int_1^4 u^{1/2}du = \frac{1}{3} \cdot \frac{2}{3}u^{3/2}]_1^4$ = $\frac{2}{9}(4^{3/2} - 1^{3/2}) = \frac{2}{9}(8-1) = \frac{14}{9}$.

31. $\Delta y_i \implies$ y is the independent variable and $f(y) = (5+\sqrt{y})/\sqrt{y} = 5y^{-1/2} + 1$, $1 \le y \le 4$. A = $\int_1^4 (5y^{-1/2}+1)dy = 10y^{1/2} + y]_1^4 = 24 - 11 = 13$.

33. A = $\int_0^1 [(6-3x^2)-3x]dx + \int_1^2 [3x-(6-3x^2)]dx$.

34. The graphs intersect when $x^2-4 = x+2 \iff x^2-x-6 = (x+2)(x-3) = 0 \implies$ x = -2,3. Only x = 3 is in [1,4]. When it is not obvious from the functions f and g, we can test values (as in Section 4.3) to see which function is larger on the interval in question. Thus, selecting k = 1 in [1,3] we find that f(1) = -3 < g(1) = 3. Thus $f(x) \le g(x)$ on [1,3]. Similarly, f(4) = 12 > g(4) = 6 $\implies f(x) \ge g(x)$ on [3,4]. (Recall f(3) = g(3) so that our interest is focused on the two intervals [1,3] and [3,4].). Thus A = $\int_1^3 (g(x)-f(x))dx$

+ $\int_3^4 (f(x)-g(x))dx = \int_1^3 (x-x^2+6)dx + \int_3^4 (-x+x^2-6)dx = \frac{x^2}{2} - \frac{x^3}{3} + 6x]_1^3$ +

$[-\frac{x^2}{2} + \frac{x^3}{3} - 6x]_3^4 = \frac{22}{3} + \frac{17}{6} = \frac{61}{6}$.

37. In the table below, $f(x_i)$ denotes the ordinate value of the upper boundary at x_i, $g(x_i)$ is that of the lower, and $h(x_i)$ is the difference, $h(x_i)$ = $f(x_i) - g(x_i)$ as the author has measured them. (Your answers may differ.)

i	x_i	$f(x_i)$	$g(x_i)$	$h(x_i)$	m	$mh(x_i)$	r	$rh(x_i)$
0	0	0	0	0	1	0	1	0
1	1	1.5	1.0	0.5	2	1.0	4	2.0
2	2	2.0	1.25	0.75	2	1.5	2	1.5
3	3	2.5	1.5	1.0	2	2.0	4	4.0
4	4	3.0	2.0	1.0	2	2.0	2	2.0
5	5	3.5	2.5	1.0	2	2.0	4	4.0
6	6	5.0	5.0	0	1	0	1	0
						8.5		13.5

(a) $(b-a)/2n = 6/12 = 1/2 \implies T = 4.25.$

(b) $(b-a)/3n = 6/18 = 1/3 \implies S = 4.5.$

EXERCISES 6.2, page 264

NOTE: When using the disc or washer method to compute the volume of a solid of revolution, you must remember that the partitioning must be done so that a typical rectangle is <u>perpendicular</u> to the line around which the revolution is taking place (the axis of revolution). Thus, if revolution takes place around a vertical line, a typical rectangle must be horizontal so that a y-interval must be partitioned and the bounding curves must be graphs of functions of y. Conversely, if we revolve about a horizontal line, the rectangle must be vertical so that an x-interval must be partitioned and the bounding curves expressed as graphs of functions of x.

1. By (6.3), $V = \pi \int_1^3 (1/x)^2 dx = \pi \int_1^3 x^{-2} dx = \pi [-\frac{1}{x}]_1^3 = \frac{2\pi}{3}$.

3. $V = \pi \int_0^2 y \, dy.$

4. Writing the equation as $x = 1/y$, $1 \le y \le 3$, we have by

(6.4), $V = \pi \int_1^3 (1/y)^2 \, dy = 2\pi/3.$

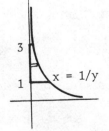

5. $V = \pi \int_0^4 (x^2 - 4x)^2 \, dx.$

7. The curves intersect when $2y = y^2$ or $y = 0,2$. For $0 \le y \le 2$, the right boundary is $x = 2y$; the left is $x = y^2$. Thus a typical rectangle, corresponding to the subinterval $[y_{i-1}, y_i]$ in a partition of $0 \le y \le 2$, sweeps out a "washer" of volume $[\pi(2w_i)^2 - \pi(w_i^2)^2]\Delta y_i$. Summing and passing to the limit as $\|P\| \to 0$, we get

$$V = \pi \int_0^2 [(2y)^2 - (y^2)^2]dy = \pi[\tfrac{4}{3}y^3 - \tfrac{1}{5}y^5]\Big|_0^2 = \frac{64\pi}{15}.$$

9. $V = \pi \displaystyle\int_{-\sqrt{2}}^{\sqrt{2}} ((4 - x^2)^2 - x^4)dx.$

10. The curves intersect when $x^{1/3} = -x^2 \iff$ $x = -x^6 \iff x(x^5+1) = 0$ yielding $x = -1,0$. Formula (6.7) cannot be used here since the functions are both negative for $-1 \le x \le 0$. The typical rectangle shown sweeps out a washer with outer radius $-w_i^{1/3}$ and inner radius w_i^2. (As <u>distances</u>, these radii must be ≥ 0.) The washer's volume is $\pi[(-w_i^{1/3})^2 - (w_i^2)^2]\Delta x_i$. Summing and passing to the limit we obtain

$$V = \int_{-1}^{0} (x^{2/3} - x^4)dx = \pi[\tfrac{3}{5}x^{5/3} - \tfrac{1}{5}x^5]\Big|_{-1}^{0} = \frac{2\pi}{5}\;.$$

(graph labels: -1, w_i, 0, w_i^2, $-w_i^{1/3}$, $(-1,-1)$, $y = x^{1/3}$, $y = x^2$)

11. $V = \pi \displaystyle\int_{-1}^{2} ((y + 2)^2 - y^4)dy.$

13. $x = y^3$, $x = 8 \Longrightarrow y = 2$. Partition the interval $0 \le y \le 2$. The typical rectangle shown sweeps out a disc (when revolved around $x = 8$) of radius $8 - w_i^3$, thickness Δy_i and volume $\pi(8-w_i^3)^2\Delta y_i$. Thus $V \approx \sum\limits_{i=1}^{n} \pi(8-w_i^3)^2\Delta y_i$. Passing to the limit as $\|P\| \to 0$, $V =$

$$\pi\int_0^2 (8-y^3)^2 dy = \pi\int_0^2 (64-16y^3+y^6)dy =$$

$$\pi[64y - 4y^4 + \tfrac{1}{7}y^7]\Big|_0^2 = \pi[128 - 64 + \tfrac{128}{7}] = 64\pi(\tfrac{9}{7}).$$

(graph labels: 2, w_i, $8 - w_i^3$, 8)

15. $V = \pi \displaystyle\int_0^8 [3^2 - (3 - x^{1/3})^2]dx.$

16. Since x = 2 is vertical, we must partition the in-
    terval $0 \le y \le 1$ and express the boundary with x
    as a function of y. Thus, the left boundary is
    $x = -\sqrt[4]{y}$, and the right boundary is $x = \sqrt[4]{y}$. The
    rectangle shown sweeps out a washer of outer
    radius $2-(-\sqrt[4]{w_i}) = 2+\sqrt[4]{w_i}$, inner radius $2-\sqrt[4]{w_i}$, and

    volume $\pi[(2+\sqrt[4]{w_i})^2 - (2-\sqrt[4]{w_i})^2]\Delta y_i = 8\pi\sqrt[4]{w_i}\Delta y_i$.

    Summing and passing to the limit we get

    $V = 8\pi\int_0^1 y^{1/4}dy = 8\pi \cdot \frac{4}{5} y^{5/4}\Big]_0^1 = \frac{32\pi}{5}$.

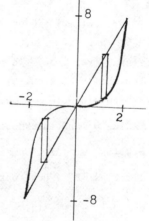

17. (a) $V = \pi\int_{-2}^2 (4-x^2)^2 dx$. (b) $V = \pi\int_{-2}^2 [(5-x^2)^2 - 1]dx$. (c) $\pi\int_0^4 [(2+\sqrt{y})^2 -$
    $(2-\sqrt{y})^2]dy$.

19. The curves intersect when $x^3 = 4x \Longrightarrow x(x^2-4)$
    $= 0 \Longrightarrow x = -2,0,2$. If $-2 \le w_i \le 0$, the
    rectangle sweeps out a washer of outer radius
    $8 - 4w_i$, inner radius $8 - w_i^3$ (both positive
    since $w_i < 0$) and volume $\pi[(8 - 4w_i)^2 -$
    $(8 - w_i^3)^2]\Delta x_i$. If $0 \le w_i \le 2$, the outer
    and inner radii are reversed from the 1st
    case. Thus, the washer volume is
    $\pi[(8 - w_i^3)^2 - (8 - 4w_i)^2]\Delta x_i$. Summing and
    passing to the limit yields the text answer.

22. Writing x-y = 1 as y = x-1, the curves intersect when $1-x^2 = x-1 \Longrightarrow x^2+x-2$
    $= (x+2)(x-1) = 0 \Longrightarrow x = -2,1$. On the interval $-2 \le x \le 1$, $x-1 \le 1-x^2 < 3$.
    Thus, when revolving a rectangle about y = 3, the outer radius is $3 - (w_i-1)$
    $= 4-w_i$. The inner radius is $3 - (1-w_i^2) = 2 + w_i^2$, and its volume is
    $\pi[(4-w_i)^2 - (2+w_i^2)^2]\Delta x_i$. As before, this yields $V = \pi\int_{-2}^1 [(4-x)^2 -$
    $(2+x^2)^2]dx$.

25. Revolve the triangle with vertices (0,0), (r,0) and (0,h) about the y-axis
    using x = (-r/h)(y-h) to obtain $V = \pi\int_0^h \frac{r^2(y-h)^2}{h^2} dy$.

28. Revolve the region between the circle $x = \sqrt{r^2 - y^2}$ and the y-axis, for r-h
    $\le y \le r$, about the y-axis to obtain $V = \pi\int_{r-h}^r (r^2-y^2)dy = (\pi h^2/3)(3r-h)$.

EXERCISES 6.3, page 269

NOTE: When using the shell method to compute the volume of a solid of revolution, the partitioning must be done so that a typical rectangle's altitude is _parallel_ to the axis of revolution. Thus, revolution about a vertical line means that an x-interval must be partitioned, the altitude of the rectangle is vertical, and the bounding curves must be expressed as functions of x. Similarly, revolution about a horizontal line means a y-interval must be partitioned and the bounding curves expressed as functions of y.

1. $V = 2\pi \int_0^4 x\sqrt{x}\ dx = 2\pi \int_0^4 x^{3/2}dx = 2\pi(\frac{2}{5})x^{5/2}]_0^4 = \frac{4\pi}{5}(2^5) = \frac{128\pi}{5}$.

3. $V = 2\pi \int_0^2 x(\sqrt{8x} - x^2)dx.$

4. $x^2-5x = x(x-5) \leq 0$ on $[0,5]$ since $x \geq 0$, $x-5 \leq 0$ there. So, with rotation about the y-axis (vertical), we partition this x interval. The shell swept out by the rectangle shown has altitude $0 - (w_i^2 - 5w_i) = 5w_i - w_i^2$, average radius w_i and thickness Δx_i. Its volume is $2\pi w_i(5w_i-w_i^2)\Delta x_i$. Summing, and passing to the limit as $\|P\| \to 0$ we obtain

$V = 2\pi \int_0^5 x(5x-x^2)dx = 2\pi \int_0^5 (5x^2-x^3)dx = 2\pi[\frac{5}{3}x^3 - \frac{x^4}{4}]_0^5 = 2\pi[\frac{625}{3} - \frac{625}{4}] =$

$\frac{1250\pi}{12} = \frac{625\pi}{6}$.

5. $V = 2\pi \int_4^7 x[(\frac{x}{2} - \frac{3}{2}) - (2x - 12)]dx.$

7. To go around the x-axis and use the shell method, we partition the y-interval, $0 \leq y \leq 4$. Solving $x^2 = 4y$ for x, we find that the left boundary is x $= -2\sqrt{y}$, and the right boundary is $x = 2\sqrt{y}$. The typical rectangle is horizontal with altitude = (right boundary) - (left boundary) = $2\sqrt{w_i} - (-2\sqrt{w_i}) =$ $4\sqrt{w_i}$. The shell has average radius w_i, thickness Δy_i, and volume

$2\pi w_i(4\sqrt{w_i})\Delta y_i = 8\pi w_i^{3/2}\Delta y_i$. Summing and passing to the limit, we obtain

$V = 8\pi \int_0^4 y^{3/2}dy = \frac{16\pi}{5} y^{5/2}]_0^4 = \frac{16\pi}{5}(32).$

9. $V = 2\pi \int_0^6 y(y/2)\,dy.$

10. $2y = x$ intersects $x = 1$ at $y = 1/2$. The right
boundary is $x = 2y$; the left is $x = 1$. Thus,
the altitude is $2w_i - 1$, radius w_i, thickness
Δy_i. The shell volume is $2\pi w_i(2w_i - 1)\Delta y_i$. Thus,
as above, $V = 2\pi \int_{1/2}^4 y(2y - 1)\,dy = 2\pi[\frac{2}{3}y^3 - \frac{y^2}{2}]_{1/2}^4$

$= 2\pi(\frac{104}{3} + \frac{1}{24}) = \frac{833\pi}{12}$.

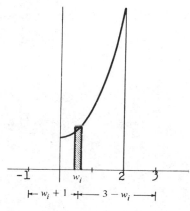

11. $V = 2\pi \int_1^4 (5-y)2y^{-1/2}\,dy.$

13. (a) Partitioning $[0,2]$, the typical rectangle
shown sweeps out a cylindrical shell of average
radius $3-w_i$, height w_i^2+1, thickness Δx_i, and
volume $2\pi(3-w_i)(w_i^2+1)\Delta x_i$. Summing and passing
to the limit, $V = 2\pi \int_0^2 (3-x)(x^2+1)\,dx = 16\pi.$

(b) Now, the average radius is w_i+1 and, as
above, $V = 2\pi \int_0^2 (x+1)(x^2+1)\,dx = 64\pi/3.$

16. (a) Partitioning the x interval $[0,4]$,
the shell swept out by the rectangle has
average radius $4-w_i$, height $\sqrt{w_i}$ and
volume $2\pi(4-w_i)\sqrt{w_i}\,\Delta x_i$. As before,

$V = 2\pi \int_0^4 (4-x)\sqrt{x}\,dx = 256\pi/15.$

(b) Now the average radius is $6-w_i$ and

$V = 2\pi \int_0^4 (6-x)\sqrt{x}\,dx = 192\pi/5.$ (c) To revolve about $y = 2$ using the shell

method, the equation of the graph must be written as $x = y^2$, and the y

interval $[0,2]$ must be partitioned. Now the typical rectangle is horizon-

tal and sweeps out a shell of average radius $2-w_i$, height $4-w_i^2$, and volume

$2 (2-w_i)(4-w_i^2)\Delta y_i$, so that $V = 2\pi \int_0^2 (2-y)(4-y^2)\,dy = 40\pi/3.$

19. Writing the equations as $y = 3-x$ and $y = 3-x^2$, the curves intersect when
    $3-x = 3-x^2 \Rightarrow x^2-x = x(x-1) = 0 \Rightarrow x = 0,1$. On the interval $[0,1]$, $3-x^2 \geq$
    $3-x$. (Use test value $k = 1/2$ to verify this.) Thus when the interval $0 \leq x$
    ≤ 1 is partitioned, the typical rectangle, when revolved about $x = 2$, sweeps
    out a shell of average radius $2-w_i$, height $(3-w_i^2) - (3-w_i) = w_i - w_i^2$,
    thickness Δx_i and volume $2\pi(2-w_i)(w_i-w_i^2)\Delta x_i$. Summing and passage to the
    limit yields the answer in the text.

22. Because the region is symmetric about the y-axis,
    we will consider only the 1st quadrant region,
    doubling the result for the entire volume. To use
    the shell method when revolving around a horizontal
    line ($y = -1$ here), y must be the independent
    variable so that the typical rectangle is horizon-
    tal. Expression the equations as $x = y^{3/2}$ and
    $x = y^{1/2}$, the curves intersect when $y^{3/2} = y^{1/2}$,
    $y \geq 0 \Rightarrow y^3 = y$, $y \geq 0 \Rightarrow y = 0,1$. Note that

    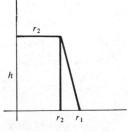

    $y^{1/2} \geq y^{3/2}$ on $0 \leq y \leq 1$. Partitioning $0 \leq y \leq 1$, the rectangle sweeps out
    a shell of radius $1+w_i$, height $= w_i^{1/2} - w_i^{3/2}$, thickness Δy_i, and volume
    $2\pi(1+w_i)(w_i^{1/2} - w_i^{3/2})\Delta y_i$. As usual, and inserting the factor of 2 as de-
    scribed in the first line, $V = (2)2\pi \int_0^1 (1+y)(y^{1/2}-y^{3/2})dy$.

25. Revolve the trapezoid with vertices $(0,0)$, $(0,h)$,
    (r_2,h) and $(r_1,0)$ about the y-axis. The upper
    boundary is $y = h$ for $0 \leq x \leq r_2$ and $y =$
    $(h/(r_2 - r_1))(x-r_1)$ for $r_2 \leq x \leq r_1$. Thus

    $V = 2\pi \int_0^{r_2} xh \, dx + 2\pi \int_{r_2}^{r_1} x(h/(r_2-r_1))(x-r_1))dx.$

28. The Δx_i tells us that $0 \leq x \leq 1$ is being partitioned. The term
    $2\pi(w_i^5 + w_i^{3/2})\Delta x_i = 2\pi w_i[w_i^4 - (-w_i^{1/2})]\Delta x_i$ is the volume of a cylin-
    drical shell with average radius w_i, height $w_i^4 - (-w_i^{1/2})$ and thickness Δx_i.
    Thus the limit is the volume of the solid obtained by revolving the region
    bounded by the graphs of $y = x^4$, $y = -\sqrt{x}$ and $x = 1$ about the y-axis.

    $V = 2\pi \int_0^1 (x^5 + x^{3/2})dx = 17\pi/15$. (Note that other answers are possible.

For example, writing the term in the sum as $2\pi w_i (w_i^4 + \sqrt{w_i})\Delta x_i$, we can correctly interpret the solid as having been obtained by revolving the region under the graph of $f(x) = x^4 + \sqrt{x}$, $0 \le x \le 1$, about the y axis.)

EXERCISES 6.4, page 272

1. If (x,y) is a point on the circle for which $y \ge 0$ then, because of the symmetry of the circle, the side of the cross-sectional square has length $2y$, and the area of the square is $A = 4y^2$. Since $x^2 + y^2 = a^2$, $A = 4(a^2 - x^2)$

and $V = \displaystyle\int_{-a}^{a} 4(a^2-x^2)\,dx = 4[a^2x - \frac{x^3}{3}]_{-a}^{a} = \frac{16a^3}{3}$.

3. $V = \displaystyle\int_{-2}^{2} [(4-x^2)/2]^2 dx$.

4. If (x,y) is on the curve $y = x^2$, the cross-sectional square has side length $(4-y) = 4-x^2$ and area $A = (4-x^2)^2$. Thus

$V = \displaystyle\int_{-2}^{2} (4-x^2)^2\,dx = \int_{-2}^{2} (16 - 8x^2 + x^4)\,dx$

$= [16x - \frac{8}{3}x^3 + \frac{1}{5}x^5]_{-2}^{2} = 2[32 - \frac{64}{3} + \frac{32}{5}] = \frac{512}{15}$.

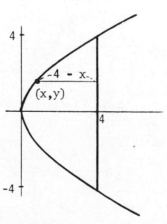

5. $V = \displaystyle\int_{0}^{h} (2a^2x^2/h^2)\,dx$.

7. If (x,y) is on $y^2 = 4x$, the base (diameter) of the cross-sectional semi-circle has length $4-x = 4 - y^2/4$. The radius is $(4-y^2/4)/2$ and the area of the semi-circle is $A(y) = \frac{\pi}{8}(4 - \frac{y^2}{4})^2$ and

$V = \frac{\pi}{8} \displaystyle\int_{-4}^{4} (4 - \frac{y^2}{4})^2 dy = \frac{\pi}{8} \int_{-4}^{4} (16 - 2y^2 + \frac{y^4}{16})\,dy$

$= \frac{\pi}{8}[16y - \frac{2}{3}y^3 + \frac{y^5}{80}]_{-4}^{4} = \frac{128\pi}{15}$.

9. $V = 2\displaystyle\int_{0}^{a} y\sqrt{a^2 - y^2}\,dy$.

10. Position the x-axis with the origin at
the point of intersection of the cylindrical axes and perpendicular to the
plane they lie in. The sketch depicts
only 1/8 of the entire solid, the nearest
1/4 of the top half.

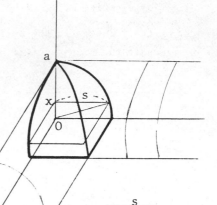

   Restricting our attention to this portion, we see that for a number $x \varepsilon$ [0,a],
the plane through x perpendicular to the
x-axis cuts the solid in a square. (The
facts that the edges of the cut are on
the cylindrical surface parallel to the
axis of the cylinder, and that the cylin-
ders are perpendicular should convince the reader of this.) If s is the
length of a side, then $s = \sqrt{a^2-x^2}$ (see insert in sketch). The area of the

square is $A(x) = s^2 = a^2-x^2$ and the volume is $\int_0^a (a^2-x^2)dx = \frac{2}{3}a^3$. The

entire solid therefore has volume $8(\frac{2}{3})a^3 = \frac{16a^3}{3}$.

11. $V = b \int_{-a}^a \sqrt{a^2-x^2} \, dx$.

13. We place a coordinate line along the 4 cm side with the origin at the vertex
shown. (See sketches at end of solution.) Consider a point on this line x
units from the vertex; a plane through this point, perpendicular to the coordinate line, intersects the solid in a triangular cross-section. Let b be
the base and h the height of this triangle. We can express b and h in terms
of x using similar triangles. From the middle sketch below, b/x = 2/4, or

b = x/2. From the last sketch, h/x = 3/4, or h = (3/4)x. The area of this

cross-sectional triangle is $A(x) = (1/2)bh = 1/2 \cdot x/2 \cdot 3x/4 = \frac{3}{16} x^2$. Thus

$V = \int_0^4 (3/16)x^2 dx = \frac{1}{16}x^3 \Big]_0^4 = \frac{64}{16} = 4$.

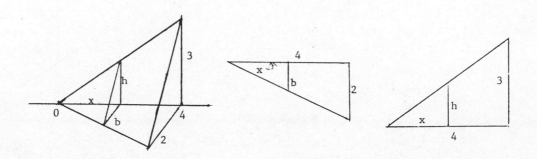

15. $V = \dfrac{\pi}{8} \displaystyle\int_0^a (a-y)^2 dy$.

16. Since a regular hexagon of side y is the union of
     6 equilateral triangles of side y, the area of the
     hexagon is 6 times the area of such a triangle, or
     $6\left(\dfrac{\sqrt{3}}{4} y^2\right) = \dfrac{3\sqrt{3}}{2} y^2$. Positioning the base triangle
     as shown, if (x,y) is on the hypotenuse, then
     y = -x + a. Thus, the cross-sectional area func-
     tion is $A(x) = \dfrac{3\sqrt{3}}{2} y^2 = \dfrac{3\sqrt{3}}{2}(-x+a)^2$. Thus,
     $V = \dfrac{3\sqrt{3}}{2} \displaystyle\int_0^a (-x+a)^2 dx = \dfrac{\sqrt{3}}{2} a^3$.

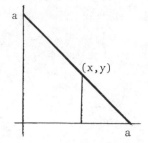

EXERCISES 6.5, page 279

1. If, as in Example 3, x is the number of units that the spring is stretched
    beyond its natural length, then f(x) = kx and f(1.5) = 8 $\Longrightarrow$ k(3/2) = 8 $\Longrightarrow$
    k = 16/3.
    (a) Here x ranges from 0 to 4 (14" is 4" beyond the natural length of 10").
    Thus $W = \displaystyle\int_0^4 (16/3)x\, dx = 128/3$.
    (b) Here, x ranges from 1 to 3 and $W = \displaystyle\int_1^3 (16/3)x\, dx = \dfrac{64}{3}$.

4. In the formula f(x) = kx, x is the amount that the spring has been stretched
    beyond its natural length. Thus if x_0 is the natural length, then we obtain
    amounts of stretch of $6-x_0$, $7-x_0$, and $8-x_0$ when the spring is stretched to
    lengths of 6, 7 and 8 cm., respectively. The data given in the problem,
    together with (6.10) and (6.11) yield: $\displaystyle\int_{6-x_0}^{7-x_0} kx\, dx = 60$ and $\displaystyle\int_{7-x_0}^{8-x_0} kx\, dx = 120$.
    We seek k and x_0. From the first relation we get: $(k/2)[(7-x_0)^2-(6-x_0)^2]$
    $= 60 \Longrightarrow k(13-2x_0) = 120 \Longrightarrow 13k - 2kx_0 = 120$. From the second relation,
    we get: $(k/2)[(8-x_0)^2-(7-x_0)^2] = 120 \Longrightarrow k(15-2x_0) = 240 \Longrightarrow 15k - 2kx_0 =$
    240. Subtracting from this equation the equation from the first relation,
    we get 2k = 120 or k = 60. Using this in either equation, we get $x_0 = 11/2$
    = 5.5 cm.

5. $W = 62.5 \displaystyle\int_0^3 8(3-y)\, dy$.

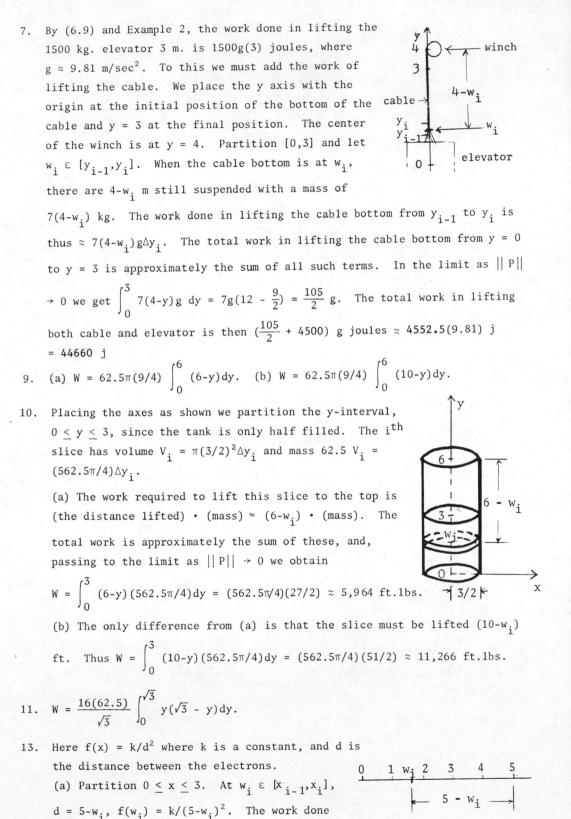

7. By (6.9) and Example 2, the work done in lifting the
    1500 kg. elevator 3 m. is 1500g(3) joules, where
    $g \approx 9.81$ m/sec^2. To this we must add the work of
    lifting the cable. We place the y axis with the
    origin at the initial position of the bottom of the
    cable and $y = 3$ at the final position. The center
    of the winch is at $y = 4$. Partition [0,3] and let
    $w_i \; \varepsilon \; [y_{i-1}, y_i]$. When the cable bottom is at w_i,
    there are $4-w_i$ m still suspended with a mass of

    $7(4-w_i)$ kg. The work done in lifting the cable bottom from y_{i-1} to y_i is

    thus $\approx 7(4-w_i)g\Delta y_i$. The total work in lifting the cable bottom from $y = 0$

    to $y = 3$ is approximately the sum of all such terms. In the limit as $\|P\|$

    $\to 0$ we get $\int_0^3 7(4-y)g \; dy = 7g(12 - \frac{9}{2}) = \frac{105}{2}$ g. The total work in lifting

    both cable and elevator is then $(\frac{105}{2} + 4500)$ g joules $\approx 4552.5(9.81)$ j
    $= 44660$ j

9. (a) $W = 62.5\pi(9/4) \int_0^6 (6-y)dy$.   (b) $W = 62.5\pi(9/4) \int_0^6 (10-y)dy$.

10. Placing the axes as shown we partition the y-interval,
    $0 \le y \le 3$, since the tank is only half filled. The ith
    slice has volume $V_i = \pi(3/2)^2\Delta y_i$ and mass 62.5 V_i =
    $(562.5\pi/4)\Delta y_i$.

    (a) The work required to lift this slice to the top is
    (the distance lifted) · (mass) $\approx (6-w_i)$ · (mass). The

    total work is approximately the sum of these, and,
    passing to the limit as $\|P\| \to 0$ we obtain

    $W = \int_0^3 (6-y)(562.5\pi/4)dy = (562.5\pi/4)(27/2) \approx 5,964$ ft.lbs.

    (b) The only difference from (a) is that the slice must be lifted $(10-w_i)$

    ft. Thus $W = \int_0^3 (10-y)(562.5\pi/4)dy = (562.5\pi/4)(51/2) \approx 11,266$ ft.lbs.

11. $W = \frac{16(62.5)}{\sqrt{3}} \int_0^{\sqrt{3}} y(\sqrt{3} - y)dy$.

13. Here $f(x) = k/d^2$ where k is a constant, and d is
    the distance between the electrons.
    (a) Partition $0 \le x \le 3$. At $w_i \; \varepsilon \; [x_{i-1}, x_i]$,
    $d = 5-w_i$, $f(w_i) = k/(5-w_i)^2$. The work done

in moving the electron from x_{i-1} to x_i is approximately (force) · (distance)

$= \dfrac{k\Delta x_i}{(5-w_i)^2}$. The total work done in moving it from $x = 0$ to $x = 3$ is ap-

proximately the sum of all such terms, and passing to the limit as $\|P\| \to$

0, we obtain $W = \displaystyle\int_0^3 \dfrac{k}{(5-x)^2}\,dx = \dfrac{k}{5-x}\Big]_0^3 = k\left(\dfrac{1}{2} - \dfrac{1}{5}\right) = \dfrac{3k}{10}$.

(b) Begin as in (a). Now, the net force,

f, on the electron at w_i is a sum $f_1 + f_2$

of the force f_1 exerted by the electron at

(-5,0) and the force f_2 exerted by the elec-

tron at (5,0). Note that f_1 and f_2 must be of opposite signs since f_2 op-

poses the motion (as in (a)), but f_1 assists it in repelling the moving elec-

tron. Thus $f(w_i) = \dfrac{-k}{(5+w_i)^2} + \dfrac{k}{(5-w_i)^2}$ and, as above,

$W = \displaystyle\int_0^3 \left[-\dfrac{k}{(5+x)^2} + \dfrac{k}{(5-x)^2}\right]dx = k\left[\dfrac{1}{5+x} + \dfrac{1}{5-x}\right]_0^3 = \dfrac{9k}{40}$.

15. $W = \displaystyle\int_0^{12} (24-y/6)\,dy$.

16. Since there were 20 lb. of water initially, the bucket will be half-filled
     when 10 lbs have leaked out. This will happen in 40 sec. since it leaks out
     at a rate of $0.25 = 1/4$ lb/sec. Since it rises at a rate of 1.5 ft/sec, it
     will rise $1.5(40) = 60$ ft while half the water leaks out. With $y = 0$ and
     $y = 60$ as initial and final locations of the bucket, we partition $0 \le y \le 60$
     and let $w_i \in [y_{i-1}, y_i]$. At height w_i, the bucket will have been rising for
     $w_i/1.5 = 2w_i/3$ sec., and during this time $(0.25)(2w_i/3) = w_i/6$ lbs of water
     will have leaked out. Since the initial mass of bucket and water was 24 lb.,
     the mass at w_i is thus $24-w_i/6$ and the work in lifting it from y_{i-1} to y_i is

     $\approx (24-w_i/6)\Delta y_i$. Summing we obtain $W = \displaystyle\int_0^{60} (24-y/6)\,dy = 1440-300 = 1140$ ft.lb.

17. $W = 115 \displaystyle\int_{32}^{40} v^{-1.2}\,dv$.

19. If $K = gm_1m_2$ then $F(s) = Ks^{-2}$ and $W = K\displaystyle\int_{4000}^{4000+h} s^{-2}\,ds = -Ks^{-}\Big]_{4000}^{4000+h}$

     $= -K\left(\dfrac{1}{4000+h} - \dfrac{1}{4000}\right) = \dfrac{Kh}{(4000+h)(4000)}$.

22. $a = 1$, $b = 9$, $n = 8 \Longrightarrow (b-a)/2n = 1/2$. Thus $W = \displaystyle\int_1^9 f(x)\,dx \approx$

     $\dfrac{1}{2}[125 + 2(120) + 2(130) + 2(146) + 2(165) + 2(157) + 2(150) + 2(143) + 140]^{-}$

$$= \frac{2287}{2} = 1143.5 \text{ joules}.$$

EXERCISES 6.6, page 284

NOTE: In these solutions, ρ is the density of water, 62.5 lbs/ft^3 .

1. (a) Introducing a coordinate system with the origin at the lower left corner, we can use (6.13) directly with $k = 1$, $f(y) = 1$, $g(y) = 0$ so that $F =$

$$\rho \int_0^1 (1-y)(1-0)dy = \rho/2.$$

(b) Similar to (a) except that $f(y) = 3$ and $F = \rho \int_0^1 (1-y)(3-0)dy = 3\rho/2.$

2. HINT: Let the diagonal be the line $y = x$. For the upper half, $f(y) = y$, $g(y) = 0$, $k = 1$. For the lower half, $f(y) = 1$, $g(y) = y$, $k = 1$.

3. (a) $F = \rho \int_0^1 (1-y)2\sqrt{3} \, y \, dy$.   (b) $F = \rho \int_0^{1/2} (1/2-y)2\sqrt{3} \, y \, dy$.

4. The end of the trough and the coordinate axes are shown. (The length is immaterial.) The upper vertices are at $x = \pm\sqrt{4-h^2}$. Thus the right boundary is $y = (h/\sqrt{4-h^2})x$ or $x = (\sqrt{4-h^2}/h)y = f(y)$. Similarly the left boundary is $x = (-\sqrt{4-h^2}/h)y$.

The coordinate points: $(-\sqrt{4-h^2},h)$ and $(\sqrt{4-h^2},h)$, with h, 2, 2 labeled.

(a) The trough full means the surface is at $y = h$. Thus $F = \rho \int_0^h (h-y)[(\sqrt{4-h^2}/h)(y-(-y))]dy = 2\rho(\sqrt{4-h^2}/h) \int_0^h (h-y)y \, dy.$

The integral is $h^3/6$ and $F = \rho h^2\sqrt{4-h^2}/3.$

(b) If half full, the surface is at $y = h/2$, and $F = 2\rho(\sqrt{4-h^2}/h) \int_0^{h/2} (h/2-y)ydy.$
The integral is $h^3/48$ and $F = \rho h^2\sqrt{4-h^2}/24.$

5. $F = 60 \int_{-2}^0 (0-y) \, 2\sqrt{4-y^2} \, dy.$

7. Place the x-axis on a sloping edge of the bottom with $x = 0$ at the 3' end and $x = \sqrt{40^2 + 6^2} = \sqrt{1636}$ at the 9' end. Partition as usual and consider the rectangle shown. Above the point w_i, the depth d is $3 + L$ where, by similar triangles, $\dfrac{L}{6} = \dfrac{w_i}{\sqrt{1636}}$ so that $d = 3 + \dfrac{6w_i}{\sqrt{1636}}$.

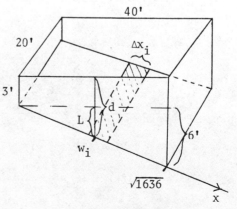

The force acting on this rectangle = (pressure) $\cdot$ (area) $\approx$ (ρd) $\cdot$

(20Δx_i). Summing over all rectangles and passing to the limit, the total

force is $F = 20\rho \int_0^{\sqrt{1636}} (3 + \frac{6x}{\sqrt{1636}}) dx = 120\sqrt{1636}\ \rho \approx 4853.7\rho$. (Another way

would be to place the axis on a horizontal edge. With a bit of work, the

area at the bottom can be shown to be $\sqrt{1636}\Delta x_i/2$ and the depth at w_i is

$3 + \frac{6w_i}{40}$.)

9. $F = \rho \int_0^4 (10-y)[(4-y/2)-(y/2-4)]dy$. (The y-axis bisects the trapezoid for

    this form of the integral.)

10. Place the coordinate axes with the origin at the
    center of the circle, the water level at y = 6.
    The right and left boundaries of the circular
    plate are $f(y) = \sqrt{4-y^2}$ and $g(y) = -\sqrt{4-y^2}$. Thus

    $F = 2\rho \int_{-2}^2 (6-y)\sqrt{4-y^2}\ dy$. To evaluate $\int_{-2}^2 \sqrt{4-y^2}\ dy$,

    note that this is the area of half a circle of
    radius 2, which is 2π. The other integral is

    $\int_{-2}^2 y\sqrt{4-y^2}\ dy = -\frac{1}{3}(4-y^2)^{3/2}\Big]_{-2}^2 = 0$. Thus $F = 24\pi\rho$.

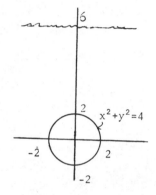

11. $F = \rho \int_0^4 (4-y)\ 2\sqrt{y}\ dy$.

13. Place the y axis with y = 0 at the bottom of the plate.
    Then the top is at y = 6, and the surface is at y = 8.
    Partition [0,6] and let $w_i\ \epsilon\ [y_{i-1}, y_i]$. By (6.14) the
    force on the typical rectangle shown is $50(8-w_i)(3\Delta y_i)$
    $= 150(8-w_i)\Delta y_i$. Summing and passing to the limit as

    $\|P\| \to 0$ we get $F = 150 \int_0^6 (8-y)dy = 150(48-18) = 4500$ lbs.

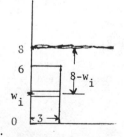

14. HINT. Let the diagonal extend from the lower left to the upper right corner.
    For the left part of the plate, by similar triangles, the area of the typical
    rectangle is $(3/6)w_i\Delta y_i$.

EXERCISES 6.7, page 290

1. $8x^2 = 27y^3 \Rightarrow y = (2/3)x^{2/3} \Rightarrow y' = (4/9)x^{-1/3} = f'(x)$. Then $\sqrt{1 + f'(x)^2}$

$= \sqrt{1 + (16/81)x^{-2/3}} = \sqrt{x^{-2/3}(x^{2/3} + 16/81)} = x^{-1/3}\sqrt{x^{2/3} + 16/81}$, and $L_1^8 =$

$\displaystyle\int_1^8 x^{-1/3}\sqrt{x^{2/3} + 16/81}\ dx$. Let $u = x^{2/3} + 16/81$ so that $du = (2/3)x^{-1/3}\ dx$

or $x^{-1/3}\ dx = (3/2)du$. $x = 1 \Rightarrow u = 1 + 16/81 = A$. $x = 8 \Rightarrow u = 8^{2/3} +$

$16/81 = 4 + 16/81 = B$. Thus $L_1^8 = (3/2)\displaystyle\int_A^B u^{1/2}\ du = u^{3/2}\Big]_A^B = B^{3/2} - A^{3/2} =$

$(4 + 16/81)^{3/2} - (1 + 16/81)^{3/2} \approx 7.29$.

3. $L_1^4 = \displaystyle\int_1^4 \sqrt{1 + (9/4)x}\ dx$.

4. Since $y = 6x^{2/3} + 1$, the calculations are similar to those in #1. The only

thing to watch out for is that $\sqrt{x^{2/3}} = -x^{1/3}$ in this problem since $-8 \le x \le$

$-1 < 0$ here. Then $L_{-8}^{-1} = \displaystyle\int_{-8}^{-1} -x^{-1/3}\sqrt{x^{2/3} + 16}\ dx = 20^{3/2} - 17^{3/2}$ with the

substitution $u = x^{2/3} + 16$. (See #10 also.)

5. $L_{2/3}^{8/3} = \displaystyle\int_{2/3}^{8/3} \sqrt{1 + (243/32)y}\ dy$.

7. $y' = \dfrac{x^2}{4} - \dfrac{1}{x^2} = f'(x)$. Then $1 + f'(x)^2 = 1 + (\dfrac{x^4}{16} - \dfrac{1}{2} + \dfrac{1}{x^4}) = \dfrac{x^4}{16} + \dfrac{1}{2} + \dfrac{1}{x^4} =$

$(\dfrac{x^2}{4} + \dfrac{1}{x^2})^2$. Thus, $L_1^2 = \displaystyle\int_1^2 (\dfrac{x^2}{4} + x^{-2})dx = \dfrac{x^3}{12} - \dfrac{1}{x}\Big]_1^2 = \dfrac{1}{6} - (-\dfrac{11}{12}) = \dfrac{13}{12}$.

9. $L_1^2 = \displaystyle\int_1^2 (\dfrac{y^4}{6} + \dfrac{3}{2}y^{-4})dy$ (by (6.19)).

10. $x = g(y) = \dfrac{y^4}{16} + \dfrac{1}{2y^2} \Rightarrow g'(y) = \dfrac{y^3}{4} - \dfrac{1}{y^3}$. Then $1 + g'(y)^2 = 1 + (\dfrac{y^6}{16} - \dfrac{1}{2} + \dfrac{1}{y^6})$

$= \dfrac{y^6}{16} + \dfrac{1}{2} + \dfrac{1}{y^6} = (\dfrac{y^3}{4} + \dfrac{1}{y^3})^2$. Here, $-2 \le y \le -1 < 0$ so that $y^3 < 0$ and the ex-

pression in the parentheses is negative. Recalling that $\sqrt{a^2} = |a| = -a$ if

$a < 0$, it follows that $\sqrt{1 + g'(y)^2} = -(\dfrac{y^3}{4} + \dfrac{1}{y^3})$. Thus, $L_{-2}^{-1} =$

$-\displaystyle\int_{-2}^{-1} (\dfrac{y^3}{4} + y^{-3})dy = -[\dfrac{y^4}{16} - \dfrac{1}{2y^2}]_{-2}^{-1} = -(-\dfrac{7}{16} - \dfrac{7}{8}) = \dfrac{21}{16}$.

13. Let the line $y = x$ and the given curve intersect when

$x = a$. Solving, we find that $2a^{2/3} = 1$ so that $a =$

$(1/2)^{3/2}$. By symmetry then, the desired length is $8 \, L_a^1$.

Solving $x^{2/3} + y^{2/3} = 1$ for y, we get $y = (1-x^{2/3})^{3/2}$ and

$y' = -(1-x^{2/3})^{1/2}/x^{1/3}$ and $\sqrt{1+y'^2} = \sqrt{1+(1-x^{2/3})/x^{2/3}}$

which simplifies to $x^{-1/3}$. Thus $8 \, L_a^1 =$

$$8 \int_a^1 x^{-1/3} \, dx = 12(1 - a^{2/3}) = 12(1 - 1/2) = 6.$$

NOTE. If we had tried to compute L_0^1 directly, we would have obtained $L_0^1 =$

$\int_0^1 1/\sqrt[3]{x} \, dx$ which does not exist because the integrand becomes infinite as

$x \to 0^+$. This type of integral is called an "improper" integral and will be
studied in Chapter 10.

16. $f(x) = x^{3/2} \implies f'(x) = (3/2)x^{1/2} \implies \sqrt{1 + f'(x)^2} = \sqrt{1 + 9x/4}$. Thus $s(x) =$

$\int_1^x \sqrt{1 + 9t/4} \, dt = \frac{8}{27} \left[(1 + 9t/4)^{3/2} \right]_1^x = \frac{8}{27} \left[(1 + \frac{9}{4}x)^{3/2} - (1 + \frac{9}{4})^{3/2} \right] =$

$\frac{1}{27} \left[(4 + 9x)^{3/2} - 13^{3/2} \right]$. $\Delta s = s(1.1) - s(1) = (\frac{1}{27}) \left[13.9^{3/2} - 13^{3/2} \right] \approx$

$(51.82 - 46.86)/27 \approx 0.184$.

$ds = \sqrt{1 + f'(x)^2} \, \Delta x$ and with $x = 1$, $\Delta x = 0.1$, $ds = \sqrt{1 + 9/4} \, (.1) = \sqrt{13}(.1)/2$
≈ 0.180.

19. $y = f(x) = 2/x \implies f'(x) = -2/x^2 \implies L_1^2 = \int_1^2 \sqrt{1+4/x^4} \, dx$. Let $g(x)$ denote

the integrand. Then with $a = 1$, $b = 2$, $n = 4$, $L_1^2 = \int_1^2 g(x) \, dx \approx$

$\frac{2-1}{3(4)}[g(1) + 4g(5/4) + 2g(3/2) + 4g(7/4) + g(2)] = 0.0833[2.2361 + 4(1.6243)$

$+ 2(1.3380) + 4(1.1944) + 1.1180] = 0.0833(17.3047) = 1.4421 \approx 1.44$.

22. $f(x) = x^4/4$, $f'(x) = x^3 \implies L_0^2 = \int_0^2 \sqrt{1+x^6} \, dx$. With $g(x)$ denoting the

integrand, with $a = 0$, $b = 2$, $n = 4$, $L_0^2 \approx \frac{2-0}{3(4)}[g(0) + 4g(0.5) + 2g(1) +$

$4g(1.5) + g(2)] \approx 0.1667[1 + 4(1.0078) + 2(1.4142) + 4(3.5200) + 8.0623] =$

$0.1667(30.0019) = 5.0003 \approx 5.00$.

EXERCISES 6.8, page 296

1. The total depreciation, $f(t)$, is $\int_0^t g(x) \, dx = \int_0^t (1-x^2/9)dx = t - t^3/27$ hundreds of dollars.

 (a) At 6 months, $t = 1/2$ and $f(1/2) = 1/2 - 1/8(27) = 107/216 \approx \$49.54$.

 (b) $f(1) = 26/27 \approx \$96.30$.   (c) $f(3/2) = 11/8 \approx \$137.50$.

 (d) $f(2) = 46/27 \approx \$170.37$.

4. Over [0,5], the amount of capital formation is $\int_0^5 2t(3t+1)dt = \int_0^5 (6t^2+2t)dt$

= 275 thousand dollars. Over [5,10], we obtain

$\int_5^{10} (6t^2+2t)dt = 2100-275 = 1825$ thousands of dollars.

7. (a) 1-item time is f(1) $\approx$ 18.16. (b) 4-item time $\approx \int_0^4 (20(x+1)^{-.4}+3)dx =$

$\frac{20}{.6}(x+1)^{.6}\Big]_0^4 +12 = \frac{20}{.6}(5^{.6}-1)+12 \approx 66.22$. (c) 8-item time $\approx \frac{20}{.6}(9^{.6}-1)+32 \approx$

115.24. (d) 16-item time $\approx \frac{20}{.6}(17^{.6}-1)+48 \approx 197.12$ min.

10. Let P(t) be the population, in thousands, t years after 1980. We are given

that P'(t) = $1.5 + 0.3t^{1/2} + .006t^2$, P(0) = 50 (thousand), and we want P(9).

(1989 is 9 years after 1980.) Antidifferentiating P'(t) we get P(t) = 1.5t +

$0.2t^{3/2} + .002t^3$ + C. P(0) = 50 $\Rightarrow$ C = 50, P(t) = $1.5t + 0.2t^{3/2} + .002t^3$ +

50, and P(9) = 13.5 + 5.4 + 1.458 + 50 = 70.358 thousand (or 70,358).

EXERCISES 6.9, page 298

1. The curves intersect at ($\pm 2,4$). Thus for x integration the interval is
    $-2 \le x \le 2$, the upper boundary is $y = -x^2$, the lower is $y = x^2 - 8$, and

$A = \int_{-2}^2 [(-x^2)-(x^2-8)]dx = \int_{-2}^2 (8-2x^2)dx = 64/3$. For the y integration the

interval is $-8 \le y \le 0$. For $-8 \le y \le -4$, the right and left boundaries are

$x = \pm(y+8)^{1/2}$, and for $-4 \le y \le 0$, the boundaries are $x = \pm(-y)^{1/2}$. Thus

$A = \int_{-8}^{-4} 2(y+8)^{1/2} dy + \int_{-4}^0 2(-y)^{1/2} dy = \frac{32}{3} + \frac{32}{3} = \frac{64}{3}$.

3. $A = \int_a^b [(1-y)-y^2]dy$ where $a = (-1 - \sqrt{5})/2$, $b = (-1 + \sqrt{5})/2$.

4. Find point A by substituting $y = -x^3$ into the
    line's equation to obtain $-3x^3 + 7x - 10 = 0$
    which has x = -2 as the only real solution.
    For point B, put $y = \sqrt{x}$, or $y^2 = x$, into the
    linear equation to obtain $3y + 7y^2 - 10 = 0$
    with positive solution y = 1. Thus the x-
    interval is $-2 \le x \le 1$ with the obvious change
    in the lower boundary at x = 0. Thus

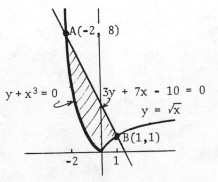

$A = \int_{-2}^0 [(-\frac{7}{3}x + \frac{10}{3}) - (-x^3)]dx +$

$$\int_0^1 \left[\left(-\frac{7}{3}x + \frac{10}{3}\right) - x^{1/2}\right]dx = \frac{1}{3}\int_{-2}^1 (-7x+10)dx + \int_{-2}^0 x^3 \, dx - \int_0^1 x^{1/2} \, dx =$$

$$\frac{27}{2} - 4 - \frac{2}{3} = \frac{53}{6} \ .$$

5. $A = \displaystyle\int_{-2}^0 (x^3 - x^2 - 6x)dx + \int_0^3 (-x^3 + x^2 + 6x)dx.$

7.   Using the disc method, $V = \pi\displaystyle\int_0^2 (\sqrt{4x + 1})^2 dx = \pi\int_0^2 (4x + 1)dx.$

9. $V = 2\pi\displaystyle\int_0^1 x(2-(x^3+1))dx.$

10. The graphs intersect when $x = 0$ and 1. $\sqrt[3]{x} \geq \sqrt{x}$ on $[0,1]$

   $\Longrightarrow$ (using the washer method) $V = \pi\displaystyle\int_0^1 (x^{2/3} - x)dx =$

   $\pi(3/5 - 1/2) = \pi/10.$

11. (a) $V = \pi\displaystyle\int_{-2}^1 [(-4x+8)^2 - (4x^2)^2]dx.$

   (b) $V = 2\pi\displaystyle\int_{-2}^1 (1-x)[(-4x+8) - 4x^2]dx.$

   (c) $V = 2\pi\displaystyle\int_{-2}^1 [(16 - 4x^2)^2 - (4x + 8)^2]dx.$

13. $y = 1 + (1/2)(x+3)^{2/3} = f(x) \Longrightarrow f'(x) = (1/3)(x+3)^{-1/3} \Longrightarrow 1 + f'(x)^2 = 1 +$

   $(1/9)(x+3)^{-2/3} = [(x+3)^{2/3} + 1/9](x+3)^{-2/3} \Longrightarrow L_{-2}^5 = \displaystyle\int_{-2}^5 \sqrt{(x+3)^{2/3} + 1/9} \ \cdot$

   $(x+3)^{-1/3}dx = [(x+3)^{2/3} + 1/9]^{3/2}\Big]_{-2}^{5} = (4 + 1/9)^{3/2} - (1 + 1/9)^{3/2} =$

   $(37^{3/2} - 10^{3/2})/27.$

   (The substitution $u = (x+3)^{2/3} + 1/9$, $du = \frac{2}{3}(x+3)^{-1/3}dx$ leads to the antiderivative above.)

15. $W = 36\pi(62.5)\displaystyle\int_0^4 (5-y)dy.$

16. Position the y-axis vertically so that $y = 0$ is the bottom and $y = 30$ is the
   top of the well. The bucket loses 8 pounds of water in the 30 feet for an
   average loss of 8/30 pounds per foot. Partition $[0,30]$, and select w_i in
   $[y_{i-1}, y_i]$. When the bucket bottom is at w_i, $(8/30)w_i$ of water has leaked out,
   and the total mass of bucket and water is $4 + (24 - (8/30)w_i)$. The work done
   in lifting the bucket from y_{i-1} to y_i, a distance of Δy_i feet, is

$(28 - (8/30)w_i)\Delta y_i$. Summing for the total work approximation and passing to the limit as $\|P\| \to 0$, we obtain $W = \int_0^{30} (28 - (8/30)y)dy = 840 - 120 = 720$.

17. $F = \rho \int_0^{2\sqrt{2}} (6-y)2(2\sqrt{2} - y)dy + \rho \int_{-2\sqrt{2}}^{0} (6-y)2(2\sqrt{2} + y)dy$.   (The y-axis bisects the plate for this form of the answer.)

19.   The limit is $\int_0^1 \pi x^4 \, dx = \pi/5$.

22.   If the force function is $f(x) = \pi x^4$ for $0 \leq x \leq 1$, then the limit is the work done in moving an object from $x = 0$ to $x = 1$.

CHAPTER 7

EXPONENTIAL AND LOGARITHMIC FUNCTIONS

<u>EXERCISES 7.1, page 302</u>

1. $(f \circ g)(x) = 9g(x) + 2 = 9(\frac{1}{9}x - \frac{2}{9}) + 2 = x - 2 + 2 = x.$ $(g \circ f)(x) = \frac{f(x)}{9} - \frac{2}{9} =$
    $\frac{9x+2}{9} - \frac{2}{9} = x.$

4. With $f(x) = \frac{1}{x-1}$, $g(x) = \frac{1+x}{x} = \frac{1}{x} + 1$, $(f \circ g)(x) = \frac{1}{g(x)-1} = \frac{1}{1/x} = x$, and
    $(g \circ f)(x) = \frac{1}{f(x)} + 1 = (x-1) + 1 = x.$

7. To find f^{-1} if $f(x) = 6-x^2$, $0 \le x \le \sqrt{6}$, we solve $y = 6-x^2 \iff x^2 = 6-y \implies$
    $x = \sqrt{6-y}$, where we chose the positive square root since $x \ge 0$. Thus $f^{-1}(x) =$
    $\sqrt{6-x}$, $0 \le x \le 6$.

10. Here, we solve $y = \sqrt{1-4x^2}$, $0 \le x \le 1/2 \implies y^2 = 1-4x^2 \iff 4x^2 = 1-y^2 \implies$
    $x = (1/2)\sqrt{1-y^2}$. Thus $f^{-1}(x) = (1/2)\sqrt{1-x^2}$ for $0 \le x \le 1$. (For the original
    function, the range was $0 \le y \le 1$. This becomes the domain of f^{-1}.)

13. $y = (x^3+8)^5 \iff x^3+8 = y^{1/5} \iff x = (y^{1/5} - 8)^{1/3}$. Thus $f^{-1}(x) =$
    $\sqrt[3]{x^{1/5} - 8}$ for all $x \in \mathbb{R}$.

19. Any polynomial function which is not one-to-one won't have an inverse, e.g.
    $f(x) = x^2$ $(f(1) = f(-1) = 1)$.

<u>EXERCISES 7.2, page 310</u>

1. $f'(x) = \frac{D_x(9x+4)}{9x+4} = \frac{9}{9x+4}$.

4. $f(x) = \ln(5x^2+1)^3 = 3 \ln(5x^2+1)$. Thus $f'(x) = 3 \frac{D_x(5x^2+1)}{5x^2+1} = \frac{3(10x)}{5x^2+1}$.

7. $f'(x) = \frac{D_x(3x^2-2x+1)}{(3x^2-2x+1)} = \frac{6x-2}{3x^2-2x+1}$.

10. $f'(x) = (\ln x)D_x \ln(x+5) + D_x(\ln x) \ln(x+5) = \frac{\ln x}{x+5} + \frac{\ln(x+5)}{x}$.

13. $f(x) = \ln\sqrt{x} + \sqrt{\ln x} = (1/2)\ln x + (\ln x)^{1/2} \implies f'(x) = 1/2x + (1/2)(\ln x)^{-1/2}$.
    $D_x(\ln x) = 1/2x + 1/2x\sqrt{\ln x}.$

16. $f(x) = \ln\sqrt{\frac{4+x^2}{4-x^2}} = \frac{1}{2} \ln \frac{4+x^2}{4-x^2} = \frac{1}{2}[\ln(4+x^2) - \ln(4-x^2)] \implies f'(x) =$
    $\frac{1}{2}(\frac{2x}{4+x^2} - \frac{-2x}{4-x^2}) = \frac{8x}{16-x^4}$.

19. $f(x) = \ln \frac{\sqrt{x^2+1}}{(9x-4)^2} = \frac{1}{2} \ln(x^2+1) - 2 \ln(9x-4) \implies f'(x) = (\frac{1}{2})2x/(x^2+1) -$
    $(2)9/(9x-4) = x/(x^2+1) - 18/(9x-4).$

22. $f'(x) = \dfrac{D_x \ln x}{\ln x} = \dfrac{1}{x \ln x}$.

25. $f'(x) = 2 \ln\sqrt{x^2+1} \; D_x \; \ln\sqrt{x^2+1}$. Using $\ln\sqrt{a} = (1/2)\ln a$, we obtain $f'(x) =$

 $\ln(x^2+1)D_x((1/2)\ln(x^2+1)) = \ln(x+1)\dfrac{(1/2)2x}{x^2+1}$.

28. $x > 0 \Longrightarrow |x| = x$, and $f'(x) = D_x \ln|x| = D_x \ln x = 1/x$. $x < 0 \Longrightarrow |x| = -x$,

 and $f'(x) = D_x \ln |x| = D_x \ln(-x) = \dfrac{D_x(-x)}{-x} = \dfrac{-1}{-x} = \dfrac{1}{x}$. Thus, for all $x \neq 0$,

 $D_x \ln |x| = 1/x$.

31. $x \ln y - y \ln x = 1 \Longrightarrow (x \dfrac{y'}{y} + \ln y) - (\dfrac{y}{x} + y' \ln x) = 0 \Longrightarrow x^2 y' + xy \ln y$

 $- y^2 - y'xy \ln x) = 0$ (having multiplied through by xy) $\Longrightarrow (x^2 - xy \ln x)y' =$

 $y^2 - xy \ln y \Longrightarrow y' = (y^2 - xy \ln y)/(x^2 - xy \ln x)$.

34. $\ln x \ln y = xy - 1 \Longrightarrow (\ln x) \dfrac{y'}{y} + \dfrac{1}{x} \ln y = xy' + y \Longrightarrow x(\ln x)y' + y \ln y$

 $= x^2 yy' + xy^2 \Longrightarrow (x \ln x - x^2 y)y' = xy^2 - y \ln y \Longrightarrow y' =$

 $y(xy - \ln y)/x(\ln x - xy)$.

40. $x^3 - x \ln y + y^3 = 2x + 5 \Longrightarrow 3x^2 - xy'/y - \ln y + 3y^2 y' = 2$. At $(2,1)$ this

 reduces to $12 - 2y' - \ln 1 + 3y' = 2$ or $y' = -10$. Thus, $(y-1) = -10(x-2)$.

43. $v(t) = 2t - 4/(t+1)$, and $a(t) = 2 + 4/(t+1)^2$. Writing $v(t) =$

 $(2t(t+1) - 4)/(t+1) = 2(t-1)(t+2)/(t+1)$ we see that $v(t) < 0$ if $0 \leq t \leq 1$;

 $v(t) > 0$ if $1 < t \leq 4$. Thus the motion is to the left from $s(0) = 0$ to

 $s(1) = 1 - 4 \ln 2$ from $t = 0$ to $t = 1$, then to the right to $s(4) = 16 -$

 $4 \ln 5$ from $t = 1$ to $t = 4$.

46. (a)   (b)

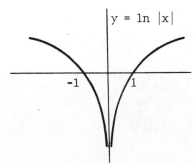

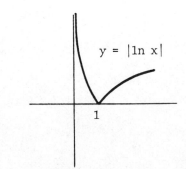

49. $D_x(x \ln x - x + C) = x \cdot \dfrac{1}{x} + \ln x - 1 + 0 = \ln x$ verifies the formula.

EXERCISES 7.3, page 318

1. $f'(x) = e^{-5x}D_x(-5x) = -5e^{-5x}$.

4. $f'(x) = e^{1-x^3}D_x(1-x^3) = -3x^2e^{1-x^3}$.

7. $f'(x) = e^{\sqrt{x+1}}D_x\sqrt{x+1} = (e^{\sqrt{x+1}})/2\sqrt{x+1}$.

10. $f'(x) = \frac{1}{2}(e^{2x}+2x)^{-1/2}D_x(e^{2x} + 2x) = \frac{1}{2}(e^{2x}+2x)^{-1/2}(2e^{2x}+2)=(2e^{2x}+2)/2\sqrt{e^{2x}+2}$.

13. $f'(x) = 3(e^{4x}-5)^2D_x(e^{4x}-5) = 3(e^{4x}-5)^2(4e^{4x})$.

16. $f'(x) = D_x(e^{x^{1/2}} + e^{x/2}) = e^{\sqrt{x}}D_x(x^{1/2}) + e^{x/2}D_x(x/2) = e^{\sqrt{x}}/2\sqrt{x} + \frac{1}{2}e^{x/2}$.

19. $f'(x) = e^{-2x}D_x(\ln x) + \ln x\, D_x(e^{-2x}) = \frac{e^{-2x}}{x} + \ln x(-2)e^{-2x}$.

22. $f'(x) = \dfrac{\ln(e^x-1)D_x \ln(e^x+1) - \ln(e^x+1)D_x \ln(e^x-1)}{[\ln(e^x-1)]^2} =$

$\{\dfrac{[\ln(e^x-1)]e^x}{e^x + 1} - \dfrac{[\ln(e^x+1)]e^x}{e^x - 1}\}/[\ln(e^x-1)]^2$.

25. $e^{xy} - x^3 + 3y^2 = 11 \implies e^{xy}(xy'+y) - 3x^2 + 6yy' = 0 \implies (xe^{xy}+6y)y' +$

$(ye^{xy}-3x^2) = 0$.

28. $xe^y - ye^x = 2 \implies (xe^yy' + e^y) - (ye^x + e^xy') = 0 \implies (xe^y - e^x)y' =$

$ye^x - e^y \implies y' = (ye^x - e^y)/(xe^y - e^x)$.

34. $y' = 4(x\, e^{x^2-1}(2x) + e^{x^2-1}) = 4(2x^2+1)e^{x^2-1}$. $x = 1 \implies y' = 4(3)e^0 = 12$.
     Thus the normal line has slope $-1/12$ and equation $y-4 = (-1/12)(x-1)$.

37. $f'(x) = -2e^{-2x} < 0 \implies$ f is decreasing on $(-\infty,\infty)$. $f''(x) = 4e^{-2x} > 0 \implies$
     graph is CU on $(-\infty,\infty)$. There are no local extrema or PI's.

40. $f'(x) = e^x - e^{-x} = e^{-x}(e^{2x} - 1)$. Thus $f'(x) = 0$ if $x = 0$, $f'(x) > 0$ if
     $x > 0$, $f'(x) < 0$ if $x < 0$. Thus f is increasingly on $[0,\infty)$, decreasing on
     $(-\infty,0]$ and $f(0) = 2$ is a local minimum. $f''(x) = e^x + e^{-x} > 0$ for all $x \implies$
     graph is CU on $(-\infty,\infty)$.

43. (a) $C'(t) = \frac{k}{a-b}(-be^{-bt} + ae^{-at}) = 0$ if $ae^{-at} = be^{-bt} \implies \ln a - at = \ln b -$
     $bt \implies \ln a - \ln b = (a-b)t \implies t = (\ln a - \ln b)/(a-b)$.

(b) $\lim_{t \to \infty} C(t) = \frac{k}{a-b} \lim_{t \to \infty} (e^{-bt} - e^{-at}) = \frac{k}{a-b} (0-0) = 0$ since each exponent $\to$ $-\infty$ as $t \to \infty$.

46. $f(x) = e^{2x} \implies f'(x) = 2e^{2x} \implies f''(x) = 2^2 e^{2x} \implies f'''(x) = 2^3 e^{2x}$, and in general, $f^{(n)}(x) = 2^n e^{2x}$.

NOTE. In #47-50, use is made of the formulas $y = e^{cx} \implies y' = ce^{cx} \implies y'' = c^2 e^{cx} \implies y''' = c^3 e^{cx}$ and the fact that $e^{cx} \neq 0$ for all x.

47. Substituting $y = e^{cx}$, $y'' - 3y' + 2y = c^2 e^{cx} - 3ce^{cx} + 2e^{cx} = (c^2 - 3c + 2)e^{cx} = 0$ if $c^2 - 3c + 2 = 0$. Factoring, $c^2 - 3c + 2 = (c-2)(c-1) = 0$ if $c=1$ and $c=2$.

49. $y''' - y'' - 4y' + 4y = 0 \implies c^3 e^{cx} - c^2 e^{cx} - 4ce^{cx} + 4e^{cx} = (c^3 - c^2 - 4c + 4)e^{cx} = 0$ if $c^3 - c^2 - 4c + 4 = 0$. Factoring: $c^3 - c^2 - 4c + 4 = c^2(c-1) - 4(c-1) = (c^2 - 4)(c-1) = 0$ if $c = 1, \pm 2$.

52. Recall: $\ln t \to -\infty \iff t \to 0^+$; $\ln t \to \infty \iff t \to \infty$. (a) $y = e^x \implies x = \ln y \to -\infty \iff y \to 0^+$, i.e. $y = e^x \to 0$ as $x \to -\infty$. (b) $x = \ln y \to \infty \iff y \to \infty$, i.e. $y = e^x \to \infty$ as $x \to \infty$.

58. $f(x) = 1 - (1-e^{-x})^3 \implies f'(x) = -3(1-e^{-x})^2(e^{-x})$ which is ≤ 0 for all x, and is zero only at $x = 0$. $f''(x) = -3e^{-x}(1-e^{-x})(3e^{-x}-1) = 0$ at $x = 0$ and $x = \ln 3$, both of which are PI's. Using $f(0) = 1$, $f(\ln 3) \approx f(1.10) = 19/27$, the graph is obtained as shown.

EXERCISES 7.4, page 325

1. Let $u = x^2 + 1$. Then $du = 2x\,dx$, $x\,dx = (1/2)du$. $\int \frac{x}{x^2+1}\,dx = \frac{1}{2}\int \frac{du}{u} = \frac{1}{2}\ln|u| + C = \frac{1}{2}\ln|x^2+1| + C = \frac{1}{2}\ln(x^2+1) + C$ since $x^2+1 > 0$. ($\ln\sqrt{x^2+1} + C$ is another correct form of the answer.)

4. Let $u = x^4 - 5$, $du = 4x^3 dx$, $x^3 dx = (1/4)du$. $\int \frac{x^3}{x^4-5}\,dx = \frac{1}{4}\int \frac{du}{u} = \frac{1}{4}\ln|u| + C = \frac{1}{4}\ln|x^4-5| + C$.

7. With $u = x^3+1$, $du = 3x^2 dx$, $\int \frac{x^2}{x^3+1}\,dx = \frac{1}{3}\int \frac{du}{u} = (1/3)\ln|u| + C = (1/3)\ln|x^3+1| + C$.

10. Let $u = 4-5x$, $du = -5dx$. When $x = -1$, $u = 9$ and when $x = 0$, $u = 4$. Thus $\int_{-1}^{0} \frac{dx}{4-5x} = -\frac{1}{5}\int_{9}^{4} \frac{du}{u} = -\frac{1}{5}\ln|u|\Big]_{9}^{4} = -\frac{1}{5}(\ln 4 - \ln 9) = \frac{1}{5}\ln(9/4)$.

13. $\int (x + e^{5x})dx = \frac{x^2}{2} + \int e^{5x}dx$. Let $u = 5x$, $du = 5\,dx$, $dx = (1/5)du$. Using

this in the remaining integral, we get $\frac{x^2}{2} + \frac{1}{5}\int e^u du = \frac{x^2}{2} + \frac{e^u}{5} + C = \frac{x^2}{2} + \frac{e^{5x}}{5} + C$.

16. With $u = \ln x$, $du = \frac{1}{x}\,dx$, $\int \frac{1}{x(\ln x)^2}\,dx = \int \frac{1}{u^2}\,du = -\frac{1}{u} + C = -\frac{1}{\ln x} + C$.

19. With $u = \sqrt{x}$, $du = \frac{1}{2\sqrt{x}}\,dx$, $\int \frac{e^{\sqrt{x}}}{\sqrt{x}}\,dx = 2\int e^u du = 2e^u + C = 2e^{\sqrt{x}} + C$.

22. With $u = e^x + 1$, $du = e^x dx$, $\int \frac{e^x}{(e^x+1)^2}\,dx = \int \frac{1}{u^2}\,du = -\frac{1}{u} + C = -1/(e^x+1) + C$.

25. Since $x^2 + 2x + 1 = (x+1)^2$, we let $u = (x+1)$, $du = dx$ so that $\int \frac{1}{x^2+2x+1}\,dx$

$= \int \frac{1}{(x+1)^2}\,dx = \int \frac{1}{u^2}\,du = \int u^{-2}du = -u^{-1} + C = -1/(x+1) + C$.

28. $\int \frac{x^2+3x+1}{x}\,dx = \int (x + 3 + \frac{1}{x})dx = \frac{x^2}{2} + 3x + \ln|x| + C$.

31. $A = \int_1^2 (\frac{1}{x} - e^{-x})dx = \ln|x| + e^{-x}\Big]_1^2 = (\ln 2 + e^{-2}) - (\ln 1 + e^{-1}) = \ln 2 +$

$e^{-2} - e^{-1} \approx 0.460$. (Recall that $\ln 1 = 0$.)

34. $V = \pi \int_1^4 (\frac{1}{\sqrt{x}})^2 dx = \pi \int_1^4 \frac{1}{x}\,dx = \pi \ln x \Big]_1^4 = \pi \ln 4 \approx 1.39\pi$.

37. (a) $f'(x) = e^x \implies L_0^1 = \int_0^1 \sqrt{1+(e^x)^2}\,dx$.

(b) With $a = 0$, $b = 1$, $n = 5$, the partitioning points are 0, .2, .4, .6, .8
and 1. With $g(x) = \sqrt{1+(e^x)^2}$ we obtain $L_0^1 \approx \frac{(1-0)}{2(5)}[g(0) + 2g(.2) + 2g(.4) +$
$2g(.6) + 2g(.8) + g(1)]$.

(c) $L_0^1 \approx (0.1)[(1.414 + 2(1.579) + 2(1.796) + 2(2.078) + 2(2.440) + 2(2.896)]$

$= 2.010$.

40. Following the outline of steps for logarithmic differentiation, we obtain:

$y = \sqrt{4x+7}(x-5)^3 = (4x+7)^{1/2}(x-5)^3 \implies \ln y = (1/2)\ln(4x+7) + 3\ln(x-5) \implies$

$\frac{y'}{y} = \frac{1}{2}\frac{4}{4x+7} + 3\frac{1}{x-5} = \frac{2x - 10 + 12x + 21}{(4x+7)(x-5)} = \frac{14x+11}{(4x+7)(x-5)}$. Thus $y' =$

$\frac{14x+11}{(4x+7)(x-5)}y = \frac{14x+11}{(4x+7)(x-5)}\sqrt{4x+7}(x-5)^3 = \frac{(14x+11)(x-5)^2}{\sqrt{4x+7}}$.

43. $\ln y = \frac{1}{3}\ln(2x+1) + 2\ln(4x-1) + 4\ln(3x+5)$. $\frac{y'}{y} = \frac{2}{3(2x+1)} + \frac{2(4)}{4x-1} + \frac{4(3)}{3x+5}$. Multiply-

ing by y and substituting for y yields the indicated answer in the text.

46. $\ln y = \frac{2}{3} \ln(x^2+3) + 4 \ln(3x-4) - \frac{1}{2} \ln x.$ $\frac{y'}{y} = \frac{2(2x)}{3(x^2+3)} + \frac{4(3)}{3x-4} - \frac{1}{2x}$.

     $y' = [\frac{4x}{3(x^2+3)} + \frac{12}{3x-4} - \frac{1}{2x}] \frac{(x^2+3)^{2/3}(3x-4)^4}{\sqrt{x}}$.

49. $f(x) = \ln|1-e^{-2x}|^3 = 3 \ln|1-e^{-2x}|.$ $f'(x) = \frac{3D_x(1-e^{-2x})}{1-e^{-2x}} = \frac{3(2e^{-2x})}{1-e^{-2x}}$.

EXERCISES 7.5, page 332

1. $f'(x) = 7^x \ln 7$ immediately from (7.20.

4. $f'(x) = 9^{\sqrt{x}} \ln 9 \, D_x\sqrt{x} = (9^{\sqrt{x}} \ln 9)/2\sqrt{x}.$

7. $f'(x) = 5^{3x-4}\ln 5 \, D_x(3x-4) = 5^{3x-4}(\ln 5) \cdot 3.$

10. $f'(x) = 10(10^x + 10^{-x})^9 D_x(10^x + 10^{-x}) = 10(10^x + 10^{-x})^9(10^x\ln 10-10^{-x}\ln 10).$

13. $f'(x) = D_x 5 \log(3x^2 + 2) = \frac{5(6x)}{(\ln 10)(3x^2+2)}$.

16. $f'(x) = D_x(\log |1-x^2| - \log |2-5x^3|) = \frac{-(2x)}{(\ln 10)(1-x^2)} - \frac{(-15x^2)}{(\ln 10)(2-5x^3)}$.

19. $f'(x) = D_x(x^e) + D_x(e^x) = ex^{e-1} + e^x$ since the first function is a power

     function; the second is the familiar exponential.

22.   Method 1. $D_x(x^{x^2+4}) = D_x e^{(x^2+4)\ln x} = e^{(x^2+4)\ln x}D_x(x^2+4)\ln x =$

     $x^{x^2+4}[(x^2+4)/x + 2x \ln x].$

     Method 2. $y = x^{x^2+4} \iff \ln y = (x^2+4) \ln x \implies \frac{y'}{y} = \frac{x^2+4}{x} + 2x \ln x \implies$

     $y' = y((x^2+4)/x + 2x \ln x).$

25.   Let $u = -x^2$, $du = -2x \, dx$, $x \, dx = -(1/2)du.$ Then $\int x3^{-x^2} dx = -\frac{1}{2} \int 3^u du =$

     $-\frac{1}{2} \frac{3^u}{\ln 3} + C = -\frac{3^{-x^2}}{2 \ln 3} + C.$

28.   Let $u = 3^x+4$, $du = 3^x \ln 3 \, dx.$ Then $3^x \, dx = (1/\ln 3)du$ and $\int \frac{3^x}{\sqrt{3^x+4}} dx =$

     $\frac{1}{\ln 3} \int \frac{du}{\sqrt{u}} = \frac{1}{\ln 3} \int u^{-1/2} du = \frac{2}{\ln 3} u^{1/2} + C = \frac{2}{\ln 3}\sqrt{3^x+4} + C.$

31.   With $u = x^3$, $du = 3x^2 dx$, $\int x^2 2^{x^3} dx = \frac{1}{3}\int 2^u du = 2^u/3 \ln 2 + C = 2^{x^3}/3 \ln 2 + C.$

34. $u = 4^x + 1 \implies du = 4^x \ln 4 \, dx \implies 4^x dx = (1/\ln 4)du.$ $\int 4^x(4^x + 1)^3 dx =$

     $\frac{1}{\ln 4} \int u^3 du = \frac{u^4}{4 \ln 4} + C = \frac{(4^x + 1)^4}{4 \ln 4} + C.$

37. The graphs intersect when $x = 0$ and on $[0,1]$, $2^x \geq 1-x$. Thus,

$$A = \int_0^1 (2^x - (1-x))dx = 2^x/\ln 2 - x + x^2/2]_0^1 = 2/\ln 2 - 1 + 1/2 - 1/\ln 2$$

$$= 1/\ln 2 - 1/2.$$

40. The given line has slope 4, and $y' = 2^x \ln 2$, so the equation to be solved is $2^x \ln 2 = 4 \implies 2^x = 4/\ln 2 \implies x = \log_2(4/\ln 2) = 2 - \log_2(\ln 2) = 2 - \ln(\ln 2)/\ln 2$.

43. Let $x = [H^+]$, $y = $ pH. Then $y = -\log x$. We are given that $x = 6.3 \times 10^{-3}$ with maximum % error $\frac{\Delta x}{x}(100) = 0.5$. Thus $\frac{\Delta x}{x} = 0.005$. The calculated pH value is $y = -\log(6.3 \times 10^{-3}) = 2.201$. We seek the maximum error, $|\Delta y|$, in this calculation. $|\Delta y| \approx |dy| = |D_x(-\log x)|\Delta x = |\frac{-1}{\ln 10\, x}|\Delta x = \frac{1}{\ln 10}\frac{\Delta x}{x} = \frac{0.005}{\ln 10} \approx 0.002$.

49. HINT: Use the definition of a^u and the properties of the ln and exp functions. For example: $(ab)^u = e^{u \ln ab} = e^{u(\ln a + \ln b)} = e^{u \ln a + u \ln b} = e^{u \ln a}e^{u \ln b} = a^u b^u$.

EXERCISES 7.6, page 341

1. $y = C_1 e^x + C_2 e^{2x} \implies y' = C_1 e^x + 2C_2 e^{2x} \implies y'' = C_1 e^x + 4C_2 e^{2x}$. Substituting these into the left side of the equation: $y'' - 3y' + 2y = (C_1 e^x + 4C_2 e^{2x}) - (3C_1 e^x + 6C_2 e^{2x}) + (2C_1 e^x + 2C_2 e^{2x}) + C_1(1-3+2)e^x + C_2(4-6+2)e^{2x} = 0e^x + 0e^{2x}$ so that the end result is 0. Thus the given function satisfies the given equation.

4. $y = cx^3 \implies y' = 3cx^2$, $y'' = 6cx$, $y''' = 6c$. Substituting into the left side of the equation: $x^3 y''' + x^2 y'' - 3xy' - 3y = x^3(6c) + x^2(6cx) - 3x(3cx^2) - 3(cx^3) = cx^3(6 + 6 - 9 - 3) = 0$. Thus, it is a solution.

7. $x\frac{dy}{dx} - y = 0$ is separable. Separating variables we obtain: $x\, dy - y\, dx = 0 \implies \frac{dy}{y} - \frac{dx}{x} = 0 \implies \ln|y| - \ln|x| = C \implies \ln\left|\frac{y}{x}\right| = C \implies \left|\frac{y}{x}\right| = e^C \implies |y| = K|x|$ where $K = e^C$. This simplifies to $y = \pm Kx$, or just $y = mx$ for any constant m.

10. $(y + yx^2)dy + (x + xy^2)dx = 0 \implies y(1+x^2)dy + x(1+y^2)dx = 0 \implies \frac{y}{1+y^2}dy + \frac{x}{1+x^2}dx = 0 \implies \frac{1}{2}\ln(1+y^2) + \frac{1}{2}\ln(1+x^2) = C \implies \ln(1+y^2)(1+x^2) = 2C = C'$

$\Rightarrow$ $(1+y^2)(1+x^2) = e^{C'} = K.$

13. $x^2y' - yx^2 = y \Rightarrow x^2dy - yx^2dx = ydx \Rightarrow x^2dy - y(x^2+1)dx = 0 \Rightarrow \dfrac{dy}{y} -$

$\dfrac{x^2+1}{x^2} dx = 0 \Rightarrow \dfrac{dy}{y} - (1 + \dfrac{1}{x^2})dx = 0 \Rightarrow \ln|y| - (x - \dfrac{1}{x}) = C \Rightarrow \ln|y| =$

$(x - \dfrac{1}{x}) + C \Rightarrow |y| = e^{x-1/x} e^C = C_1 e^{x-1/x}.$ Thus the solutions are

$y = \pm C_1 e^{(x-1/x)}$ or just $y = C_2 e^{(x-1/x)}.$

16. $\sqrt{x}\, y' - \sqrt{y} = x\sqrt{y} \Rightarrow \sqrt{x}\, dy = \sqrt{y}(x+1)dx \Rightarrow y^{-1/2}dy = x^{-1/2}(x+1)dx =$

$(x^{1/2} + x^{-1/2})dx \Rightarrow 2y^{1/2} = \dfrac{2}{3} x^{3/2} + 2x^{1/2} + C.$ Using the condition that

$y = 4$ when $x = 9$, we obtain the following equation for C: $2 \cdot 4^{1/2} = \dfrac{2}{3} 9^{3/2}$

$+ 2 \cdot 9^{1/2} + C \Rightarrow 4 = \dfrac{2}{3} \cdot 27 + 2 \cdot 3 + C \Rightarrow C = 4-18-6 = -20.$ Thus

$2y^{1/2} = \dfrac{2}{3} x^{3/2} + 2x^{1/2} - 20$ or $y = (\dfrac{1}{3} x^{3/2} + x^{1/2} - 10)^2.$

19. Let $y = q(t)$ be the number of bacteria present after t hours. We are given

that $y_0 = q(0) = 5,000$, $q(10) = 15,000$, and $\dfrac{dy}{dt} = cy.$ By the theorem, $y =$

$q(t) = y_0 e^{ct} = 5000\, e^{ct}.$ To find c, set $t = 10$, $y = 15,000$ to obtain

$15,000 = 5000e^{10c} \Rightarrow e^{10c} = 3 \Rightarrow 10c = \ln 3$ or $c = (\ln 3)/10.$ Thus $q(t) =$

$5000e^{((\ln 3)/10)t} = 5000(e^{\ln 3})^{t/10} = 5000 \cdot 3^{t/10}.$ After 20 hours, $y =$

$q(20) = 5000 \cdot 3^{20/10} = 5000 \cdot 3^2 = 45,000.$ To determine at what value of t,

y will be 50,000, we set $q(t) = 50,000$ and solve for t. Thus $5000 \cdot$

$3^{t/10} = 50,000 \Rightarrow 3^{t/10} = 10 \Rightarrow \dfrac{t}{10} \ln 3 = \ln 10 \Rightarrow t = \dfrac{10 \ln 10}{\ln 3} \approx 21$ hrs.

22. If $P(t) =$ the population t years from the present, then $\dfrac{dP}{dt} = .05P$ and $P(t) =$

$P(0)e^{.05t} = 500,000\, e^{.05t}.$ In 10 years $t = 10$ and $p(10) = 500,000e^{.5} \approx$

$500,000(1.65) = 825,000.$

25. Let $y(t)$ be the temperature of the thermometer t minutes after it's brought

in. (Assume that the reading is the same as the actual temperature.) Then

$\dfrac{dy}{dt} = c(y-70)$, and $y(10) = 40$ which yields $\dfrac{dy}{y-70} = c\, dt \Rightarrow \ln|y-70| = ct + b$

$\Rightarrow |y-70| = ke^{ct}.$ Since the instrument is cooler than 70, $y-70 < 0$ and the

last formula becomes $70-y = ke^{ct}.$ Setting $t = 0$, $y(0) = 40$ and $k = 30.$

Using $y(5) = 60$ we obtain $10 = 30e^{5c}$ or $c = (-1/5)\ln 3.$ To find when it

registers 65, we solve $70-65 = 30e^{(-1/5)(\ln 3)t} \Longleftrightarrow (-1/5)(\ln 3)t = \ln(1/6)$

$= -\ln 6 \Rightarrow t = (5 \ln 6)/\ln 3 \approx 5(1.792)/1.099 \approx 8.2$ minutes.

28. The data given yields $\frac{dy}{dt} = c(k-y)$, $y(0) = 0$ where c is the proportionality

constant. (The initial value is 0 since at the start no sugar is decomposed.)

Solving, as in Example 3 or Exercise 7, $\frac{dy}{k-y} = c\ dt \implies -\ln(k-y) = ct + b$

(since $k > y$). Setting t = 0, we get $-\ln k = b$. Thus $\ln(k-y) = -ct +$

$\ln k \implies k-y = ke^{-ct} \implies y = k(1 - e^{-ct})$.

31. (a) Writing $G'(t) = ABke^{-Bt}e^{-Ae^{-Bt}}$, we see that if $t = (\ln A)/B$ then $e^{Bt} =$

$e^{\ln A} = A$, $e^{-Bt} = 1/A$, and $G'((\ln A)/B) = ABk(1/A)e^{-A/A} = Bke^{-1}$. That this

is a maximum for G' follows from the first derivative test. All factors in

$G''(t)$ are positive except $(-1 + Ae^{-Bt})$ which is < 0 if $t > (\ln A)/B$ and > 0

if $t < (\ln A)/B$.

(b) $B > 0 \implies e^{-Bt} \to 0$ as $t \to \infty$ and $e^{-Ae^{-Bt}} \to e^0 = 1$. Thus $\lim\limits_{t\to\infty} G'(t) =$
$ABk(0)1 = 0$.

(c) $G(t) = ke^{-Ae^{-Bt}} \to ke^{-(A)(0)} = k$ as $t \to \infty$.

34. Since $f(n) = 3 + 20(1 - e^{-0.1n})$ is approximately the number of items pro-

duced after n days, in (a) we must round off our answers to the nearest in-

teger. (a) $f(5) = 3 + 20(1 - e^{-0.5}) \approx 10.87 \approx 11$ items; $f(9) = 3 +$

$20(1 - e^{-0.9}) \approx 15$; $f(24) \approx 21$; $f(30) \approx 22$.

(b) and (c) $f(x) = 3 + 20(1 - e^{-0.1x}) \implies f'(x) =$

$2e^{-0.1x} > 0 \implies$ f is increasing. $f''(x) = -0.2e^{-0.1x}$

$< 0 \implies$ CD. $\lim\limits_{x\to\infty} f(x) = 23$. These yield the graph

shown.

37. Let V(t) be the value t years after purchase. We are given that $V(t) = Ae^{kt}$

where $k < 0$. $V(0) = 20,000 \implies A = 20,000$ so that $V(t) = 20,000\ e^{kt}$. $V(2)$

$= 16,000 \implies 20,000\ e^{2k} = 16,000 \implies e^{2k} = 0.8 \implies e^k = \sqrt{0.8}$. Thus $V(t) =$

$20,000(e^k)^t = 20,000\sqrt{0.8}^{\ t} = 20,000(0.8)^{t/2}$. Then after one more year,

$t = 3$ and $V(3) = 20,000(0.8)^{3/2} \approx 14,311$.

40. $\frac{dh}{dt} = -\frac{V}{Q}\frac{h}{k+h} \implies \frac{k+h}{h}\ dh = -\frac{V}{Q}\ dt \implies (\frac{k}{h} + 1)dh + \frac{V}{Q}\ dt = 0 \implies k\ln h + h +$

$\frac{V}{Q}\ t = C$.

EXERCISES 7.7, page 348

1. $y' + 2y = e^{2x}$ is in the required form (i.e. coefficient of y' is 1) with

    $P(x) = 2$. Thus $\int P = 2x$ and the integrating factor is $e^{\int P} = e^{2x}$. Multiply-

    ing the equation by this factor we obtain: $e^{2x}y' + 2e^{2x}y = e^{4x} \implies \frac{d}{dx}(e^{2x}y) =$

    $e^{4x} \implies e^{2x}y = \frac{1}{4} e^{4x} + C \implies y = \frac{1}{4} e^{2x} + Ce^{-2x}$.

4. Here, $P(x) = -6x$, $\int P = -3x^2$, and the integrating factor is e^{-3x^2}. Multiply-

    ing the equation by this factor yields $e^{-3x^2}y' - 6xe^{-3x^2}y = xe^{-3x^2}$ or

    $D_x(e^{-3x^2}y) = xe^{-3x^2}$. Integrating, $e^{-3x^2}y = -\frac{1}{6} e^{-3x^2} + C \implies y = -\frac{1}{6} +$

    Ce^{3x^2}.

7. Rearrange terms and divide by x^2 to obtain $y' + \frac{2}{x} y = \frac{e^x}{x^2}$. Then $P(x) = \frac{2}{x}$

    and $e^{\int P} = e^{2 \ln x} = e^{\ln x^2} = x^2$. Multiplying by this factor yields $x^2y' +$

    $2xy = e^x$ or $D_x(x^2y) = e^x \implies x^2y = e^x + C \implies y = (e^x + C)/x^2$.

10. Rewriting the equation as $y' + \frac{5}{x+4}y = \frac{x^2+8x+16}{x+4} = \frac{(x+4)^2}{x+4} = x+4$, we have

    $P(x) = \frac{5}{x+4}$, $\int P = 5 \ln(x+4) = \ln(x+4)^5$ and $e^{\int P} = (x+4)^5$. Multiplying, we get

    $(x+4)^5 y' + 5(x+4)^4 y = (x+4)^6 \implies \frac{d}{dx}((x+4)^5 y) = (x+4)^6 \implies (x+4)^5 y = \frac{(x+4)^7}{7} +$

    $C \implies y = \frac{(x+4)^2}{7} + \frac{C}{(x+4)^5}$.

13. Divide by x to obtain $y' - \frac{1}{x} y = x + 1$. Then $P(x) = -1/x$ and $e^{\int P} = e^{-\ln x} =$

    $e^{\ln 1/x} = \frac{1}{x}$. Multiplying yields $\frac{1}{x} y' - \frac{1}{x^2} y = 1 + \frac{1}{x}$ or $(\frac{1}{x} y)' = 1 + \frac{1}{x} \implies$

    $\frac{1}{x} y = x + \ln x + C \implies y = x(x + \ln x + C)$. Setting $x = 1$, $y = 2$ we get

    $2 = (1 + 0 + C)$ or $C = 1$.

16. $P(x) = 2x \implies e^{\int P} = e^{x^2}$. Multiplying yields $e^{x^2}y' + 2xe^{x^2}y = 1 + xe^{x^2} \implies$

    $(e^{x^2}y)' = 1 + xe^{x^2} \implies e^{x^2}y = x + \frac{1}{2} e^{x^2} + C \implies y = xe^{-x^2} + \frac{1}{2} + Ce^{-x^2}$.

    Setting $x = 0$, $y = 1$ we get $1 = 0 + \frac{1}{2} + C$, or $C = 1/2$.

19. Let $y(t)$ denote the amount of salt (in pounds) in the tank at time t. Then
    $y(0) = k$. The hard part of this problem is to find out what differential
    equation y satisfies. We know that dy/dt is the rate at which the amount of
    salt is changing. Thus dy/dt = (rate at which salt enters the tank) - (rate
    at which salt leaves the tank). The rate of salt entry is the input concen-
    tration (1/3 lbs/gal) times the input flow rate (6 gal/min) or 2 lbs/min.

Next, at time t, there are y(t) lbs of salt in the 80 gal. tank. Thus the
concentration of salt then is $y(t)/80$ lbs/gal. Thus the rate of salt elimination from the tank is this concentration ($y(t)/80$ lbs/gal) times the exit
flow rate (6 gal/min) or $6y(t)/80$ lbs/min. Combining these results we obtain

$\frac{dy}{dt} = 2 - \frac{6}{80} y = 2 - 0.075y$, or $\frac{dy}{dt} + 0.075y = 2$. The integrating factor is

$e^{0.075t}$, and we obtain: $e^{0.075t} \frac{dy}{dt} + 0.075 e^{0.075t} y = 2e^{0.075t} \implies$

$\frac{d}{dt}(e^{0.075t} y) = 2e^{0.075t} \implies e^{0.075t} y = \frac{2}{0.075} e^{0.075t} + C = \frac{80}{3} e^{0.075t} + C$

$\implies y = \frac{80}{3} + Ce^{-0.075t}$. Setting $t = 0$ and $y = k$ yields $k = 80/3 + C$ or
$C = k - 80/3$.

22.   (a) Let v(t) be the volume of CO in the room at time t. Since the room
volume is 1200 cu. ft. and the initial concentration of CO is 0.001% =
0.00001, we have $v(0) = 0.012$ cu. ft. Now, dv/dt is the rate of change of
CO volume, and dv/dt = (rate of CO entry) - (rate of CO elimination). The
rate of entry is the input fraction (5%) times the entry rate (0.12) or
0.006. The elimination rate is the fraction of CO in the eliminated air
($v(t)/1200$) times the elimination rate (0.12), or 0.0001 v. Thus the dif-
ferential equation is $\frac{dv}{dt} = .006 - .0001v$ or $\frac{dv}{dt} + .0001v = .006$, linear
with integrating factor $e^{.0001t}$. Multiplying: $\frac{d}{dt}(e^{.0001t} v) = .006e^{.0001t}$

$\implies e^{.0001t} v = 60e^{.0001t} + C \implies v = 60 + Ce^{-.0001t}$. Using $v(0) = .012$,
$C = -59.988$.

(b) We seek t such that $v(t)/1200 = .00015 \iff v(t) = 60 - 59.988e^{-.0001t}$

$= .18 \implies t = 10^4 \ln \frac{59.988}{59.82} \approx 28$ min.

EXERCISES 7.8, page 353

1. $f'(x) = 1/\sqrt{2x+3} > 0 \implies$ f is increasing on [1,11]
and has an inverse with domain $[f(1),f(11)] =$
$[\sqrt{5},5]$. As in Sec. 7.1, we find f^{-1} by solving $y =$
$\sqrt{2x+3}$ to obtain $y^2 = 2x+3$ and $x = (y^2-3)/2$. Thus
$f^{-1}(x) = (x^2-3)/2$. Directly, $D_x f^{-1}(x) = x$. Using
(7.31) with $g = f^{-1}$, $D_x f^{-1}(x) = 1/f'(f^{-1}(x)) =$
$\sqrt{2f^{-1}(x) + 3}$ (from the formula for f' in the first
line) $= \sqrt{(x^2-3) + 3} = x$ since $x > 0$.

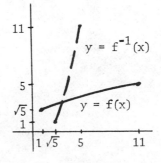

4. $f'(x) = 2x-4 < 0 \Longrightarrow$ f is decreasing on $[-1,1]$ and has an inverse with domain $[f(1),f(-1)] = [2,10]$. Setting $y = x^2-4x+5$ and solving for x, we get $x = 2 - \sqrt{y-1}$ by the quadratic formula. (The negative sign must be selected for x to lie in $[-1,1]$.) Thus $f^{-1}(x) = 2 - \sqrt{x-1}$. Using (7.31), $D_x f^{-1}(x) = 1/(2f^{-1}(x) - 4) = -1/2\sqrt{x-1}$, the same as computing it directly.

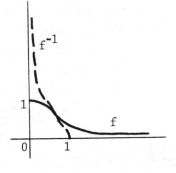

7. $f'(x) = -2xe^{-x^2} < 0$ if $x > 0$. Thus f is decreasing on $[0,\infty)$ and has an inverse with domain equal to the range of f. Since $f(0) = 1$ and $f(x) \to 0$ as $x \to \infty$, f^{-1} has domain $(0,1]$. Solving $y = e^{-x^2}$ we get $-x^2 = \ln y \Longrightarrow x = \sqrt{-\ln y}$. Thus $f^{-1}(x) = \sqrt{-\ln x}$ and $D_x f^{-1}(x) = -1/2\sqrt{-\ln x}$ by either method.

10. $f'(x) = e^x - e^{-x} > 0$ if $x > 0$. Thus f is increasing on $[0,\infty)$ and has an inverse with domain equal to the range of f. Since $f(0) = 2$ and $f(x) \to \infty$ as $x \to \infty$, the domain of f^{-1} is $[2,\infty)$.

Next, $y = e^x + e^{-x} \Longrightarrow e^x - y + e^{-x} = 0$
$\Longrightarrow e^{2x} - ye^x + 1 = 0$. Now solve for e^x by the quadratic formula! $e^x = (y \pm \sqrt{y^2-4})/2$.
The + sign must be chosen so that $x = \ln[(y + \sqrt{y^2-4})/2]$. Thus $f^{-1}(x) = \ln[(x + \sqrt{x^2-4})/2]$ and $Df^{-1}(x) = [1 + x/\sqrt{x^2-4}]/(x + \sqrt{x^2-4}) = 1/\sqrt{x^2-4}$.

(NOTE: The quadratic formula can be used since $e^{2x} = (e^x)^2$. Also, if the - sign had been selected, we would have $x = \ln[(y - \sqrt{y^2-4})/2]$. But as $y \to \infty$, $y - \sqrt{y^2-4} \to 0$ and x would tend to $-\infty$ contrary to the earlier observation that $y = f(x)$ and x go to ∞ simultaneously.)

13. $f'(x) = 4e^{2x}/(e^{2x}+1)^2 > 0 \Longrightarrow$ f has an inverse. Using 7.31, if g is the inverse function, $g'(0) = 1/f'(g(0)) = 1/f'(0) = 1$.

16. Since $|x-2| = -(x-2)$, if $x \leq 2$ and $|x-2| = x-2$ if $x \geq 2$, f is decreasing on $(-\infty, 2]$, increasing on $[2, \infty)$ and, thus, has no inverse. On any subset of either of these intervals, f will have an inverse.

EXERCISES 7.9, page 353

1. $f'(x) = (1-2x)D_x \ln|1-2x| + \ln|1-2x| \cdot D_x(1-2x) = \dfrac{(1-2x)(-2)}{(1-2x)} + (-2)\ln|1-2x| = -2(1 + \ln|1-2x|)$.

4. $f(x) = \log|2-9x| - \log|1-x^2| \implies f'(x) = \dfrac{1}{\ln 10}\left(\dfrac{-9}{2-9x} - \dfrac{-2x}{1-x^2}\right)$.

7. $f(x) = e^{\ln(x^2+1)} = x^2+1$, and $f'(x) = 2x$.

10. $f(x) = \dfrac{1}{4}\ln\dfrac{x}{3x+5} = \dfrac{1}{4}(\ln x - \ln(3x+5)) \implies f'(x) = \dfrac{1}{4}\left(\dfrac{1}{x} - \dfrac{3}{3x+5}\right) = \dfrac{5}{4x(3x+5)}$.

13. $f'(x) = x^2 e^{1-x^2}(-2x) + 2xe^{1-x^2} = 2x(1-x^2)e^{1-x^2}$.

16. $f'(x) = 5^{3x}(\ln 5)(3) + 5(3x)^4 \cdot 3$.

19. $f'(x) = 10^{\ln x}(\ln 10)D_x \ln x = 10^{\ln x}(\ln 10)/x$.

22. $f'(x) = 7^{\ln|x|} \ln 7 \, D_x \ln|x| = 7^{\ln|x|}(\ln 7)x^{-1}$.

25. $1 + xy = e^{xy} \implies xy'+y = e^{xy}(xy'+y) \implies x(1-e^{xy})y' = y(e^{xy}-1) \implies y' = y(e^{xy}-1)/x(1-e^{xy}) = -y/x$ if $xy \neq 0$.

28. $v(t) = f'(t) = [-(t^2+2t) + (2t+2)]e^{-t} = (-t^2 + 2)e^{-t}]$

    (a) $v(t) = 0 \iff -t^2 + 2 = 0 \implies t = \pm\sqrt{2}$. Note also that $|t| < \sqrt{2} \implies -t^2 + 2 > 0 \implies v(t) > 0$ and $|t| > \sqrt{2} \implies v(t) < 0$. Hence:

    (c) motion to the right in $[-\sqrt{2}, \sqrt{2}]$, and

    (d) motion to the left in $[-5, -\sqrt{2}]$ and $[\sqrt{2}, 5]$.

    (b) $a(t) = v'(t) = (t^2 - 2 - 2t)e^{-t} = 0 \iff t^2 - 2t - 2 = 0 \iff t = (2 \pm \sqrt{4+8})/2 = 1 \pm \sqrt{3}$.

31. With $u = \sqrt{x}$, $du = dx/2\sqrt{x} \implies dx/\sqrt{x} = 2du$. $x = 1, 4 \implies u = 1, 2$ and

    $\displaystyle\int_1^4 (1/\sqrt{x}e^{\sqrt{x}})dx = 2\int_1^2 (1/e^u)du = 2\int_1^2 e^{-u}du = -2e^{-u}\Big]_1^2 -2(e^{-2} - e^{-1})$

34. $\displaystyle\int_1^2 \dfrac{x^2+1}{x^3+3x}\,dx = (1/3)\int_1^2 \dfrac{3x^2+3}{x^3+3x}\,dx = (1/3)\ln|x^3+3x|\Big]_1^2 = (1/3)(\ln 14 - \ln 4)$

    $= (1/3)\ln(7/2)$.

37. $u = x^2$, $du = 2x\,dx$, $x\,dx = (1/2)du$. $x = 0, 1 \implies u = 0, 1$. Thus $\displaystyle\int_0^1 x\,4^{x^2}\,dx$

    $= \dfrac{1}{2}\int_0^1 4^u\,du = \dfrac{1}{2\ln 4}\,4^u\Big]_0^1 = \dfrac{3}{2\ln 4}$.

40. Since $x^4 + 2x^2 + 1 = (x^2+1)^2$, let $u = x^2+1$, $du = 2x\ dx$. $\int \dfrac{x}{x^4+2x^2+1}\ dx =$

$\int \dfrac{x}{(x^2+1)^2}\ dx = \dfrac{1}{2} \int u^{-2}\ du = -\dfrac{1}{2}\ u^{-1} + C = -1/2(x^2+1) + C.$

43. $\int 5^x e^x\ dx = \int (5e)^x\ dx = \dfrac{1}{\ln(5e)}\ (5e)^x + C = \dfrac{5^x e^x}{\ln 5 + 1} + C.$

46. $u = 1 + 5^x$, $du = 5^x \ln 5\ dx \implies 5^x\ dx = (1/\ln 5)du$ and $\int 5^x(1 + 5^x)^{1/2}\ dx =$

$\dfrac{1}{\ln 5} \int u^{1/2}\ du = \dfrac{2}{3 \ln 5}\ u^{3/2} + C = \dfrac{2}{3 \ln 5}\ (1 + 5^x)^{3/2} + C.$

49. Rewriting as $y' + (3/x^2)y = 1/x^2$, $P(x) = 3/x^2 \implies e^{\int P} = e^{-3/x}$. Multiplying

yields: $e^{-3/x}y' + (3/x^2)e^{-3/x}y = (1/x^2)e^{-3/x}$ or $(e^{-3/x}y)' = (1/x^2)e^{-3/x}$

$\implies e^{-3/x}y = (1/3)e^{-3/x} + C \implies y = 1/3 + Ce^{3/x}.$

52. Rewriting as $y' + 4x^3y = 8x^3$ we have $P(x) = 4x^3$, $e^{\int P} = e^{x^4} \implies e^{x^4}y' +$

$4x^3 e^{x^4}y = 8x^3 e^{x^4} \implies (e^{x^4}y)' = 8x^3 e^{x^4} \implies e^{x^4}y = 2e^{x^4} + C \implies y = 2 +$

Ce^{-x^4}. Setting $x = 0$, $y = 5$ we get $5 = 2 + C$, or $C = 3$.

55. $y' = xe^{1/x^3}(-3/x^4) + e^{1/x^3} - 2x/(2-x^2)$. When $x = 1$, $y' = -3e + e - 2 =$
$-2(1+e)$. Thus, the tangent line is $y-e = -2(1+e)(x-1)$.

58. $f'(x) = 6x^2-8 < 0$ on $[-1,1]$. Thus f is decreasing and has an inverse g.
Since $f(0) = 5$, $g(5) = 0$ and $g'(5) = 1/f'(g(5)) = 1/f'(0) = -1/8$.

61. Let $y = y(t)$ be the amount (in lbs) dissolved t hours after 1:00 PM. Then

$10-y$ remain and $\dfrac{dy}{dt} = k(10-y) \implies \dfrac{dy}{10-y} = k\ dt \implies \ln(10-y) = -kt - C$. The

conditions to be used are $y(0) = 0$ and $y(3) = 5$. (At 4 PM, $t = 3$, and half
is dissolved.) These conditions imply $C = -\ln 10$, $k = (\ln 2)/3$ and thus

$y = 10(1 - e^{-(\ln 2)t/3}) = 10(1 - (\tfrac{1}{2})^{t/3})$.

(a) 2 more lbs will be dissolved (after the 5 that were dissolved at 4 PM)

when $y = 7$. Set $y = 7$ and solve for t: $1 - (\tfrac{1}{2})^{t/3} = .7 \implies (1/2)^{t/3} = .3$

$\implies (t/3)\ln(.5) = \ln(.3) \implies t = 3 \ln(.3)/\ln(.5) \approx 3(-1.204)/(-0.693) \approx 5.21$

(i.e. at 6.21 PM or $\approx$ 6:14 PM).

(b) At 8 PM. $t = 7$ and $y = 10(1 - (1/2)^{7/3}) \approx 10(1 - .1984) = 8.016$ lbs.

64. $p\ dv + c\ v\ dp = 0 \implies \dfrac{1}{c} \dfrac{dv}{v} + \dfrac{dp}{p} = 0 \implies \dfrac{1}{c} \ln v + \ln p = C \implies \ln v^{1/c}p = C$

$\implies v^{1/c}p = e^C = K \implies p = Kv^{-1/c}.$

CHAPTER 8

OTHER TRANSCENDENTAL FUNCTIONS

EXERCISES 8.1, page 360

1. $\lim\limits_{x\to 0} \dfrac{x}{\sin x} = \lim\limits_{x\to 0} \dfrac{1}{(\sin x/x)} = \dfrac{1}{1} = 1.$

4. $\lim\limits_{\theta\to 0} \dfrac{3\theta + \sin \theta}{\theta} = \lim\limits_{\theta\to 0} (\dfrac{3\theta}{\theta} + \dfrac{\sin \theta}{\theta}) = \lim\limits_{\theta\to 0} 3 + \lim\limits_{\theta\to 0} \dfrac{\sin \theta}{\theta} = 3 + 1 = 4.$

7. $\lim\limits_{\theta\to 0} \dfrac{2 \cos \theta - 2}{3\theta} = \lim\limits_{\theta\to 0} \dfrac{2}{3} \dfrac{\cos \theta - 1}{\theta} = -\dfrac{2}{3} \lim\limits_{\theta\to 0} \dfrac{1 - \cos \theta}{\theta} = -\dfrac{2}{3} \cdot 0 = 0.$

10. $\lim\limits_{x\to 0} \dfrac{x \sin x}{x^2 + 1} = \lim\limits_{x\to 0} \dfrac{x}{x^2+1} \lim\limits_{x\to 0} \sin x = 0 \cdot 0 = 0.$

13. $\lim\limits_{t\to 0} \dfrac{4t^2 + 3t \sin t}{t^2} = \lim\limits_{t\to 0} (4 + 3 \dfrac{\sin t}{t}) = 4 + 3 \cdot 1 = 7.$

16. $\lim\limits_{t\to 0} \dfrac{\sin t}{1 + \cos t} = \dfrac{0}{1+1} = 0.$

19. $\lim\limits_{x\to 0} \dfrac{x + \tan x}{\sin x} = \lim\limits_{x\to 0} (\dfrac{x}{\sin x} + \dfrac{\tan x}{\sin x}) = \lim\limits_{x\to 0} (\dfrac{1}{(\sin x/x)} + \dfrac{\sin x}{\cos x} \cdot \dfrac{1}{\sin x}) = \dfrac{1}{1} +$

   $\lim\limits_{x\to 0} \dfrac{1}{\cos x} = 1 + \dfrac{1}{1} = 2.$ (This is the proof of the limit considered in

   Exercise 34, Sec. 2.1.)

22. $\lim\limits_{x\to 0} \dfrac{\csc 2x}{\cot x} = \lim\limits_{x\to 0} \dfrac{1}{\sin 2x} \tan x = \lim\limits_{x\to 0} \dfrac{1}{2 \sin x \cos x} \dfrac{\sin x}{\cos x} = \lim\limits_{x\to 0} \dfrac{1}{2 \cos^2 x} =$

   $\dfrac{1}{2 \cdot 1^2} = \dfrac{1}{2}.$

25. $\lim\limits_{v\to 0} \dfrac{\cos(v + \pi/2)}{v} = \lim\limits_{v\to 0} \dfrac{\cos v \cos \pi/2 - \sin v \sin \pi/2}{v} = \lim\limits_{v\to 0} \dfrac{0 - \sin v}{v} = -1.$

28. $\lim\limits_{x\to 0} \dfrac{1 - \cos ax}{bx} = \dfrac{a}{b} \lim\limits_{x\to 0} \dfrac{1 - \cos ax}{ax}.$ With $t = ax$, $t \to 0$ as $x \to 0$. Thus the

   limit is $\dfrac{a}{b} \lim\limits_{t\to 0} \dfrac{1 - \cos t}{t} = \dfrac{a}{b} \cdot 0 = 0.$

EXERCISES 8.2, page 369

1. $D_x \cot u = D_x \dfrac{\cos u}{\sin u} = \dfrac{\sin u\, D_x \cos u - \cos u\, D_x \sin u}{\sin^2 u}$

   $= \dfrac{- \sin^2 u\, D_x u - \cos^2 u\, D_x u}{\sin^2 u} = \dfrac{-1}{\sin^2 u} D_x u = -\csc^2 u\, D_x u.$ (Recall: $-\sin^2 u -$

   $\cos^2 u = -(\sin^2 u + \cos^2 u) = -1.$) Next, $D_x \csc u = D_x (\sin u)^{-1} =$

$-(\sin u)^{-2}D_x \sin u = -(\sin u)^{-2}\cos u \ D_x u = -\dfrac{1}{\sin u} \cdot \dfrac{\cos u}{\sin u} \ D_x u =$

$-\csc u \cot u \ D_x u.$

4. $f'(x) = -\sin(4 - 3x)D_x(4 - 3x) = -(-3)\sin(4 - 3x) = 3 \sin(4 - 3x).$

7. $f'(x) = x^3 D_x \cos(1/x) + D_x(x^3) \cos(1/x) = -x^3 \sin(1/x) \ D_x(1/x) +$

$3x^2 \cos(1/x) = -x^3 \sin(1/x)(-1/x^2) + 3x^2 \cos(1/x) = x \sin(1/x) +$

$3x^2 \cos(1/x).$

10. $f'(x) = -\csc^2(x/2) \ D_x(x/2) = -(1/2)\csc^2(x/2).$

13. $f'(x) = -\csc^2(x^3-2x) \ D_x(x^3-2x) = -[\csc^2(x^3-2x)](3x^2-2),$ or, better,

$-(3x^2-2)\csc^2(x^3-2x).$

16. $f'(x) = 3(\tan^2 6x) \ D_x \tan 6x = 3 \tan^2 6x \ \sec^2 6x \ D_x(6x) = 18 \tan^2 6x \ \sec^2 6x.$

19. $f'(x) = x^2 \ D_x \csc 5x + (D_x \ x^2)\csc 5x = -x^2 \csc 5x \cot 5x \ D_x(5x) + 2x \csc 5x$

$= -5x^2 \csc 5x \cot 5x + 2x \csc 5x.$

22. $f'(x) = x^2 \cdot 3 \sec^2 4x \cdot D_x \sec 4x + D_x(x^2)\sec^3 4x = 3x^2 \sec 4x(\sec 4x \tan 4x)$

$\cdot \ D_x(4x) + 2x \sec^3 4x = 12x^2 \sec^3 4x \tan 4x + 2x \sec^3 4x.$

25. $f'(x) = 3 \cot^2(3x+1) \ D_x \cot(3x+1) = 3 \cot^2(3x+1)(-\csc^2(3x+1)) \cdot 3.$

28. $f'(x) = \dfrac{[(\tan 2x + 1)(\sec 2x \tan 2x)(2) - \sec 2x(\sec^2 2x)(2)]}{(\tan 2x + 1)^2}.$

31. $f'(x) = e^{-3x} \ D_x \tan \sqrt{x} + \tan \sqrt{x} \ D_x \ e^{-3x} = (e^{-3x} \sec^2 \sqrt{x})/2\sqrt{x} - 3(\tan \sqrt{x})e^{-3x}.$

34. $f'(x) = -\csc(\cot 4x)\cot(\cot 4x)D_x \cot 4x$

$= (\csc(\cot 4x))(\cot(\cot 4x))(\csc^2 4x)(4).$

37. $f'(x) = [(x^3+1) \ D_x \csc 3x - \csc 3x \ D_x(x^3+1)]/(x^3+1)^2$

$= [-(x^3+1)\csc 3x \cot 3x \ D_x(3x) - 3x^2 \csc 3x]/(x^3+1)^2$

$= -3[(x^3+1)\csc 3x \cot 3x + x^2\csc 3x]/(x^3+1)^2.$

40. Using logarithmic differentiation, $y = (\tan x)^{3x} \Rightarrow \ln y = 3x \ln(\tan x) \Rightarrow$

$\dfrac{y'}{y} = 3x \dfrac{D_x(\tan x)}{\tan x} + 3 \ln(\tan x) = 3x \dfrac{\sec^2 x}{\tan x} + 3 \ln(\tan x) \Rightarrow y' =$

$(3x \dfrac{\sec^2 x}{\tan x} + 3 \ln(\tan x))(\tan x)^{3x}.$

43. $\dfrac{dy}{dx} = \cos x - x(-\sin x) - \cos x = x \sin x$

$\dfrac{d^2 y}{dx^2} = x \cos x + \sin x.$

46. $\dfrac{dy}{dx} = \dfrac{(\cos x + 1)(-\sin x) - (\cos x - 1)(-\sin x)}{(\cos x + 1)^2} = (-2 \sin x)/(\cos x + 1)^2.$

$$\frac{d^2y}{dx^2} = \frac{(\cos x + 1)^2(-2\cos x) + 2\sin x(2)(\cos x + 1)(-\sin x)}{(\cos x + 1)^4}$$

$$= (-2\cos x(\cos x + 1) - 4\sin^2 x)/(\cos x + 1)^3.$$

49. $e^x \cot y = xe^{2y} \implies -e^x(\csc^2 y)y' + e^x \cot y = 2xe^{2y}y' + e^{2y} \implies$

   $(e^x \cot y + 2xe^{2y})y' = (e^x \cot y - e^{2y}).$

52. $f'(x) = -\sin x - \cos x = 0$ if $\sin x = -\cos x$, or $\tan x = -1 \implies x = 3\pi/4$,
   $7\pi/4$. Tabulating as before:

Interval	$[0, 3\pi/4)$	$(3\pi/4, 7\pi/4)$	$(7\pi/4, 2\pi]$
k	$\pi/2$	π	$11\pi/6$
$f'(k)$	-1	1	$(1-\sqrt{3})/2$
$f'(x)$	$-$	$+$	$-$
Variation of f	decreasing on $[0, 3\pi/4]$	increasing on $[3\pi/4, 7\pi/4]$	decreasing on $[7\pi/4, 2\pi]$

Thus $f(3\pi/4) = -2/\sqrt{2} = -\sqrt{2}$ is a local minimum and $f(7\pi/4) = \sqrt{2}$ is a local maximum.

55. $f'(x) = -2\sin x + 2\cos 2x = -2\sin x + 2(1 - 2\sin^2 x) = -4\sin^2 x - 2\sin x$
   $+ 2 = -4(\sin x - 1/2)(\sin x + 1) = 0$ if $\sin x = 1/2$ at $x = \pi/6$, $5\pi/6$ and if
   $\sin x = -1$ at $x = 3\pi/2$. Since $(\sin x + 1) \geq 0$ always, the sign of $f'(x)$ is
   the same as that of $-4(\sin x - 1/2)$ and, thus, opposite to that of $\sin x -$
   $1/2$. (This follows from the final factored form of $f'(x)$ above.) On
   $(\pi/6, 5\pi/6)$, $\sin x > 1/2$, $\sin x - 1/2 > 0$ and, thus $f'(x) < 0$. On the remainder of $[0, 2\pi]$, namely on $[0, \pi/6]$ and $(5\pi/6, 2\pi]$, $\sin x < 1/2$ and $f'(x) >$
   0. Thus f is decreasing on $[\pi/6, 5\pi/6]$ and increasing on $[0, \pi/6]$ and
   $[5\pi/6, 2\pi]$. Thus $f(\pi/6)$ is a local maximum, and $f(5\pi/6)$ is a local minimum.
   (There is no extremum at $x = 3\pi/2$, only a horizontal tangent.)

58. $f'(x) = e^{-x}\sec x \cdot \tan x - e^{-x}\sec x = e^{-x}\sec x(\tan x - 1) = 0$ only if $\tan x$
   $= 1$ since e^{-x} and $\sec x$ are never 0. Thus the critical numbers are $x = \pi/4$
   and $5\pi/4$. Now, $f''(x) = e^{-x}\sec^3 x + e^{-2x}\sec^2 x (\tan x - 1)^2$. $f''(\pi/4) =$
   $e^{-\pi/4}\sqrt{2}^3 > 0 \implies f(\pi/4)$ is a local minimum. $f(5\pi/4) = e^{-5\pi/4}(-\sqrt{2})^3 < 0 \implies$
   $f(5\pi/4)$ is a local maximum.

61. $y' = \frac{3}{8}\csc^2 x \, D_x \csc x = -\frac{3}{8}\csc^3 x \cot x$. $x = \pi/6 \implies y' = -\frac{3}{8}(2)^2\sqrt{3} = -3\sqrt{3}$.
   Thus the tangent line is $y - 1 = -3\sqrt{3}(x - \pi/6)$. Since $-1/y' = 1/3\sqrt{3}$, the
   normal line is $y - 1 = (1/3\sqrt{3})(x - \pi/6)$.

64. With $f(x) = \cot x$, $x = 45° = \pi/4$ rad., $\Delta x = 1° = \pi/180$ rad. $\Delta y \approx dy =$
   $f'(\pi/4)(\pi/180) = -(\csc^2(\pi/4))(\pi/180) = -2\pi/180 \approx -0.035.$

67. Refer to my sketch for Exercise 49 of Sec. 8.5. If A and B are the angles shown between the horizontal and the top and bottom, respectively, of the billboard, then $\theta = A-B$ is to be maximized. Note that $0 < B < A < \pi/2$ so that $0 < \theta = A-B < \pi/2$. If the viewer is x feet from the building, then by elementary trigonometry, $\tan A = 80/x$ and $\tan B = 60/x$. Thus $\tan \theta =$
$\tan(A-B) = \dfrac{\tan A - \tan B}{1 + \tan A \tan B} = \dfrac{80/x - 60/x}{1 + 4800/x^2} = \dfrac{20x}{x^2+4800}$. Differentiating, we obtain: $\sec^2\theta \dfrac{d\theta}{dx} = \dfrac{20(x^2+4800) - 40x^2}{(x^2+4800)^2}$, or $\dfrac{d\theta}{dx} = \dfrac{96,000 - 20x^2}{(x^2+4800)^2} \cos^2\theta$. Since $0 < \theta < \pi/2$, $\cos \theta$ can not be zero. Thus the critical numbers are solutions of $96000 - 20x^2 = 0$ (and $x > 0$, of course). Solving, we obtain $x^2 = 4800$ $\implies$ $x = \sqrt{4800} = 40\sqrt{3} \approx 69.3$ ft.

70. (a) $f(x) = x \sin \dfrac{1}{x} \implies f'(x) = x \cos \dfrac{1}{x}(-\dfrac{1}{x^2}) + \sin \dfrac{1}{x} = -\dfrac{1}{x}\cos \dfrac{1}{x} + \sin \dfrac{1}{x} =$ 0 if $\sin \dfrac{1}{x} = \dfrac{1}{x}\cos \dfrac{1}{x}$ or $\tan \dfrac{1}{x} = \dfrac{1}{x}$. (b) $y = \pm x$ will be tangent to the graph of f at any point $(x, f(x))$ at which $f(x) = \pm x$ and $f'(x) = \pm 1$. $f(x) =$ $x \sin \dfrac{1}{x} = \pm x \implies \sin \dfrac{1}{x} = \pm 1 \implies \dfrac{1}{x} = \dfrac{\pi}{2} + n\pi \implies x = 1/(\pi/2 + n\pi)$ where if n is even $f(x) = x$, and if n is odd $f(x) = -x$. At such values of x, $f'(x) =$ $-\dfrac{1}{x}\cos \dfrac{1}{x} + \sin \dfrac{1}{x} = -(\dfrac{\pi}{2} + n\pi)\cos(\dfrac{\pi}{2} + n\pi) + \sin(\dfrac{\pi}{2} + n\pi) = 0 \pm 1$, with +1 if n

73. Strangely, this maximum problem is solved by considering a minimum problem. Let $L = L_1 + L_2$ be, as shown, the distance between points on the walls measured on a line touching the inner corner. As $\theta \to 0$ or $\theta \to \pi/2$, $L \to \infty$, and it is clear that there is an angle θ_0 which makes L a minimum. Let L_0 be the minimum value of L. A rod of length L_0 <u>will</u> just fit around the corner. It will touch both walls when the turning angle is θ_0, but there is excess room for any other angle. However, any rod of

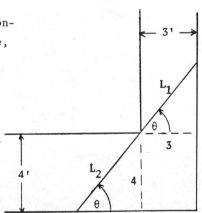

length $> L_0$ will not fit around the corner. It will be jammed tight touching the corner and the walls, at some angle $\theta \neq \theta_0$, and further rotation will be impossible. So, our problem is to minimize L as a function of θ. By elementary trigonometry, $L = L_1 + L_2 = \dfrac{3}{\cos \theta} + \dfrac{4}{\sin \theta} \cdot \dfrac{dL}{d\theta} = \dfrac{3 \sin \theta}{\cos^2\theta} - \dfrac{4 \cos \theta}{\sin^2\theta} =$

76. Let a = altitude and b = base of this triangle. (The base is opposite to θ, and is not one of the equal sides.) Then $a = 12 \cos(\theta/2)$ and $b = 24 \sin(\theta/2)$. Then, the area, A, is $A = \dfrac{1}{2}ab = 144 \cos \dfrac{\theta}{2} \sin \dfrac{\theta}{2} = 72 \sin \theta$. $\theta = 30° = \dfrac{\pi}{6}$, $\theta + \Delta\theta = 33° \implies \Delta\theta = d\theta = 3° = \pi/60$ radians. Thus $dA = 72 \cos \theta \, d\theta$

$$= 72 \cos \frac{\pi}{6} \cdot \frac{\pi}{60} = \frac{6}{5} \cdot \frac{\sqrt{3}}{2} \cdot \pi = \frac{3\sqrt{3}\,\pi}{5} \approx 3.26 \text{ sq. in.}$$

79. (a) $v(t) = s'(t) = \sqrt{3} - 2 \sin 2t \implies v(\pi/4) = \sqrt{3} - 2 \sin \pi/2 = \sqrt{3} - 2$.
$a(t) = v'(t) = -4 \cos 2t \implies a(\pi/4) = -4 \cos \pi/2 = 0$. (b) The point moves
in the positive direction when $v(t) > 0$. Now, $v(t) = 0$ if $\sin 2t = \sqrt{3}/2$.
Since t is between 0 and 2π, $2t$ is between 0 and 4π. The solutions of
$v(t) = 0$ in $[0,4\pi]$ are $2t = \pi/3$, $2\pi/3$, $7\pi/3$, and $8\pi/3$. Now, $v(t) > 0$ if
$\sin 2t < \sqrt{3}/2$. This occurs if $2t$ is in $(0,\pi/3)$, $(2\pi/3, 7\pi/3)$ or $(8\pi/3, 4\pi)$,
or, equivalently, if t is in $(0,\pi/6)$, $(\pi/3, 7\pi/6)$ or $(4\pi/3, 2\pi)$.

82. $s(t) = 4 \sin \pi t \implies$ amplitude $= |4| = 4$, period $= 2\pi/\pi = 2$, frequency $=$
$\pi/2\pi = 1/2$. Note that $v(t) = 4\pi \cos \pi t < 0$ if $\pi/2 < \pi t < 3\pi/2$ or $1/2 < t$
$< 3/2$. Similarly, $v(t) > 0$ if $0 \le t < 1/2$ or $3/2 < t \le 2$. Thus the motion
is in the "+" direction (from $s = 0$ to $s = 4$) during the time interval
$0 \le t \le 1/2$; then in the "-" direction (from $s = 4$ to $s = -4$) during the
interval $1/2 \le t \le 3/2$, and, finally in the "+" direction (from $s = -4$ to
$s = 0$) in the interval $3/2 \le t \le 2$. This motion repeats itself every 2
seconds, and the motion is oscillatory.

88. Preliminary analysis: writing the equation as $\cos x + x - 2 = 0$, let $f(x)$
$= \cos x + x - 2$. Then $f(\pi/2) = \pi/2 - 2 < 0$ and $f(\pi) = -1 + \pi - 2 > 0$.
Thus the root lies between $\pi/2 \approx 1.57$ and $\pi \approx 3.14$. Our initial guess will
be $x_1 = 3$.

i	x_i	$f(x_i)$
1	3.0000	0.0100
2	2.9883	0.0001
3	2.9883	0.0000

Thus, the root is 2.9883 to 4 places.

EXERCISES 8.3, page 376

1. With $u = 4x$, $du = 4\,dx$, $dx = (1/4)du$ and $\int \cos 4x\,dx = \frac{1}{4}\int \cos u\,du =$
$\frac{1}{4} \sin u + C = \frac{1}{4} \sin 4x + C$.

4. With $u = x^3$, $\int x^2 \cot x^3 \csc x^3 dx = (1/3)\int \cot u \csc u\,du = -(1/3)\csc u + C$
$= -(1/3)\csc x^3 + C$.

7. $\int \frac{1}{\cos 2x}\,dx = \int \sec 2x\,dx = \frac{1}{2}\ln|\sec 2x + \tan 2x| + C$, ($u = 2x$ could be
used as in #1).

10. $\int (x + \csc 8x)\,dx = x^2/2 + (1/8)\ln|\csc 8x - \cot 8x| + C.$

13. With $u = \sin 3x$, $du = 3\cos 3x\,dx$, $\cos 3x\,dx = (1/3)\,du$ and

$$\int \cos 3x \sqrt[3]{\sin 3x}\,dx = \frac{1}{3}\int u^{1/3}\,du = \frac{1}{3}\cdot\frac{3}{4}u^{4/3} + C = \frac{1}{4}(\sin 3x)^{4/3} + C.$$

16. With $u = \sin x$, $du = \cos x\,dx$ and $\int \sin^3 x \cos x\,dx = \int u^3\,du =$

$\frac{1}{4}u^4 + C = \frac{1}{4}\sin^4 x + C.$

19. With $u = \tan x$, $du = \sec^2 x\,dx$, $\displaystyle\int_0^{\pi/4} \tan x\,\sec^2 x\,dx = \int_0^1 u\,du = 1/2.$

22. $\displaystyle\int_{\pi/6}^{\pi/2} \frac{\cos^2 x}{\sin x}\,dx = \int_{\pi/6}^{\pi/2} \frac{1 - \sin^2 x}{\sin x}\,dx = \int_{\pi/6}^{\pi/2} (\csc x - \sin x)\,dx = \ln|\csc x - \cot x|$

$\displaystyle + \cos x]_{\pi/6}^{\pi/2} = 0 - (\ln|2-\sqrt{3}| + \sqrt{3}/2).$

25. With $u = x + \cos x$, $du = (1 - \sin x)\,dx$ and $\int \frac{1 - \sin x}{x + \cos x}\,dx = \int \frac{du}{u} = \ln|u| + C$

$= \ln|x + \cos x| + C.$

28. $\displaystyle\int_0^{\pi/4} (1 + \sec x)^2\,dx = \int_0^{\pi/4} (1 + 2\sec x + \sec^2 x)\,dx = [x + 2\ln|\sec x + \tan x|$

$\displaystyle + \tan x]_0^{\pi/4} = \pi/4 + 2\ln|\sqrt{2}+1| + 1.$

31. Since $\sin x = \dfrac{1}{\csc x}$, $\int \dfrac{e^{\cos x}}{\csc x}\,dx = \int e^{\cos x}\sin x\,dx.$ Let $u = \cos x$, $du =$

$-\sin x$ and the integral is $-\int e^u\,du = -e^u + C = -e^{\cos x} + C.$

34. With $u = 1 + 3\sec x$, $du = 3\sec x \tan x\,dx$, and $\int \dfrac{\sec x \tan x}{1 + 3\sec x}\,dx = \dfrac{1}{3}\int \dfrac{du}{u} =$

$\frac{1}{3}\ln|u| + C = \frac{1}{3}\ln|1 + 3\sec x| + C.$

37. For $x \in [-\pi/4, \pi/4]$, $x \le \pi/4 < 1 \le \sec x$. Thus $A = \displaystyle\int_{-\pi/4}^{\pi/4} (\sec x - x)\,dx =$

$\displaystyle \ln|\sec x + \tan x| - \frac{x^2}{2}\Big]_{-\pi/4}^{\pi/4} = \ln|\sqrt{2} + 1| - \ln|\sqrt{2} - 1|.$

40. Using the shell method, $V = 2\pi\displaystyle\int_0^{\sqrt{\pi}/2} x \tan x^2\,dx.$ With $u = x^2$, $du = 2x\,dx$,

$x = 0 \Longrightarrow u = 0$, $x = \sqrt{\pi}/2 \Longrightarrow u = \pi/4$, $V = \pi\displaystyle\int_0^{\pi/4} \tan u\,du = \pi \ln|\sec u|\,]_0^{\pi/4}$

$= \pi(\ln\sqrt{2} - \ln 1) = \pi \ln\sqrt{2}$ or $(\pi \ln 2)/2.$

43. $D_x(\frac{1}{2}\tan^2 x + C) = \frac{2}{2}\tan x\, D_x \tan x + 0 = \tan x \sec^2 x.$

46. (a) $f'(x) = \sec^2 x \implies L = \int_0^{\pi/4} \sqrt{1 + \sec^4 x}\ dx.$

   (b) With $a = 0$, $b = \pi/4$, $n = 4$, the partitioning points are 0, $\pi/16$, $2\pi/16 = \pi/8$, $3\pi/16$ and $\pi/4$. If $g(x) = \sqrt{1 + \sec^4 x}$, $L \approx \frac{(\pi/4 - 0)}{3(4)}[g(0) + 4g(\pi/16) + 2g(\pi/8) + 4g(3\pi/16) + g(\pi/4)].$

   (c) $L \approx (\pi/48)[1.414 + 4(1.442) + 2(1.540) + 4(1.758) + 2.236] \approx (.06545)(19.530) \approx 1.278.$

49. We obtain with $f(x) = \sqrt{\sin x}$, $(b-a)/n = \pi/6$:

i	x_i	$f(x_i)$	m	$mf(x_i)$	r	$rf(x_i)$
0	0	0.0000	1	0.0000	1	0.0000
1	$\pi/6$	0.7071	2	1.4142	4	2.8284
2	$\pi/3$	0.9306	2	1.8612	2	1.8612
3	$\pi/2$	1.0000	2	2.0000	4	4.0000
4	$2\pi/3$	0.9306	2	1.8612	2	1.8612
5	$5\pi/6$	0.7071	2	1.4142	4	2.8284
6	π	0.0000	1	0.0000	1	0.0000
				8.5508		13.3792

   Since $(b-a)/2n = \pi/12 \approx 0.2618$, $T = (\pi/12)(8.5508) = 2.2386 \approx 2.24.$
   Since $(b-a)/3n = \pi/18 \approx 0.1745$, $S = (\pi/18)(13.3792) = 2.3351 \approx 2.34.$

EXERCISES 8.4, page 381

1. $\sin^{-1}(\pm\sqrt{3}/2) = \pm\pi/3$ since $\sin(\pm\pi/3) = \pm\sqrt{3}/2$ and both angles are in $[-\pi/2, \pi/2]$.

4. (a) $\arcsin(-1) = -\pi/2$ since $\sin(-\pi/2) = -1$ and $-\pi/2 \in [-\pi/2, \pi/2].$
   (b) $\cos^{-1}(-1) = \pi$ since $\cos \pi = -1$ and $\pi \in [0, \pi].$

7. $\sin(\cos^{-1}(\sqrt{3}/2)) = \sin \pi/6 = 1/2.$

10. $\tan(\tan^{-1} 10) = 10$ since $\tan x$, $\tan^{-1} x$ are inverse functions.

13. Let $a = \sin^{-1} 3/5$. Then $\sin a = 3/5$, $\cos a = \sqrt{1 - 9/25} = 4/5$. Let $b = \tan^{-1} 4/3$. Then $\sin b = 4/5$, $\cos b = 3/5$. $\cos(\sin^{-1} 3/5 + \tan^{-1} 4/3) = \cos(a+b) = \cos a \cos b - \sin a \sin b = (\frac{4}{5})(\frac{3}{5}) - (\frac{3}{5})(\frac{4}{5}) = 0.$

16. Let $a = \sin^{-1} 8/17$. Then $\sin a = \frac{8}{17}$, $\cos a = \sqrt{1 - (8/17)^2} = \frac{15}{17}$. Then
   $\cos(2\sin^{-1} 8/17) = \cos(2a) = \cos^2 a - \sin^2 a = (\frac{15}{17})^2 - (\frac{8}{17})^2 = \frac{161}{289}.$

19. The method of Examples 3 and 4 can be used: let $y = \tan^{-1}x$ so that $x =$
     $\tan y = \sin y/\sqrt{1 - \sin^2 y}$, and now solve for $\sin y$. An alternate method
     is to sketch a right triangle with y as interior
     angle whose tangent is x. We can do this by mak-
     ing the opposite side of length x and the adjacent
     side of length 1. Then the hypotenuse is $\sqrt{x^2+1}$
     and $\sin(\tan^{-1}x) = \sin y = $ opposite/hypotenuse
     $= x/\sqrt{x^2+1}$.

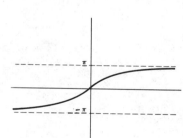

22. Let $y = \tan^{-1}x$. Then $\cos 2y = \cos^2 y - \sin^2 y = (1/\sqrt{x^2+1})^2 - (x/\sqrt{x^2+1})^2 =$
     $(1-x^2)/(x^2+1)$. (Refer to the sketch for #19.)

25. Let $y = \arctan x$. Then the right side of the desired identity is $2y$. Now,
     from #19 above, $\sin y = \sin(\arctan x) = x/\sqrt{x^2+1}$. By the figure there, $\cos y$
     $= 1/\sqrt{x^2+1}$. Thus $2 \sin y \cos y = 2x/(x^2+1)$, and the left side of the identity
     is $\arcsin(2x/(x^2+1)) = \arcsin(2 \sin y \cos y) = \arcsin(\sin 2y) = 2y$, the same
     as the right side.

28. $\cos(\arccos(-x)) = -x$ and, from the formula $\cos(\pi-\theta) = -\cos\theta$ we obtain
     $\cos(\pi-\arccos x) = -\cos(\arccos x) = -x$. The identity is thus established
     since $\cos x$ is one-to-one on $[0,\pi]$.

34.   37.

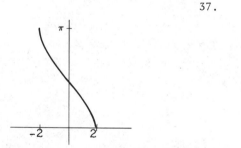

40. Let $a = \arccos x$. Then $x = \cos a$ and $y = \sin a$. Since $0 \le \arccos x \le \pi$,
     $0 \le \sin a \le 1$ and hence, $0 \le y \le 1$. $y = \sin a = \sqrt{1-\cos^2 a} = \sqrt{1-x^2} \Longrightarrow y^2 =$
     $1-x^2 \Longrightarrow x^2 + y^2 = 1$. Since $y \ge 0$, the graph is the upper half of the unit
     circle centered at $(0,0)$.

43. Set $x = 1$. The left side is $\tan^{-1}1 = \pi/4 \approx 0.785$. The right side is
     $1/\tan 1 \approx 1/1.557 \approx 0.642$; definitely not $\pi/4$.

EXERCISES 8.5, page 387

1. $f'(x) = \dfrac{D_x(3x-5)}{1 + (3x-5)^2} = \dfrac{3}{9x^2-30x+26}$.

2. $f'(x) = \dfrac{D_x(x/3)}{\sqrt{1 - (x/3)^2}} = \dfrac{1/3}{\sqrt{1 - x^2/9}} = \dfrac{1}{\sqrt{9 - x^2}}$.

4. $f'(x) = 2x/(1 + (x^2)^2) = 2x/(1+x^4)$.

7. $f'(x) = x^2 \cdot \dfrac{2x}{1+x^4} + 2x \arctan(x^2)$.

10. $f'(x) = x^2 \cdot \dfrac{5}{5x\sqrt{(5x)^2-1}} + 2x \sec^{-1}5x = x/\sqrt{25x^2-1} + 2x \sec^{-1}5x$.

13. $f'(x) = D_x(\sin^{-1}x)^{-1} = -(\sin^{-1}x)^{-2} D_x\sin^{-1}x = -1/\sqrt{1-x^2}\,(\sin^{-1}x)^2$.

16. $f'(x) = 4(\dfrac{1}{x} - \arcsin\dfrac{1}{x})^3 D_x(\dfrac{1}{x} - \arcsin\dfrac{1}{x})$. The last derivative is

$-\dfrac{1}{x^2} - \dfrac{D_x(1/x)}{\sqrt{1-1/x^2}} = -\dfrac{1}{x^2}(1 - \dfrac{1}{\sqrt{1-1/x^2}})$.

19. $f'(x) = \sqrt{x} D_x \sec^{-1}\sqrt{x} + \sec^{-1}\sqrt{x} D_x \sqrt{x} = \dfrac{\sqrt{x} D_x \sqrt{x}}{\sqrt{x}\sqrt{(\sqrt{x})^2-1}} + \dfrac{\sec^{-1}\sqrt{x}}{2\sqrt{x}}$

$= \dfrac{1/2\sqrt{x}}{\sqrt{x-1}} + \dfrac{\sec^{-1}\sqrt{x}}{2\sqrt{x}}$.

22. $f'(x) = x D_x \arccos\sqrt{4x+1} + \arccos\sqrt{4x+1} D_x x = \dfrac{-x D_x\sqrt{4x+1}}{\sqrt{1 - \sqrt{4x+1}^2}} + \arccos\sqrt{4x+1}$

$= \dfrac{-x(4/2\sqrt{4x+1})}{\sqrt{-4x}} + \arccos\sqrt{4x+1} = -2x/\sqrt{4x+1}\sqrt{-4x} + \arccos\sqrt{4x+1}$.

(Note that the domain of f is [-1/4,0], so there's no problem with $\sqrt{-4x}$.)

25. $x^2 + x \sin^{-1}y = ye^x \Rightarrow 2x + xy'/\sqrt{1-y^2} + \sin^{-1}y = ye^x + y'e^x \Rightarrow$

$(x/\sqrt{1-y^2} - e^x)y' = ye^x - 2x - \sin^{-1}y$ which yields the given answer.

28. With $u = e^x$, $du = e^x dx$, $\displaystyle\int_0^1 \dfrac{e^x}{1+e^{2x}} dx = \int_1^e \dfrac{du}{1+u^2} = \tan^{-1}u\Big]_1^e = \tan^{-1}e - \tan^{-1}1$

$= \tan^{-1}e - \pi/4$.

31. With $u = \cos x$, $du = -\sin x\, dx$, $\displaystyle\int \dfrac{\sin x}{\cos^2 x + 1} dx = -\int \dfrac{du}{u^2+1} = -\tan^{-1}u + C$

$= -\tan^{-1}(\cos x) + C$.

34. First, $\displaystyle\int \dfrac{dx}{e^x\sqrt{1-e^{-2x}}} = \int \dfrac{e^{-x}}{\sqrt{1 - e^{-2x}}} dx$. Let $u = e^{-x}$ so that this becomes

$-\displaystyle\int \dfrac{du}{\sqrt{1-u^2}} = -\sin^{-1}u + C = -\sin^{-1}(e^{-x}) + C$.

37. First multiply and divide by x^2 so that $\displaystyle\int \dfrac{1}{x\sqrt{x^6-4}} dx = \int \dfrac{x^2}{x^3\sqrt{x^6-4}} dx$.

Let $u = x^3$, $du = 3x^2 dx$, $x^2 dx = (1/3)du$. The integral becomes $\dfrac{1}{3}\displaystyle\int \dfrac{1}{u\sqrt{u^2-4}} du$

$= \dfrac{1}{3} \cdot \dfrac{1}{2} \sec^{-1}\dfrac{u}{2} + C = \dfrac{1}{6} \sec^{-1}\dfrac{x^3}{2} + C$.

40. We use a slightly different substitution, or change of variable, technique.
Let $u = \sqrt{x}$. Then $x = u^2$ and $dx = 2u\ du$, and

$$\int \frac{1}{x\sqrt{x-1}}\ dx = \int \frac{2u}{u^2\sqrt{u^2-1}}\ du = 2\int \frac{1}{u\sqrt{u^2-1}}\ du = 2\ sec^{-1}u + C = 2\ sec^{-1}\sqrt{x} + C.$$

43. $A = \displaystyle\int_{-2}^{2} \frac{4}{\sqrt{16-x^2}}\ dx = 4\ sin^{-1}\left.\frac{x}{4}\right]_{-2}^{2} = 4[\frac{\pi}{6} - (-\frac{\pi}{6})] = \frac{4\pi}{3}$.

46. With $f(x) = \arcsin x$, $x = .25$, $\Delta x = .01$, $\Delta f \approx df = f'(.25)(.01) =$

$$\frac{1}{\sqrt{1-.25^2}}\ (.01) = \frac{.01}{\sqrt{1 - 1/16}} = .04/\sqrt{15}.$$

49. If A and B are the angles shown, between the
horizontal and the top and bottom, respectively,
of the billboard, then $\theta = A-B$ is to be
maximized. If the viewer is x feet from the
base of the building then $\theta = tan^{-1}(80/x)$

$- tan^{-1}(60/x)$ and $\dfrac{d\theta}{dx} = \dfrac{-80x^2}{1+(80/x)^2} - \dfrac{-60/x^2}{1+(60/x)^2}$

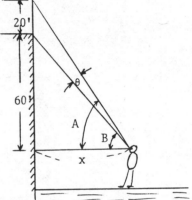

$= \dfrac{60}{x^2 + 3600} - \dfrac{80}{x^2 + 6400}$; $\dfrac{d\theta}{dx} = 0$ if $60(x^2+6400)$

$- 80(x^2 + 3600) = 0$ or $96,000 - 20x^2 = 0$. Thus
$x = \sqrt{4800} = 40\sqrt{3} \approx 69.3$ ft.

52. $f(x) = \arccos(\cos x) \implies f'(x) =$

$\dfrac{-D_x \cos x}{\sqrt{1 - \cos^2 x}} = \dfrac{\sin x}{\sqrt{\sin^2 x}} = \dfrac{\sin x}{|\sin x|}.$ Thus

$f'(x) = 1$ on any interval where $\sin x >$
0; $(0,\pi)$, $(2\pi,3\pi)$, ..., $(2n\pi,(2n+1)\pi)$.
Also, $f'(x) = -1$ on any interval where
$\sin x < 0$; $(-\pi,0)$, $(\pi,2\pi)$, ...,
$((2n-1)\pi,2n\pi)$. The critical numbers

of f are $x = n\pi$ at which f' fails to exist. By the first derivative test
$f(n\pi)$ is a local minimum if n is even, a local maximum if n is odd. $f''(x)$
$= 0$ if $x \neq n\pi$, so there is no concavity to discuss. Since $f'(x)$ is alternately $+1$ and -1, the graph of f is made up of straight line segments as
shown.

55. $y' = 1/(1+x^2)$ and $y'' = -2x/(1+x^2)^2 > 0$ if $x < 0$ and < 0 if $x > 0$. Thus CU on
$(-\infty,0)$ and CD on $(0,\infty)$ with a PI at $x = 0$.

58. Recall that if s is arc length of the graph of $y = f(x)$ then $\Delta s \approx ds =$
$\sqrt{1 + f'(x)^2}\ \Delta x$. Here $f'(x) = 1/(1+x^2)$, $x = 0$ and $\Delta x = 0.1$. $f'(0) = 1$ so
that $\Delta s \approx \sqrt{1 + f'(0)^2}\ \Delta x = \sqrt{2}(0.1) \approx 0.14$.

EXERCISES 8.6, page 393

1. and 4. These are immediate from the definitions and some easy calculations.

7. $2 \sinh x \cosh x = (2/4)(e^x - e^{-x})(e^x + e^{-x}) = (1/2)(e^{2x} - e^{-2x}) = \sinh 2x.$

10. $\tanh 2x = \dfrac{\sinh 2x}{\cosh 2x} = \dfrac{2 \sinh x \cosh x}{\cosh^2 x + \sinh^2 x}$ (by #7,8)

$= \dfrac{2 \tanh x}{1 + \tanh^2 x}$ (dividing numerator and denominator by $\cosh^2 x$).

13. $2 \sinh \dfrac{x+y}{2} \cosh \dfrac{x-y}{2} = 2\dfrac{(e^{\frac{x+y}{2}} - e^{\frac{-x-y}{2}})}{2} \dfrac{(e^{\frac{x-y}{2}} + e^{\frac{-x-y}{2}})}{2}$. When the first terms

in each parentheses are multiplied together, we get: $e^{\frac{x+y}{2}} e^{\frac{x-y}{2}} = e^{\frac{x+y+x-y}{2}} =$

$e^{\frac{2x}{2}} = e^x$. Similarly, the other three products can be simplified, and we ob-

tain for the entire expression: $(e^x + e^y - e^{-y} - e^{-x})/2 =$

$(e^x - e^{-x})/2 + (e^y - e^{-y})/2 = \sinh x + \sinh y$, as desired.

16. $f'(x) = \sinh\sqrt{4x^2+3} \; D_x\sqrt{4x^2+3} = \dfrac{(\sinh\sqrt{4x^2+3})(8x)}{2\sqrt{4x^2+3}}$.

19. $f'(x) = \dfrac{(x^2+1)(-\text{sech } x^2 \tanh x^2)D_x x^2 - (\text{sech } x^2)D_x(x^2+1)}{(x^2+1)^2}$

$= \dfrac{-[(x^2+1)(\text{sech } x^2 \tanh x^2)2x + (\text{sech } x^2)(2x)]}{(x^2+1)^2}$.

22. $f'(x) = \cosh(x^2+1) \; D_x(x^2+1) = 2x \cosh(x^2+1).$

25. $f'(x) = \dfrac{D_x \sinh 2x}{\sinh 2x} = \dfrac{2 \cosh 2x}{\sinh 2x} = 2 \coth 2x$.

28. $f'(x) = (1/2)(\text{sech } 5x)^{-1/2} D_x \text{ sech } 5x = -(5 \text{ sech } 5x \tanh 5x)/2\sqrt{\text{sech } 5x}.$

31. $\sinh xy = ye^x \implies (\cosh xy)(xy' + y) = ye^x + y'e^x \implies (x \cosh xy - e^x)y' = $

$y(e^x - \cosh xy).$

34. With $u = \ln x$, $du = (1/x)dx$, $\displaystyle\int \dfrac{\cosh \ln x}{x} dx = \int \cosh u \; du = \sinh u + C$

$= \sinh \ln x + C.$

37. With $u = \sinh x$, $\displaystyle\int \sinh x \cosh x \; dx = \int u \; du = u^2/2 + C = (\sinh^2 x)/2 + C.$

40. Let $u = \cosh x$, $du = \sinh x \; dx$. Then $\displaystyle\int \sinh x\sqrt{\cosh x} \; dx = \int \sqrt{u} \; du = \dfrac{2}{3}u^{3/2}$

$+ C = \dfrac{2}{3}(\cosh x)^{3/2} + C.$

43. Let $u = 1 - 2 \tanh x$, $du = -2 \text{ sech}^2 x \; dx$. Then $\displaystyle\int \dfrac{\text{sech}^2 x}{1 - 2 \tanh x} dx = -\dfrac{1}{2}\int \dfrac{du}{u}$

$= -\dfrac{1}{2} \ln|u| + C = -\dfrac{1}{2} \ln|1 - 2 \tanh x| + C.$

46. $L_0^1 = \int_0^1 \sqrt{1 + (D_x \cosh x)^2}\, dx = \int_0^1 \sqrt{1 + \sinh^2 x}\, dx = \int_0^1 \cosh x\, dx = \sinh x]_0^1$

$= \sinh 1 \approx 1.175.$

52.

EXERCISES 8.7 , page 398

1. $y = \cosh^{-1} x \implies x = \cosh y = (e^y + e^{-y})/2,\ (x \geq 1),\ \implies e^{2y} - 2xe^y + 1 = 0$

$\implies e^y = (2x \pm \sqrt{4x^2-4})/2 \implies e^y = x + \sqrt{x^2-1}.$ (The + sign must be chosen to guarantee that $x \to \infty \iff y \to \infty$.)

4. $D_x(\tanh^{-1} u) = D_u(\tfrac{1}{2} \ln \tfrac{1+u}{1-u})\, D_x u$ 10.

$= \tfrac{1}{2} D_u(\ln(1+u) - \ln(1-u)D_x u$

$= \tfrac{1}{2}(\tfrac{1}{1+u} + \tfrac{1}{1-u})D_x u = \tfrac{1}{1-u^2} D_x u.$

$y = \operatorname{sech}^{-1} x$

13. $f'(x) = \dfrac{D_x \sqrt{x}}{\sqrt{(\sqrt{x})^2 - 1}} = 1/2\ \sqrt{x}\ \sqrt{x-1}.$

16. $f'(x) = \dfrac{D_x \sin 3x}{1 - \sin^2 3x} = \dfrac{3 \cos 3x}{\cos^2 3x} = 3 \sec 3x.$

19. $f'(x) = \dfrac{D_x \cosh^{-1} 4x}{\cosh^{-1} 4x} = 4/(\sqrt{16x^2-1}\ \cosh^{-1} 4x).$

22. With $u = 4x$, $\displaystyle\int \frac{1}{\sqrt{16x^2-9}}\, dx = \frac{1}{4}\int \frac{du}{\sqrt{u^2-9}} = (1/4)\cosh^{-1}(\tfrac{u}{3}) + C =$

$(1/4)\cosh^{-1}(4x/3) + C.$

25. With $u = e^x$, $\displaystyle\int \frac{e^x}{\sqrt{e^{2x}-16}} = \int \frac{du}{\sqrt{u^2-16}} = \cosh^{-1}(u/4) + C = \cosh^{-1}(e^x/4) + C.$

28. First multiply and divide the integrand by e^x. Then let $u = e^x$, $du = e^x dx$

and $\displaystyle\int \frac{1}{\sqrt{5-e^{2x}}}\, dx$ and $\displaystyle\int \frac{e^x dx}{e^x\sqrt{5-e^{2x}}} = \int \frac{du}{u\sqrt{5-u^2}} = -\frac{1}{\sqrt{5}}\operatorname{sech}^{-1} \frac{|u|}{5} + C =$

$-\dfrac{1}{\sqrt{5}}$ sech$^{-1}\dfrac{e^x}{5}$ + C.   ($|e^x| = e^x$ since $e^x > 0$.)

EXERCISES 8.8, page 398

1. $\lim\limits_{x\to0}\dfrac{x^2}{\sin x} = \lim\limits_{x\to0} x \cdot \dfrac{x}{\sin x} = \lim\limits_{x\to0} x\,\dfrac{1}{(\sin x)/x} = 0 \cdot \dfrac{1}{1} = 0.$

4. $\lim\limits_{x\to0}\dfrac{2 - \cos x}{1 + \sin x} = \dfrac{2 - 1}{1 + 0} = 1.$

7. $f'(x) = -\sin\sqrt{3x^2+x}\; D_x\sqrt{3x^2+x} = (-\sin\sqrt{3x^2+x})(\tfrac{1}{2})(3x^2+x)^{-1/2} D_x(3x^2+x)$

   $= (-\sin\sqrt{3x^2+x})(6x+1)/2\sqrt{3x^2+x}.$

10. $f'(x) = D_x(x^3 + \csc 6x)^{1/3} = (1/3)(x^3 + \csc 6x)^{-2/3} D_x(x^3 + \csc 6x) =$

    $(1/3)(x^3 + \csc 6x)^{-2/3}(3x^2 - 6\csc 6x \cot 6x)$ or

    $(3x^2 - 6\csc 6x \cot 6x)/3\sqrt[3]{(x^3 + \csc 6x)^2}.$

13. $f'(x) = (\sin^{-1}5x\; D_x(3x+7)^4 - (3x+7)^4 D_x\sin^{-1}5x)/(\sin^{-1}5x)^2$

    $= [(\sin^{-1}5x)4(3x+7)^3 3 - (3x+7)^4 \cdot \dfrac{5}{\sqrt{1-25x^2}}]/(\sin^{-1}5x)^2.$

16. $f'(x) = 5^{\tan 2x}(\ln 5) D_x \tan 2x = 5^{\tan 2x}(\ln 5)(2\sec^2 2x).$

19. $f(x) = \ln(\csc^3 2x) = 3\ln\csc 2x \Longrightarrow f'(x) = 3\cdot\dfrac{D_x\csc 2x}{\csc 2x} =$

    $3\cdot\dfrac{-(\csc 2x \cot 2x)(2)}{\csc 2x} = -6\cot 2x.$

22. $f(x) = \cot(1/x) + 1/\cot x = \cot(1/x) + \tan x \Longrightarrow f'(x) = -\csc^2(1/x)D_x(1/x)$

    $+ \sec^2 x = (1/x^2)\csc^2(1/x) + \sec^2 x.$

25. $f'(x) = \sinh e^{-5x} D_x e^{-5x} = (\sinh e^{-5x})(-5e^{-5x}).$

28. $f'(x) = \sec(\sec x)\tan(\sec x)D_x \sec x = \sec(\sec x)\tan(\sec x)(\sec x \tan x).$

31. $f'(x) = 3\sin^2 e^{-2x} D_x\sin e^{-2x} = 3\sin^2 e^{-2x}\cos e^{-2x} D_x(e^{-2x}) =$

    $3\sin^2 e^{-2x}\cos e^{-2x}(-2e^{-2x}).$

34. $f'(x) = \sec 5x\; D_x \tan 5x + \tan 5x\; D_x \sec 5x = 5\sec^3 5x + 5\tan^2 5x \sec 5x.$

37. $f'(x) = \dfrac{D_x\sqrt{1-x^2}}{\sqrt{1-(\sqrt{1-x^2})^2}} = \dfrac{-x}{\sqrt{1-x^2}\,\sqrt{x^2}} = \pm\dfrac{1}{\sqrt{1-x^2}}, +$if $x < 0$, $-$ if $x > 0$.

40. $f'(x) = \tfrac{1}{2}(\sin\sqrt{x})^{-1/2} D_x\sin\sqrt{x} = \dfrac{\cos\sqrt{x}\; D_x\sqrt{x}}{2\sqrt{\sin\sqrt{x}}} = \dfrac{\cos\sqrt{x}}{4\sqrt{x}\sqrt{\sin\sqrt{x}}}.$

43. $f'(x) = \dfrac{D_x \tan^{-1}x}{1+(\tan^{-1}x)^2} = 1/(1+x^2)\ [1 + (\tan^{-1}x)^2]$.

46. $f'(x) = \dfrac{D_x \tanh(5x+1)}{\tanh(5x+1)} = \dfrac{5\ \mathrm{sech}^2(5x+1)}{\tanh\ (5x+1)}$

49. $f'(x) = (D_x x^2)/\sqrt{(x^2)^2+1} = 2x/\sqrt{x^4+1}$.

52. With $u = x/2$, $2\ du = dx$, $\displaystyle\int \csc(x/2)\cot(x/2)\,dx = 2\int \csc u \cot u\ du =$
$-2\ \csc u + C = -2\ \csc(x/2) + C$.

55. With $u = 9x$, $dx = (1/9)du$, $\displaystyle\int (\cot 9x + \csc 9x)dx = (1/9)\int (\cot u + \csc u)du$
$= (1/9)(\ln|\sin u| + \ln|\csc u - \cot u|) + C$, where $u = 9x$.

58. $\displaystyle\int \cot 2x\ \csc 2x\ dx = -(1/2)\csc 2x + C$.

61. $\displaystyle\int \dfrac{\sin 4x}{\tan 4x}\ dx = \int \cos 4x\ dx = (1/4)\sin 4x + C$.

64. $u = \cos 2x \Longrightarrow du = -2\sin 2x\ dx$ and $\sin 2x\ dx = -(1/2)du$. $x = 0$ or $\pi/4$
$\Longrightarrow u = 0$ or 1. Thus $\displaystyle\int_0^{\pi/4} \sin 2x\ \cos^2 2x\ dx = -\frac{1}{2}\int_1^0 u^2 du = +\frac{1}{2}\int_0^1 u^2 du =$
$\frac{1}{2}\cdot\frac{1}{3} = \frac{1}{6}$.

67. $u = \sin 3x \Longrightarrow du = 3\cos 3x\ dx$, and $\cos 3x\ dx = (1/3)du$.
$\displaystyle\int \cos 3x(\sin 3x)^{-3}dx = \frac{1}{3}\int u^{-3}du = \frac{1}{3}\frac{u^{-2}}{-2} + C = -\frac{1}{6}(\sin 3x)^{-2} + C =$
$-\frac{1}{6}\csc^2 3x + C$.

70. $\displaystyle\int \dfrac{1}{4+9x^2}\ dx = \frac{1}{9}\int \dfrac{dx}{(4/9) + x^2} = \frac{1}{9}\cdot\frac{3}{2}\tan^{-1}\dfrac{x}{2/3} + C = \frac{1}{6}\tan^{-1}(\dfrac{3x}{2}) + C$.

73. With $u = x^2$, $\displaystyle\int \dfrac{x}{\mathrm{sech}\ x^2}\ dx = \frac{1}{2}\int \cosh u\ du = \frac{1}{2}\sinh u + C = \frac{1}{2}\sinh(x^2) + C$.

76. $\displaystyle\int_0^{\pi/2} \dfrac{\cos x}{1 + \sin^2 x}\ dx = \tan^{-1}(\sin x)\Big]_0^{\pi/2} = \tan^{-1}1 - \tan^{-1}0 = \dfrac{\pi}{4}$.

79. $u = 2 + \cot x \Longrightarrow du = -\csc^2 x\ dx$. $\displaystyle\int \dfrac{\csc^2 x}{2 + \cot x}\ dx = -\int \dfrac{du}{u} = -\ln|u| + C =$
$-\ln|2 + \cot x| + C$.

82. $u = 1 - 2x \Longrightarrow dx = -(1/2)du$. $\displaystyle\int \mathrm{sech}^2(1-2x)dx = -(1/2)\int \mathrm{sech}^2 u\ du =$
$-(1/2)\tanh u + C = -(1/2)\tanh(1-2x) + C$.

85. $u = 2x \Longrightarrow dx = (1/2)du$ and $x = u/2$. $\displaystyle\int \dfrac{1}{x\sqrt{9-4x^2}}\ dx = \int \dfrac{(1/2)du}{(u/2)\sqrt{9-u^2}} =$
$\displaystyle\int \dfrac{1}{u\sqrt{3^2-u^2}}\ du = -\frac{1}{3}\mathrm{sech}^{-1}\dfrac{|u|}{3} + C = -\frac{1}{3}\mathrm{sech}^{-1}\dfrac{|2x|}{3} + C$.

88. Instead of changing variables, we proceed as follows. $\displaystyle\int \frac{1}{\sqrt{25x^2+36}}\, dx =$

$$\int \frac{1}{\sqrt{25(x^2+36/25)}}\, dx = \frac{1}{5}\int \frac{1}{\sqrt{x^2+(6/5)^2}}\, dx = \frac{1}{5}\sinh^{-1}\frac{x}{6/5} + C = \frac{1}{5}\sinh^{-1}\frac{5x}{6} + C.$$

91. $\displaystyle f'(x) = 8\sec x \tan x - \csc x \cot x = \frac{8\sin x}{\cos^2 x} - \frac{\cos x}{\sin^2 x} = \frac{8\sin^3 x - \cos^3 x}{\sin^2 x \cos^2 x} = 0$

$\Rightarrow 8\sin^3 x = \cos^3 x \Rightarrow 2\sin x = \cos x \Rightarrow \tan x = 1/2 \Rightarrow x = \tan^{-1} 1/2.$
If $0 < x < \tan^{-1} 1/2$, we find, by retracing our steps above with the "$=$"
replaced by "$<$", that $f'(x) < 0$ and f is decreasing on $(0, \tan^{-1} 1/2)$.
Similarly, f is increasing on $(\tan^{-1} 1/2, \pi/2)$, and $f(\tan^{-1} 1/2) = 5\sqrt{5}$ is a
local minimum.

94. With $u = x^2$, $\displaystyle A = \int_0^1 \frac{x}{1+x^4}\, dx = \frac{1}{2}\int_0^1 \frac{du}{1+u^2} = \frac{1}{2}\tan^{-1}u\Big]_0^1 = \frac{\pi}{8}$.

97. All distances will be in meters. Thus the observer
is 500 m (1/2 km) from the point below the balloon.
With y the distance of the balloon above ground and
θ as shown, we are given that $\dfrac{dy}{dt} = 2$ m/sec and seek
$\dfrac{d\theta}{dt}$ when $y = 100$. $\tan\theta = y/500 \Rightarrow \theta = \arctan(y/500)$

$\rightarrow \dfrac{d\theta}{dt} = \dfrac{D_y(y/500)}{1+(y/500)^2}\dfrac{dy}{dt} = \dfrac{1}{500}\dfrac{1}{1+(y/500)^2}\cdot\dfrac{dy}{dt}$. Substituting $y = 100$, dy/dt

$= 2$, we obtain: $\dfrac{d\theta}{dt} = \dfrac{1}{500}\dfrac{1}{1+(1/5)^2}(2) = \dfrac{1}{500}\cdot\dfrac{25}{26}(2) = \dfrac{1}{260}$ rad/sec.

CHAPTER 9

ADDITIONAL TECHNIQUES AND

APPLICATIONS OF INTEGRATION

EXERCISES 9.1, page 407

1. $u = x$, $dv = e^{-x}dx \implies du = dx$, $v = -e^{-x}$. $\int xe^{-x}dx = -xe^{-x} - \int (-e^{-x})dx =$
    $-(x+1)e^{-x} + C$.

4. $u = x^2$, $dv = \sin 4x\ dx \implies du = 2x\ dx$, $v = -(1/4)\cos 4x$, $I = \int x^2 \sin 4x\ dx$
    $= x^2(-1/4)\cos 4x - \int (-1/4)\cos 4x(2x)dx = -(x^2/4)\cos 4x + (1/2)\int x \cos 4x\ dx$.
    Another integration by parts is necessary. $u = x$, $dv = \cos 4x\ dx \implies du = dx$,
    $dv = (1/4)\sin 4x$, and $\int x \cos 4x\ dx = (x/4)\sin 4x - (1/4)\int \sin 4x\ dx =$
    $(x/4)\sin 4x + (1/16)\cos 4x$. Combining results we obtain:
    $I = -(x^2/4)\cos 4x + (1/2)[(x/4)\sin 4x + (1/16)\cos 4x] + C$.

7. $u = x$, $dv = \sec x \tan x\ dx \implies du = dx$, $v = \sec x$. $\int x \sec x \tan x\ dx =$
    $x \sec x - \int \sec x\ dx = x \sec x - \ln|\sec x + \tan x| + C$.

10. $u = x^3$, $dv = e^{-x}dx \implies du = 3x^2 dx$, $v = -e^{-x}$. $I = \int x^3 e^{-x}dx = -x^3 e^{-x} +$
    $3\int x^2 e^{-x}dx$. Now, $u = x^2$, $dv = e^{-x}dx \implies du = 2x\ dx$, $v = -e^{-x}$. So, $I =$
    $-x^3 e^{-x} + 3[-x^2 e^{-x} + 2\int xe^{-x}dx]$. The last integral was done in #1. So, com-
    bining all, $I = -(x^3 + 3x^2 + 6x + 6)e^{-x} + C$.

13. $u = \ln x$, $dv = \sqrt{x}\ dx \implies du = \frac{1}{x}dx$, $v = \frac{2}{3}x^{3/2}$. $\int \sqrt{x}\ \ln x\ dx = \frac{2}{3}x^{3/2} \ln x -$
    $\frac{2}{3}\int \frac{x^{3/2}}{x}\ dx = \frac{2}{3}x^{3/2} \ln x - \frac{4}{9}x^{3/2} + C$. N.B. $\int \frac{x^{3/2}}{x}dx = \int x^{1/2}dx = \frac{2}{3}x^{3/2} + D$.

16. $u = \tan^{-1}x$, $dv = x\ dx \implies du = \frac{1}{1+x^2}\ dx$, $v = \frac{x^2}{2}$. $\int x \tan^{-1}x\ dx = \frac{x^2}{2}\tan^{-1}x -$
    $\frac{1}{2}\int \frac{x^2}{1+x^2}\ dx = \frac{x^2}{2}\tan^{-1}x - \frac{1}{2}\int (1 - \frac{1}{1+x^2})dx = \frac{x^2}{2}\tan^{-1}x - \frac{x}{2} + \frac{1}{2}\tan^{-1}x + C$.
    N.B. $\frac{x^-}{1+x^2} = 1 - \frac{1}{1+x^2}$ by ordinary long division.

19. With $y = \cos x$, $dy = -\sin x\ dx$, $\int \sin x \ln \cos x\ dx = -\int \ln y\ dy = -(y \ln y - y)$
    $+ C$ (by Example 3) $= -\cos x \ln \cos x + \cos x + C$.

21. $u = \sec x$, $dv = \sec^2 x\ dx \implies du = \sec x \tan x\ dx$, $v = \tan x$. Then $I =$
    $\int \sec^3 x\ dx = \sec x \tan x - \int \sec x \tan^2 x\ dx = \sec x \tan x - \int \sec^3 x\ dx +$
    $\int \sec x\ dx$. (Recall: $\tan^2 x = \sec^2 x - 1$.) Thus $2I = \sec x \tan x +$
    $\ln|\sec x + \tan x| + C$.

22. $u = \csc^3 x$, $dv = \csc^2 x\ dx \implies du = -3 \csc^3 x \cot x\ dx$, $v = -\cot x$. After

using $\cot^2 x = \csc^2 x - 1$, this yields $4 \int \csc^5 x \, dx = -\cot x \csc^3 x + 3 \cdot$

$\int \csc^3 x \, dx$. The last integral is evaluated using the procedure of #21 but with

$u = \csc x$, $dv = \csc^2 x \, dx$. Ultimately, $\int \csc^5 x \, dx = \frac{1}{8}[3 \ln|\csc x - \cot x| -$

$\cot x \csc x \, (3 + 2\csc^2 x)] + C.$

25. $u = x$, $dv = \sin 2x \, dx \implies du = dx$, $v = -\frac{1}{2} \cos 2x$ and $\int_0^{\pi/2} x \sin 2x \, dx =$

$-\frac{x}{2} \cos 2x \, \Big]_0^{\pi/2} + \frac{1}{2} \int_0^{\pi/2} \cos 2x \, dx = (\frac{\pi}{4} - 0) + \frac{1}{4} \sin 2x \, \Big]_0^{\pi/2} = \frac{\pi}{4} + 0 = \frac{\pi}{4}$.

28. This is a tricky one to get started correctly. We have to break up the

integrand as follows: $u = x^3$, $dv = \dfrac{x^2}{\sqrt{1-x^3}} \, dx \implies du = 3x^2 dx$, $v = \int \dfrac{x^2}{\sqrt{1-x^3}} \, dx$.

To evaluate v, let $y = 1-x^3$, $dy = -3x^2 dx$, $x^2 dx = -(1/3)dy$. Then $v =$

$-\frac{1}{3} \int y^{-1/2} \, du = -(2/3)y^{1/2} = -(2/3)\sqrt{1-x^3}$. Using these results, $I = \int \dfrac{x^5}{\sqrt{1-x^3}} dx$

$= -\frac{2}{3}x^3\sqrt{1-x^3} - \frac{2}{3} \int \sqrt{1-x^3} \, 3x^2 dx$. This last integral can be done with the same

substitution, $y = 1-x^3$, as above to obtain $I = -\frac{2}{3}x^3\sqrt{1-x^3} - \frac{2}{3} \cdot \frac{2}{3}(1-x^3)^{3/2} +$

C. By factoring out $\sqrt{1-x^3}$, and simplifying, this reduces to $-(2/9)\sqrt{1-x^3}(x^3+2)$ $+ C.$

31. $u = (\ln x)^2$, $dv = dx \implies du = (2 \ln x)\frac{1}{x} \, dx$, $v = x \cdot \int (\ln x)^2 dx = x(\ln x)^2 -$

$2\int (\ln x)\frac{1}{x} x \, dx = x(\ln x)^2 - 2\int \ln x \, dx = x(\ln x)^2 - 2(x \ln x - x) + C$ by

the result of Example 3.

34. $u = x+4$, $dv = \cosh 4x \, dx \implies du = dx$, $v - (1/4)\sinh 4x$. $\int (x+4)\cosh 4x \, dx =$

$(1/4)(x+4)\sinh 4x - (1/4)\int \sinh 4x \, dx = (1/4)(x+4)\sinh 4x - (1/16)\cosh 4x + C.$

37. $u = \cos^{-1} x$, $dv = dx \implies du = -1/\sqrt{1-x^2} \, dx = -(1-x^2)^{-1/2} dx$, $v = x$. $\int \cos^{-1} x \, dx$

$= x \cos^{-1} x - \int (1-x^2)^{-1/2}(-x) dx = x \cos^{-1} x - (1-x^2)^{1/2} + C.$

40. Let $u = x^m$, $dv = \sin x \, dx$, and the formula follows immediately.

43. $\int x^5 e^x dx = x^5 e^x - 5\int x^4 e^x dx = x^5 e^x - 5[x^4 e^x - 4\int x^3 e^x dx] = x^5 e^x - 5x^4 e^x +$

$20[x^3 e^x - 3\int x^2 e^x dx] = x^5 e^x - 5x^4 e^x + 20x^3 e^x - 60[x^2 e^x - 2\int x \, e^x] =$

$x^5 e^x - 5x^4 e^x + 20x^3 e^x - 60x^2 e^x + 120[x \, e^x - \int e^x]$. The last integral is

just $e^x + C.$

45. $A = \int_0^{\pi^2} \sin\sqrt{x} \, dx$. First, $y = \sqrt{x}$, $dy = (1/2\sqrt{x})dx \implies dx = 2\sqrt{x} \, dy = 2y \, dy$, and

$A = 2\int_0^{\pi} y \sin y \, dy$. Now, $u = y$, $dv = \sin y \, dy \implies du = dy$; $v = -\cos y$, and

$$A = 2(-y \cos y]_0^\pi + \int_0^\pi \cos y \, dy) = 2(\pi + \sin y]_0^\pi) = 2\pi.$$

46. By the disc method, $V = \pi \int_0^{\pi/2} x^2 \sin x \, dx$. Using #40, $\int x^2 \sin x \, dx =$

$-x^2 \cos x + 2\int x \cos x \, dx$. In the last integral, $u = x$, $dv = \cos x \, dx \implies du$

$= dx$, $v = \sin x$, and $\int x \cos x \, dx = x \sin x - \int \sin x \, dx = x \sin x + \cos x$.

Combining these results: $V = \pi(-x^2 \cos x + 2x \sin x + 2 \cos x)]_0^{\pi/2}$

$= \pi[(0 + 2(\frac{\pi}{2}) + 0) - (0 + 0 + 2)] = \pi(\pi - 2)$.

49. Because of symmetry, we can compute the force
on the right half and double it to get the
total force. The left boundary of this half
is $x = 3\pi/2$. The right boundary is $y =$
$\sin x$, $3\pi/2 \le x \le y$. We must express this
equation in terms of y as the independent
variable. We obtain for such x, $\sin^{-1} y =$
$x - 2\pi$, or $x = \sin^{-1} y + 2\pi$, since, by the
definition, $-\pi/2 \le \sin^{-1} y \le \pi/2$, and here,
$3\pi/2 \le x \le 2\pi$. Then by (6.13), if F is the force on the right half, F =

$$\rho \int_{-1}^0 (0-y)[(\sin^{-1} y + 2\pi) - 3\pi/2] \, dy = -\rho \int_{-1}^0 y(\sin^{-1} y + \pi/2) \, dy = \rho \int_{-1}^0 y \sin^{-1} y \, dy$$

$-\frac{\pi\rho}{2} \int_{-1}^0 y \, dy$. Let $I = \int_{-1}^0 y \sin^{-1} y \, dy$. $u = y$, $dv = \sin^{-1} y \, dy \implies du = dy$,

$v = y \sin^{-1} y + \sqrt{1-y^2}$ (by #12). So, $I = y^2 \sin^{-1} y + y\sqrt{1-y^2}]_{-1}^0 - \int_{-1}^0 (y \sin^{-1} y + \sqrt{1-y^2}) \, dy$

$= (0 - \sin^{-1}(-1)) - I - \int_{-1}^0 \sqrt{1-y^2} \, dy$. We cannot evaluate the last integral

by antidifferentiation yet. However, it is the area of a quarter circle of
radius one. (It's the area of the region in the 4th quadrant enclosed by
$x^2 + y^2 = 1$.) Thus its value is $\pi/4$, and, using $\sin^{-1}(-1) = -\pi/2$ and trans-
posing the I term, we obtain $2I = -(-\pi/2) - \pi/4 = \pi/4$, or $I = \pi/8$. Since the

value of $\int_{-1}^0 y \, dy$ is $-1/2$, we obtain: $F = -\rho(\pi/8) - (\pi\rho/2)(-1/2) =$

$(\pi\rho/4)(1-1/2) = \pi\rho/8$. The total force is thus $\pi\rho/4 = 62.5 \, \pi/4$.

EXERCISES 9.2, page 413

1. $\int \cos^3 x \, dx = \int \cos^2 x \cos x \, dx = \int (1 - \sin^2 x) \cos x \, dx = \int (1-u^2) \, du$ (with

$u = \sin x) = u - \dfrac{u^3}{3} + C = \sin x - \dfrac{\sin^3 x}{3} + C.$

4. $\int \cos^7 x \, dx = \int (1-\sin^2 x)^3 \cos x \, dx = \int (1-u^2)^3 du = \int (1 - 3u^2 + 3u^4 - u^6) du$

(with $u = \sin x) = u - u^3 + \dfrac{3}{5}u^5 - \dfrac{1}{7}u^7 + C = \sin x - \sin^3 x + \dfrac{3}{5}\sin^5 x -$

$\dfrac{1}{7}\sin^7 x + C.$

7. $\int \sin^6 x \, dx = \int [\dfrac{1}{2}(1 - \cos 2x)]^3 dx = \dfrac{1}{8}\int (1 - 3 \cos 2x + 3 \cos^2 2x - \cos^3 2x) \, dx$

$= \dfrac{1}{8}(A - B + C - D)$ where $A = \int 1 \, dx = x,$ $B = 3 \int \cos 2x \, dx = \dfrac{3}{2}\sin 2x,$

$C = 3 \int \cos^2 2x \, dx = \dfrac{3}{2}\int (1 + \cos 4x) dx = \dfrac{3}{2}(x + (\sin 4x)/4),$

$D = \int \cos^3 2x \, dx = \dfrac{1}{2}\int \cos^3 t \, dt$ (with $t = 2x) = \dfrac{1}{2}(\sin t - \dfrac{\sin^3 t}{3})$ (by Exercise 1)

$= \dfrac{1}{2}(\sin 2x - \dfrac{\sin^3 2x}{3}).$ Now combine these to obtain the answer in the text.

10. $\int \sec^6 x \, dx = \int \sec^4 x \sec^2 x \, dx = \int (1 + \tan^2 x)^2 \sec^2 x \, dx = \int (1 + u^2)^2 \, du = (u = \tan x)$

$\int (1 + 2u^2 + u^4) du = u + \dfrac{2}{3}u^3 + \dfrac{1}{5}u^5 + C = \tan x + \dfrac{2}{3}\tan^3 x + \dfrac{1}{5}\tan^5 x + C.$

11. $\int \tan^3 x \sec^3 x \, dx = \int \tan^2 x \sec^2 x \sec x \tan x \, dx = \int (\sec^2 x - 1)\sec^2 x \sec x \cdot$

$\tan x \, dx = \int (u^2-1)u^2 du = \dfrac{1}{5}u^5 - \dfrac{1}{3}u^3 + C$ $(u = \sec x) = \dfrac{1}{5}\sec^5 x - \dfrac{1}{3}\sec^3 x + C.$

13. $\int \tan^6 x \, dx = \int \dfrac{\tan^6 x}{\sec^2 x} \sec^2 x \, dx = \int \dfrac{\tan^6 x}{\tan^2 x + 1} \sec^2 x \, dx = \int \dfrac{u^6}{u^2+1} \, du$ $(u = \tan x)$

$= \int (u^4 - u^2 + 1 - \dfrac{1}{u^2+1}) du$ (by long division) $= \dfrac{1}{5}u^5 - \dfrac{1}{3}u^3 + u - \tan^{-1} u + C =$

$\dfrac{1}{5}\tan^5 x - \dfrac{1}{3}\tan^3 x + \tan x - x + C.$

16. $\int \dfrac{\cos^3 x}{\sqrt{\sin x}} \, dx = \int \sin^{-1/2} x(1-\sin^2 x) \cos x \, dx = \int (u^{-1/2} - u^{3/2}) du = 2u^{1/2} -$

$\dfrac{2}{5}u^{5/2} + C$ $(u = \sin x) = 2\sqrt{\sin x} - \dfrac{2}{5}\sqrt{\sin^5 x} + C.$

19. $\displaystyle\int_0^{\pi/4} \sin^3 x \, dx = \int_0^{\pi/4} (1-\cos^2 x)\sin x \, dx = -\cos x + \dfrac{1}{3}\cos^3 x \ \Big]_0^{\pi/4} =$

$(-1 + \dfrac{1}{6})/\sqrt{2} - (-\dfrac{2}{3}) = 2/3 - 5/6\sqrt{2}.$

22. By the product formula, $\cos x \cos 5x = \dfrac{1}{2}(\cos 4x + \cos 6x).$ So,

$$\int_0^{\pi/4} \cos x \cos 5x\, dx = \frac{1}{2}\int_0^{\pi/4} (\cos 4x + \cos 6x)dx = \frac{1}{2}[\frac{\sin 4x}{4} + \frac{\sin 6x}{6}]_0^{\pi/4}$$

$$= \frac{1}{2}[(0 - \frac{1}{6}) - (0-0)] = -1/12.$$

25. $\displaystyle\int \csc^4 x\, \cot^4 x\, dx = \int \csc^2 x\, \cot^4 x\, \csc^2 x\, dx = \int (1 + \cot^2 x)\cot^4 x\, \csc^2 x\, dx =$

$-\displaystyle\int (1 + u^2)u^4 du$ (u = cot x) $= -u^5/5 - u^7/7 + C = -(\cot^5 x)/5 - (\cot^7 x)/7 + C.$

28. $\cos x = 1/\sec x$, $\tan x = \sin x/\cos x \implies \dfrac{\tan^2 x - 1}{\sec^2 x} = \sin^2 x - \cos^2 x = -\cos 2x.$

Thus $\displaystyle\int \frac{\tan^2 - 1}{\sec^2 x}\, dx = -\int \cos 2x\, dx = -\frac{1}{2}\sin 2x + C = -\sin x \cos x + C.$

(Note that if tan x and sec x had been retained, we would have obtained:

$\displaystyle\int \frac{\tan^2 x - 1}{\sec^2 x}\, dx = \int \frac{\tan^2 x - 1}{\sec^4 x}\, \sec^2 x\, dx = \int \frac{(\tan^2 x - 1)\sec^2 x}{(\tan^2 x + 1)^2}\, dx = \int \frac{u^2 - 1}{(u^2 + 1)^2}\, du,$

an integral which we can not yet evaluate.)

31. $\displaystyle V = \pi\int_0^{2\pi} (\cos^2 x)^2 dx = \pi\int_0^{2\pi} (\frac{1+\cos 2x}{2})^2 dx = \frac{\pi}{4}\int_0^{2\pi} (1 + 2\cos 2x + \cos^2 2x)dx$

$\displaystyle = \frac{\pi}{4}\int_0^{2\pi} (1 + 2\cos 2x + (\frac{1 + \cos 4x}{2}))dx = \frac{\pi}{4}\int_0^{2\pi} (\frac{3}{2} + 2\cos 2x + \frac{\cos 4x}{4})dx$

$\displaystyle = \frac{\pi}{4}[\frac{3}{2}x + \sin 2x + \frac{\sin 4x}{8}]_0^{2\pi} = \frac{\pi}{4}\cdot\frac{3}{2}\cdot 2\pi = \frac{3\pi^2}{4}.$

34. $a(t) = \sin^2 t \cos t \implies v(t) = \frac{1}{3}\sin^3 t + C.$ Using v(0) = 10, we get C = 10.

$v(t) = \frac{1}{3}\sin^3 t + 10 \implies s(t) = -\frac{1}{3}\cos t + \frac{1}{9}\cos^3 t + 10t + D$ (using the result

of Exercise 19). Using s(0) = 0, we get $0 = -1/3 + 1/9 + D \implies D = 2/9.$

Thus $s(t) = \frac{1}{9}(-3\cos t + \cos^3 t + 90t + 2).$

EXERCISES 9.3, page 418

1. Let $x = 2\sin\theta$, $dx = 2\cos\theta\, d\theta$, $\sqrt{4-x^2} = 2\cos\theta$. $\displaystyle\int \frac{x^2}{\sqrt{4-x^2}}\, dx =$

$\displaystyle\int \frac{4\sin^2\theta\,(2\cos\theta)d\theta}{2\cos\theta} = 2\int (1 - \cos 2\theta)d\theta =$

$2(\theta - \frac{\sin 2\theta}{2}) + C = 2(\theta - \sin\theta\cos\theta) + C =$

$2(\sin^{-1}\frac{x}{2} - \frac{x}{2}\cdot\frac{\sqrt{4-x^2}}{2}) + C.$

4. Let $x = 3\tan\theta$, $dx = 3\sec^2\theta\, d\theta$, $\sqrt{x^2+9} = 3\sec\theta$. $\displaystyle\int \frac{dx}{x^2\sqrt{x^2+9}} =$

$$\int \frac{3\sec^2\theta\ d\theta}{9\tan^2\theta\ (3\sec\theta)} = \frac{1}{9}\int \frac{\sec\theta}{\tan^2\theta}\ d\theta = \frac{1}{9}\int \frac{(1/\cos\theta)}{(\sin\theta/\cos\theta)^2}\ d\theta =$$

$$\frac{1}{9}\int \frac{\cos\theta}{\sin^2\theta}\ d\theta = \frac{1}{9}\int \cot\theta\ \csc\theta\ d\theta =$$

$$-\frac{1}{9}\csc\theta + C = -\frac{\sqrt{x^2+9}}{9x} + C.$$

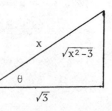

7. You could use $x = 2\sin\theta$, but the quickest way is the simpler substitution $u = 4-x^2$, $du = -2x\ dx$ so that $\int \frac{x}{\sqrt{4-x^2}}\ dx = -\frac{1}{2}\int u^{-1/2}\ du = -u^{1/2} + C = -\sqrt{4-x^2} + C.$

10. Noting that $\sqrt{4x^2-25} = 2\sqrt{x^2 - 25/4}$, we let $x = \frac{5}{2}\sec\theta$, $dx = \frac{5}{2}\sec\theta\tan\theta\ d\theta$,

$\sqrt{x^2 - 25/4} = \frac{5}{2}\tan\theta$. Then $\int \frac{dx}{\sqrt{4x^2-25}} = \frac{1}{2}\int \frac{dx}{\sqrt{x^2 - 25/4}} =$

$\frac{1}{2}\int \frac{\frac{5}{2}\sec\theta\tan\theta}{\frac{5}{2}\tan\theta}\ d\theta = \frac{1}{2}\int \sec\theta d\theta = \frac{1}{2}\ln|\sec\theta + \tan\theta| + C$

$= \frac{1}{2}\ln\left|\frac{2x}{5} + \frac{\sqrt{4x^2-25}}{5}\right| + C = \frac{1}{2}\ln|2x + \sqrt{4x^2-25}| + C',$

$C' = C - \frac{1}{2}\ln 5.$

13. Noting that $\sqrt{9-4x^2} = 2\sqrt{9/4 - x^2}$, we let $x = \frac{3}{2}\sin\theta$, $dx = \frac{3}{2}\cos\theta\ d\theta$,

$\sqrt{9/4 - x^2} = \frac{3}{2}\cos\theta$. $\int \sqrt{9-4x^2}\ dx = 2\int \sqrt{9/4 - x^2}\ dx =$

$2\int (\frac{3}{2}\cos\theta)(\frac{3}{2}\cos\theta)d\theta = \frac{9}{2}\int \cos^2\theta\ d\theta = \frac{9}{4}\int (1 + \cos 2\theta)d\theta$

$= \frac{9}{4}(\theta + \frac{\sin 2\theta}{2}) + C = \frac{9}{4}(\theta + \sin\theta\cos\theta) + C =$

$\frac{9}{4}(\sin^{-1}\frac{2x}{3} + (\frac{2x}{3})(\frac{\sqrt{9-4x^2}}{3})) + C.$

16. We could let $x = 3\sec\theta$, but the quickest way is to let $u = x^2-9$, $du = 2x\ dx$, and $\int x\sqrt{x^2-9}\ dx = \frac{1}{2}\int u^{1/2}\ du = \frac{1}{3}u^{3/2} + C = \frac{1}{3}(x^2-9)^{3/2} + C.$

19. Let $x = \sqrt{3}\sec\theta$, $dx = \sqrt{3}\sec\theta\tan\theta\ d\theta$, $\sqrt{x^2-3} = \sqrt{3}\tan\theta$. $\int \frac{1}{x^4\sqrt{x^2-3}}\ dx$

$= \int \frac{\sqrt{3}\sec\theta\tan\theta}{9\sec^4\theta(\sqrt{3}\tan\theta)}\ d\theta = \frac{1}{9}\int \frac{1}{\sec^3\theta}\ d\theta = \frac{1}{9}\int \cos^3\theta\ d\theta$

$= \frac{1}{9}\int (1 - \sin^2\theta)\cos\theta\ d\theta = \frac{1}{9}\int (1-u^2)du$ (with $u = $

$\sin\theta) = \frac{1}{9}(u - \frac{u^3}{3}) + C = \frac{1}{9}(\sin\theta - \frac{\sin^3\theta}{3}) + C$

$= \frac{\sin\theta}{27}(3 - \sin^2\theta) + C = \frac{\sqrt{x^2-3}}{27x}(3 - \frac{x^2-3}{x^2}) + C$

$= \frac{\sqrt{x^2-3}(2x^2+3)}{27x^3} + C.$

22.   Let $x = \sin\theta$, $dx = \cos\theta\,d\theta$, $\sqrt{1-x^2} = \cos\theta$. $\displaystyle\int \frac{3x-5}{\sqrt{1-x^2}}\,dx$

$= \displaystyle\int (3\sin\theta - 5)\,d\theta = -3\cos\theta - 5\theta + C = -3\sqrt{1-x^2} -$
$5 \sin^{-1}x + C$.

25.   This is a special case of #28 with $a = 1$.

28.   Let $u = a\sec\theta$, $du = a\sec\theta\tan\theta\,d\theta$, $\sqrt{u^2-a^2} = a\tan\theta$. Then $\displaystyle\int \frac{1}{u\sqrt{u^2-a^2}}\,du$

$= \dfrac{1}{a}\displaystyle\int d\theta = \dfrac{1}{a}\theta + C = \dfrac{1}{a}\sec^{-1}\dfrac{u}{a} + C$.

31. $L_0^2 = \displaystyle\int_0^2 \sqrt{1+y'^2}\,dx = \int_0^2 \sqrt{1+x^2}\,dx$. Let $x = \tan\theta$, $dx = \sec^2\theta\,d\theta$, $\sqrt{1+x^2} = \sec\theta$.

Then $\displaystyle\int \sqrt{1+x^2}\,dx = \int \sec^3\theta\,d\theta = \dfrac{1}{2}(\sec\theta\tan\theta +$

$\ln|\sec\theta + \tan\theta|\,) + C$ by Exercise 21, Sec. 9.1.

Thus $L_0^2 = \dfrac{1}{2}[x\sqrt{x^2+1} + \ln|\sqrt{x^2+1} + x|\,]\Big|_0^2 =$

$\dfrac{1}{2}[2\sqrt{5} + \ln|\sqrt{5} + 2| - 0] \approx 2.46$.

34.   The graph is an ellipse, and by symmetry we can double the area of the upper
half. $4x^2 + y^2 = 16 \Longrightarrow y = 2\sqrt{4-x^2}$, $-2 \le x \le 2$ is the upper boundary.

$A = 2\displaystyle\int_{-2}^2 2\sqrt{4-x^2}\,dx$. Let $x = 2\sin\theta$, $dx = 2\cos\theta\,d\theta$, $\sqrt{4-x^2} = 2\cos\theta$.

Since $\theta = \sin^{-1}(x/2)$, $x = \pm 2 \Longrightarrow \theta = \pm\,\pi/2$. Thus $A = 16\displaystyle\int_{-\pi/2}^{\pi/2} \cos^2\theta\,d\theta =$

$8\displaystyle\int_{-\pi/2}^{\pi/2}(1 + \cos 2\theta)\,d\theta = 8[\theta + \dfrac{\sin 2\theta}{2}]\Big|_{-\pi/2}^{\pi/2} = 8\pi$.

37.   The one identity to remember is $\cosh^2 u = 1 + \sinh^2 u$. Let $x = 5\sinh u$, $dx =$
$5\cosh u$, $\sqrt{25+x^2} = \sqrt{25(1 + \sinh^2 u)} = 5\cosh u$. Then $\displaystyle\int \frac{1}{x^2\sqrt{25+x^2}}\,dx =$

$\displaystyle\int \frac{5\cosh u}{25\sinh^2 u(5\cosh u)}\,du = \frac{1}{25}\int \frac{1}{\sinh^2 u}\,du = \frac{1}{25}\int \operatorname{csch}^2 u\,du = -\frac{1}{25}\coth u + C$

$= -\dfrac{1}{25}\dfrac{\cosh u}{\sinh u} + C = -\dfrac{1}{25}\dfrac{\sqrt{1 + \sinh^2 u}}{\sinh u} + C = -\dfrac{1}{25}\dfrac{\sqrt{1 + x^2/25}}{x/5} + C = -\dfrac{1}{25}\dfrac{\sqrt{25+x^2}}{x} + C$.

40.   Let $x = 4\tanh u$, $dx = 4\operatorname{sech}^2 u\,du$, $16-x^2 = 16(1 - \tanh^2 u) = 16\operatorname{sech}^2 u$.

$\displaystyle\int \frac{1}{16-x^2}\,dx = \int \frac{4\operatorname{sech}^2 u}{16\operatorname{sech}^2 u}\,du = \frac{1}{4}\int du = \frac{1}{4}u + C = \frac{1}{4}\tanh^{-1}\frac{x}{4} + C$.

43. $u = a \sin\theta$, $du = a\cos\theta$, $\sqrt{a^2-u^2} = a\cos\theta \Rightarrow I = \int u^2\sqrt{a^2-u^2}\,du =$

$a^4\int \sin^2\theta\,\cos^2\theta\,d\theta = a^4\int (\frac{1-\cos 2\theta}{2})(\frac{1+\cos 2\theta}{2})d\theta = \frac{a^4}{4}\int (1-\cos^2 2\theta)d\theta =$

$\frac{a^4}{4}\int (1 - \frac{1+\cos 4\theta}{2})d\theta = \frac{a^4}{8}\int (1 - \cos 4\theta)d\theta =$

$\frac{a^4}{8}(\theta - \frac{\sin 4\theta}{4}) + C$. Now, $\sin 4\theta = 2\sin 2\theta \cos 2\theta$

$= 4\sin\theta \cos\theta(\cos^2\theta - \sin^2\theta)$. Since $\theta =$

$\sin^{-1}(u/a)$, $\sin\theta = u/a$ and $\cos\theta = \sqrt{a^2-u^2}/a$.

Combining results, $I = \frac{a^4}{8}(\theta - \frac{u}{a}\frac{\sqrt{a^2-u^2}}{a}(\frac{a^2-u^2}{a^2} - \frac{u^2}{a^2}) + C$

which easily reduces to the formula.

46. $u = a\sec\theta$, $du = a\sec\theta\tan\theta\,d\theta$, $\sqrt{u^2-a^2} = a\tan\theta$

$\Rightarrow I = \int \frac{u^2}{\sqrt{u^2-a^2}}\,du = a^2\int \frac{\sec^2\theta \cdot \sec\theta\tan\theta}{\tan\theta}\,d\theta =$

$a^2\int \sec^3\theta\,d\theta$. By #21, Sec. 9.1, $I =$

$\frac{a^2}{2}(\sec\theta\tan\theta + \ln|\sec\theta + \tan\theta|) + C' =$

$\frac{a^2}{2}(\frac{u}{a}\cdot\frac{\sqrt{u^2-a^2}}{a} + \ln|\frac{u}{a} + \frac{\sqrt{u^2-a^2}}{a}|) + C' =$

$\frac{u}{2}\sqrt{u^2-a^2} + \frac{a^2}{2}\ln|u + \sqrt{u^2-a^2}| - \frac{a^2}{2}\ln|a| + C'$

which is equivalent to Formula 44 with

$C = c' - \frac{a^2}{2}\ln|a|$.

EXERCISES 9.4, page 424

1. $\frac{5x-12}{x(x-4)} = \frac{A}{x} + \frac{B}{x-4}$. Multiplying by $x(x-4)$, we get $5x-12 = A(x-4) + Bx$. Letting $x = 4$ we find that $20-12 = A(0) + 4B$, or $8 = 4B$, or $B = 2$. Letting $x = 0$, we get $-12 = -4A$, or $A = 3$. Thus $\int \frac{5x-12}{x(x-4)}\,dx = \int (\frac{3}{x} + \frac{2}{x-4})dx = 3\ln|x| + 2\ln|x-4| + C = \ln|x|^3 + \ln|x-4|^2 + C = \ln|x|^3|x-4|^2 + C$.

4. $\frac{4x^2 +54x+134}{(x-1)(x+5)(x+3)} = \frac{A}{x-1} + \frac{B}{x+5} + \frac{C}{x+3}$. Multiplying by $(x-1)(x+5)(x+3)$, we get $4x^2+54x+134 = A(x+5)(x+3) + B(x-1)(x+3) + C(x-1)(x+5)$.

     Set $x = 1$ to obtain $192 = 24A$,   or $A = 8$.

     Set $x = -5$ to obtain $-36 = 12B$,   or $B = -3$.

     Set $x = -3$ to obtain $8 = -8C$,   or $C = -1$.

$$\int \frac{4x^2+54x+134}{(x-1)(x+5)(x+3)} \, dx = \int \left(\frac{8}{x-1} - \frac{3}{x+5} - \frac{1}{x+3}\right) dx = 8 \ln|x-1| - 3 \ln|x+5| - \ln|x+3|$$

$+ C$, or $\ln \dfrac{|x-1|^8}{|x+5|^3|x+3|} + C$ where now C is the usual arbitrary constant.

7. $\dfrac{x+16}{x^2+2x-8} = \dfrac{x+16}{(x+4)(x-2)} = \dfrac{A}{x+4} + \dfrac{B}{x-2}$. Multiplying by $(x+4)(x-2)$ we get $x+16 =$

$A(x-2) + B(x+4)$, and letting $x = 2$ we find $18 = 6B$ or $B = 3$, and letting $x =$

-4, we find $12 = -6A$ or $A = -2$. Thus $\displaystyle\int \frac{x+16}{x^2+2x-8} \, dx = \int \left(\frac{-2}{x+4} + \frac{3}{x-2}\right) dx =$

$-2 \ln|x+4| + 3 \ln|x-2| + C.$

10. $\dfrac{4x^2-5x-15}{x^3-4x^2-5x} = \dfrac{4x^2-5x-15}{x(x-5)(x+1)} = \dfrac{A}{x} + \dfrac{B}{x-5} + \dfrac{C}{x+1}$. $4x^2-5x-15 = A(x-5)(x+1) + Bx(x+1) +$

$Cx(x-5).$

      Set $x = 0$ to obtain $-15 = -5A$ or $A = 3$.

      Set $x = -1$ to obtain $-6 = 6C$ or $C = -1$.

      Set $x = 5$ to obtain $60 = 30B$ or $B = 2$.

$$\int \frac{4x^2-5x-15}{x^3-4x^2-5x} \, dx = \int \left(\frac{3}{x} + \frac{2}{x-5} - \frac{1}{x+3}\right) dx = 3 \ln|x| + 2 \ln|x-5| - \ln|x+3| + C =$$

$\ln \dfrac{|x|^3|x-5|^2}{|x+1|} + C$ where now C is arbitrary.

13. The integrand is $\dfrac{9x^4+17x^3+3x^2-8x+3}{x^4(x+3)} = \dfrac{A}{x} + \dfrac{B}{x^2} + \dfrac{C}{x^3} + \dfrac{D}{x^4} + \dfrac{E}{x+3}$.

$9x^4 + 17x^3 + 3x^2 - 8x + 3 = Ax^3(x+3) + Bx^2(x+3) + Cx(x+3) + D(x+3) + Ex^4$

Set $x = 0$ to obtain $3 = 3D$ or $D = 1$.

Set $x = -3$ to obtain $324 = 81E$ or $E = 4$.

To obtain the other constants, we set the coefficients of like powers of x

equal to each other:

      x^4: $9 = A + E = A + 4$,   or $A = 5$

      x^3: $17 = 3A + B = 15 + B$,   or $B = 2$

      x^2: $3 = 3B + C = 6 + C$,   or $C = -3$.

$$\int \frac{9x^4 + 17x^3 + 3x^2 - 8x + 3}{x^4(x+3)} \, dx = \int \left(\frac{5}{x} + \frac{2}{x^2} - \frac{3}{x^3} + \frac{1}{x^4} + \frac{4}{x+3}\right) dx =$$

$5 \ln|x| - \dfrac{2}{x} + \dfrac{3}{2x^2} - \dfrac{1}{3x^3} + 4 \ln|x+3| + C.$

16. With $u = x-7$, $\displaystyle\int \frac{1}{(x-7)^5} \, dx = \int u^{-5} du = \frac{u^{-4}}{-4} + C = -1/4(x-7)^4 + C.$

19. $\dfrac{x^2+3x+1}{x^4+5x^2+4} = \dfrac{x^2+3x+1}{(x^2+4)(x^2+1)} = \dfrac{Ax+B}{x^2+4} + \dfrac{Cx+D}{x^2+1}$

$x^2+3x+1 = (Ax+B)(x^2+1) + (Cx+D)(x^2+4) = (A+C)x^3 + (B+D)x^2 + (A+4C)x + (B+4D)$

Equating coefficients of like powers of x, we obtain

$$x^3:\ \ 0 = A \qquad + C$$

$$x^2:\ \ 1 = \qquad B \qquad + D$$

$$x^1:\ \ 3 = A \qquad +4C$$

$$x^0:\ \ 1 = \qquad B \qquad +4D$$

Taking the 1st and 3rd, we get A = -1, C = 1, and from the 2nd and 4th, we get B = 1, D = 0. The integral of the original function reduces to

$$\int \left(\frac{-x}{x^2+4} + \frac{1}{x^2+4} + \frac{x}{x^2+1}\right)dx = -\frac{1}{2}\ln(x^2+4) + \frac{1}{2}\tan^{-1}\left(\frac{x}{2}\right) + \frac{1}{2}\ln(x^2+1) + C.$$

22. $\dfrac{x^4 + 2x^2 + 4x + 1}{(x^2+1)^3} = \dfrac{Ax+B}{x^2+1} + \dfrac{Cx+D}{(x^2+1)^2} + \dfrac{Ex+F}{(x^2+1)^3}$

$x^4+2x^2+4x+1 = (Ax+B)(x^2+1)^2 + (Cx+D)(x^2+1) + Ex + F$

$= Ax^5 + Bx^4 + (2A+C)x^3 + (2B+D)x^2 + (A+C+E)x + (B+D+F).$

Equating coefficients as above:

$$x^5:\ \ 0 = A \qquad\qquad x^4:\ \ 1 = B$$

$$x^3:\ \ 0 = 2A + C \qquad\qquad x^2:\ \ 2 = 2B + D$$

$$x^1:\ \ 4 = A + C + E \qquad\qquad x^0:\ \ 1 = B + D + F$$

yielding A = C = D = F = 0, B = 1, E = 4. The integral reduces to

$$\int \left[\frac{1}{x^2+1} + \frac{4x}{(x^2+1)^3}\right]dx = \tan^{-1}x - \frac{1}{(x^2+1)^2} + C.$$

25. By long division $\dfrac{x^6-x^3+1}{x^4+9x^2} = x^2 - 9 + \dfrac{-x^3+81x^2+1}{x^4 + 9x^2} \cdot \dfrac{-x^3+81x^2+1}{x^4+ 9x^2} = \dfrac{-x^3+81x^2+1}{x^2(x^2+9)} =$

$\dfrac{A}{x} + \dfrac{B}{x^2} + \dfrac{Cx+D}{x^2+9}$.

$-x^3+81x^2+1 = Ax(x^2+9) + B(x^2+9) + (Cx+D)x^2 = (A+C)x^3 + (B+D)x^2 + 9Ax + 9B.$

From x^0 and x^1 we get immediately A = 0, B = 1/9. From x^3, -1 = A+C = C;

from x^2, $81 = \frac{1}{9} + D$, or $D = 81 - \frac{1}{9} = \frac{728}{9}$. The integral reduces to

$$\int \left(x^2 - 9 + \frac{1}{9x^2} - \frac{x}{x^2+9} + \frac{728}{9}\cdot\frac{1}{x^2+9}\right)dx = \frac{x^3}{3} - 9x - \frac{1}{9x} - \frac{1}{2}\ln(x^2+9)+\frac{728}{27}\tan^{-1}\frac{x}{3}+C.$$

28. $\dfrac{-2x^4-3x^3-3x^2+3x+1}{x^2(x+1)^3} = \dfrac{A}{x} + \dfrac{B}{x^2} + \dfrac{C}{x+1} + \dfrac{D}{(x+1)^2} + \dfrac{E}{(x+1)^3}$.

$-2x^4 - 3x^3 - 3x^2 + 3x + 1 = Ax(x+1)^3 + B(x+1)^3 + Cx^2(x+1)^2 + Dx^2(x+1) + Ex^2.$

Set x = 0 to get 1 = B, and set x = -1 to get -4 = E. To obtain the remaining constants, equate coefficients of three powers of x.

$$x^4:\ \ -2 = A \qquad + C$$

$$x^2:\ \ -3 = 3A + 3B + C + D + E$$

$$x :\ \ 3 = A + 3B \qquad\qquad = A + 3 \Rightarrow A = 0$$

Using A = 0 in the first equation, we get C = -2. Using these in the second equation, we get -3 = 0 + 3 - 2 + D - 4, or D = 0. Thus the given integral reduces to $\int \left(\frac{1}{x^2} - \frac{2}{x+1} - \frac{4}{(x+1)^3}\right)dx = -\frac{1}{x} - 2\ln|x+1| + \frac{2}{(x+1)^2} + C.$

31. Note that $x^3-x^2+x-1 = x^2(x-1) + (x-1) = (x-1)(x^2+1)$, and, by long division, the integrand can be written as $2x + (4x^2-3x+1)/(x-1)(x^2+1)$.

$\dfrac{4x^2-3x+1}{(x-1)(x^2+1)} = \dfrac{A}{x-1} + \dfrac{Bx+C}{x^2+1}$. $4x^2-3x+1 = A(x^2+1) + (Bx+C)(x-1)$.

Set $x = 1$ to obtain $2 = 2A$, or $A = 1$, and set $x = 0$ to obtain $1 = A-C = 1-C$. Thus $C = 0$. For the third constant we could equate some coefficient or simply pick another value of x. Let's set $x = -1$ to obtain $8 = 2A + 2B - 2C = 2 +$ $2B$, or $B = 3$. Thus the original integral reduces to $\displaystyle\int (2x + \dfrac{1}{x-1} + \dfrac{3x}{x^2+1})\,dx =$ $x^2 + \ln|x-1| + \dfrac{3}{2}\ln(x^2+1) + C.$

34. $1/u(a + bu) = A/u + B/(a + bu) \implies 1 = A(a + bu) + Bu$. Set $u = 0$ to obtain $1 = Aa$, or $A = 1/a$. Set $u = -a/b$ to obtain $1 = -Ba/b$, or $B = -b/a$. Thus $\displaystyle\int \dfrac{1}{u(a+bu)}\,du = \int (\dfrac{1/a}{u} - \dfrac{b/a}{a+bu})\,du = (1/a)(\ln|u| - \ln|a+bu|) + C = \dfrac{1}{a}\ln\left|\dfrac{u}{a+bu}\right| + C.$

37. $f(x) = x/(x^2-2x-3) = x/(x-3)(x+1)$. Since $x-3 < 0$, $x \geq 0$, and $(x+1) > 0$ on $[0,2]$, it follows that $f(x) \leq 0$ there. Thus, by (6.2), $A = -\displaystyle\int_0^2 f(x)\,dx$.

Now, $f(x) = \dfrac{x}{(x-3)(x+1)} = \dfrac{A}{x-3} + \dfrac{B}{x+1} \implies x = A(x+1) + B(x-3)$. Setting $x = 3$ and -1, we obtain $3 = 4A$, or $A = 3/4$, and $-1 = -4B$, or $B = 1/4$. Thus $A =$

$-\displaystyle\int_0^2 (\dfrac{3/4}{x-3} + \dfrac{1/4}{x+1})\,dx = -[\dfrac{3}{4}\ln|x-3| + \dfrac{1}{4}\ln|x+1|]_0^2 = -\dfrac{1}{4}[(3\ln|-1| + \ln 3) -$ $(3\ln|-3| + \ln 1)] = -\dfrac{1}{4}(0 + \ln 3 - 3\ln 3 + 0) = \dfrac{2\ln 3}{4}$.

40. The distance travelled in the time interval $[1,2]$ is $s(2) - s(1) = \displaystyle\int_1^2 v(t)\,dt$ $= \displaystyle\int_1^2 (t+3)/(t^3+t)\,dt$. Now, $\dfrac{t+3}{t^3+t} = \dfrac{t+3}{t(t^2+1)} = \dfrac{A}{t} + \dfrac{Bt+C}{t^2+1} \implies t+3 = A(t^2+1) +$

$(Bt+C)t$ or $t+3 = (A+B)t^2 + Ct + A$. Thus $A = 3$, $C = 1$ and $A+B = 0$, or $B =$ $-A = -3$. Thus $s(2) - s(1) = \displaystyle\int_1^2 (\dfrac{3}{t} - \dfrac{3t}{t^2+1} + \dfrac{1}{t^2+1})\,dt = 3\ln|t|]_1^2 - \dfrac{3}{2}\ln(t^2+1)]_1^2 +$ $\tan^{-1}t]_1^2 = 3\ln 2 - (\dfrac{3}{2}\ln 5 - \dfrac{3}{2}\ln 2) + \tan^{-1}2 - \tan^{-1}1 = (9/2)\ln 2 -$ $(3/2)\ln 5 + \tan^{-1}2 - \pi/4 \approx 1.027.$

EXERCISES 9.5, page 428

1. $x^2-4x+8 = (x-2)^2 + 4$. So, with $u = x-2$, $du = dx$, $\displaystyle\int \frac{dx}{x^2-4x+8} = \int \frac{dx}{(x-2)^2+4}$

$= \displaystyle\int \frac{du}{u^2+4} = \frac{1}{2}\tan^{-1}\frac{u}{2} + C = \frac{1}{2}\tan^{-1}\frac{x-2}{2} + C$. Alternately, after completing the

square, we could have let $x-2 = 2\tan\theta$, $dx = 2\sec^2\theta\, d\theta$ and $(x-2)^2 + 4 = 4\sec^2\theta$. Note also that $\tan\theta = (x-2)/2 \Rightarrow \theta = \tan^{-1}((x-2)/2)$. The integral

then becomes $\displaystyle\int \frac{2\sec^2\theta}{4\sec^2\theta} d\theta = \frac{1}{2}\int d\theta = \frac{1}{2}\theta + C = \frac{1}{2}\tan^{-1}\frac{x-2}{2} + C$ as before. Both

methods are equivalent. Use whichever you prefer.

2. $7 + 6x - x^2 = 16 - (x-3)^2$. So, with $u = x-3$, $du = dx$. $\displaystyle\int \frac{dx}{\sqrt{7+6x-x^2}} = \int \frac{du}{\sqrt{16-u^2}}$

$= \sin^{-1}\frac{u}{4} + C = \sin^{-1}\frac{x-3}{4} + C$.

4. Proceed as in #1 using $x^2-2x+2 = (x-1)^2 + 1$ to get $\tan^{-1}(x-1) + C$.

7. $(x^3-1) = (x-1)(x^2+x+1) = (x-1)[(x + \frac{1}{2})^2 + \frac{3}{4}]$. Let $u = x + \frac{1}{2}$ so that $x-1 =$

$u - \frac{3}{2}$ and $\displaystyle\frac{1}{x^3-1} = \frac{1}{(u - \frac{3}{2})(u^2+\frac{3}{4})} = \frac{A}{u - \frac{3}{2}} + \frac{Bu+C}{u^2+\frac{3}{4}}$. As in the previous section,

this yields $1 = A(u^2 + \frac{3}{4}) + (Bu + C)(u - \frac{3}{2})$.

Set $u = 3/2$ to obtain $1 = 3A$ or $A = 1/3$.

Set $u = 0$ to obtain $1 = \frac{3}{4}A - \frac{3}{2}C$ or $C = -1/2$.

Equate u^2 coefficients: $0 = A+B$, or $B = -1/3$. Now we can finally tie this

all together:

$\displaystyle\int \frac{1}{x^3-1} dx = \int [\frac{1/3}{u - 3/2} - \frac{1/3\, u}{u^2 + 3/4} - \frac{1/2}{u^2 + 3/4}] du = \frac{1}{3}\ln|u - \frac{3}{2}| - \frac{1}{6}\ln(u^2+\frac{3}{4})$

$- \frac{1}{\sqrt{3}}\tan^{-1}\frac{2u}{\sqrt{3}} + C = \frac{1}{3}\ln|x-1| - \frac{1}{6}\ln(x^2+x+1) - \frac{1}{\sqrt{3}}\tan^{-1}\frac{2x+1}{\sqrt{3}} + C$.

10. $x^4 - 4x^3 + 13x^2 = x^2(x^2-4x+13) = x^2[(x-2)^2 + 9]$. Let $u = x-2$ so that $x = u+2$ and $\displaystyle\frac{1}{x^4-4x^3+13x^2} = \frac{1}{(u+2)^2(u^2+9)} = \frac{A}{u+2} + \frac{B}{(u+2)^2} + \frac{Cu+D}{u^2+9}$. Proceeding as in

the previous section, the solution is $A = 4/169$, $B = 1/13$, $C = -4/169$,

$D = -5/169$, and $\displaystyle\int \frac{1}{x^4-4x^3+13x^2} dx = \frac{4}{169}\ln|u+2| - \frac{1}{13}\cdot\frac{1}{u+2} - \frac{2}{169}\ln(u^2+9)$

$- \frac{5}{3(169)}\tan^{-1}\frac{u}{3} + C = \frac{4}{169}\ln|x| - \frac{1}{13x} - \frac{2}{169}\ln(x^2-4x+13) - \frac{5}{507}\tan^{-1}\frac{x-2}{3} + C$.

13. $2x^2 - 3x + 9 = 2(x^2 - \frac{3}{2}x + \frac{9}{16} + (\frac{9}{2} - \frac{9}{16})) = 2((x-3/4)^2 + 63/16)$. So, with

$u = x - \frac{3}{4}$, $\displaystyle\int \frac{1}{2x^2-3x+9} dx = \frac{1}{2}\int \frac{1}{(x-3/4)^2+63/16} dx = \frac{1}{2}\int \frac{1}{u^2+(3\sqrt{7}/4)^2} du =$

$\frac{1}{2}\cdot\frac{4}{3\sqrt{7}}\tan^{-1}\frac{4u}{3\sqrt{7}} + C = \frac{2}{3\sqrt{7}}\tan^{-1}\frac{4(x-3/4)}{3\sqrt{7}} + C = \frac{2}{3\sqrt{7}}\tan^{-1}\frac{(4x-3)}{3\sqrt{7}} + C$.

16. By the quadratic formula, $2x^2 + 3x - 4$ has roots $a = (-3 + \sqrt{41})/4$ and $b = (-3 - \sqrt{41})/4$. Thus $2x^2 + 3x - 4 = 2(x-a)(x-b)$. As in the previous section $f(x) = \dfrac{x}{2x^2 + 3x - 4} = \dfrac{x}{2(x-a)(x-b)} = \dfrac{A}{x-a} + \dfrac{B}{x-b}$ where $A = \dfrac{a}{2(a-b)}$, $B = -\dfrac{b}{2(a-b)}$. Thus $f(x) = \dfrac{1}{2(a-b)}(\dfrac{a}{x-a} - \dfrac{b}{x-b})$ and $\int f(x)dx =$

$\dfrac{1}{2(a-b)}(a \ln|x-a| - b \ln|x-b|)$, which may be written in many equivalent forms. (Note $2(a-b) = \sqrt{41}$).

19. $A = \displaystyle\int_0^1 \dfrac{1}{x^3+1}\, dx$. An antiderivative of $1/(x^3+1)$ is found in a manner similar to that of problem 7 of this section using $x^3+1 = (x+1)(x^2-x+1) = (x+1)((x-1/2)^2 + 3/4)$. $u = x - 1/2$, $x + 1 = u + 3/2$. In this case, an antiderivative is $F(x) = (1/3)\ln|u+3/2| - (1/6)\ln|u^2+3/4| + (1/\sqrt{3})\tan^{-1}(2u/\sqrt{3})$

$= (1/3)\ln|x+1| - (1/6)\ln(x^2-x+1) + (1/\sqrt{3})\tan^{-1}\dfrac{(2x-1)}{\sqrt{3}}$. Then $A = F(1) - F(0)$

$= [(1/3)\ln 2 - (1/6)\ln 1 + (1/\sqrt{3})\tan^{-1}(1/\sqrt{3})]$

$- [(1/3)\ln 1 - (1/6)\ln 1 + (1/\sqrt{3})\tan^{-1}(-1/\sqrt{3})]$. Using $\tan^{-1}/(\pm 1/\sqrt{3}) = (\pm\pi/6)$, we have $A = (1/3)\ln 2 + (2/\sqrt{3})(\pi/6) \approx 0.83565$.

22. $s(5) - s(0) = \displaystyle\int_0^5 v(t)dt = \int_0^5 \dfrac{1}{\sqrt{75 + 10t - t^2}}\, dt$. Now, $75 + 10t - t^2 = 100 - (t-5)^2$, so with $u = t-5$, $du = dt$. $t = 0, 5 \Rightarrow u = -5,0$, and $s(5) - s(0) = \displaystyle\int_{-5}^0 \dfrac{1}{\sqrt{100-u^2}}\, du = \sin^{-1}(u/10)]_{-5}^0 = \sin^{-1}0 - \sin^{-1}(-1/2) = 0 - (-\pi/6) = \pi/6$.

EXERCISES 9.6, page 432

1. Let $u = \sqrt[3]{x+9}$. Then $u^3 = x+9$, $x = u^3-9$, $dx = 3\,u^2 du$. $\displaystyle\int x\sqrt[3]{x+9}\, dx = \int (u^3-9)u(3u^2)du = 3\int (u^6-9u^3)du = 3(\dfrac{u^7}{7} - \dfrac{9}{4}u^4) + C$, where $u = (x+9)^{1/3}$.

4. Let $u = (x+3)^{1/3}$. Then $u^3 = x+3$, $x = u^3-3$, $dx = 3\,u^2 du$. $\displaystyle\int \dfrac{5x}{(x+3)^{2/3}}\, dx$

$= 5\displaystyle\int \dfrac{(u^3-3)(3u^2)}{u^2}\, du = 15\int (u^3-3)du = 15(\dfrac{u^4}{4} - 3u) + C$

$= 15(\dfrac{(x+3)^{4/3}}{4} - 3(x+3)^{1/3}) + C.$

7. As in Example 2, let $x = u^6$. Then $dx = 6u^5 du$, $\sqrt{x} = u^3$, $\sqrt[3]{x} = u^2$. $\displaystyle\int \dfrac{\sqrt{x}}{1+\sqrt[3]{x}}\, dx$

$= \displaystyle\int \dfrac{u^3(6u^5)}{1+u^2}\, du = 6\int \dfrac{u^8}{1+u^2}\, du = 6\int (u^6-u^4+u^2-1+\dfrac{1}{1+u^2})du$ (by long division) $=$

$6[\dfrac{u^7}{7} - \dfrac{u^5}{5} + \dfrac{u^3}{3} - u + \tan^{-1}u] + C = 6[\dfrac{x^{7/6}}{7} - \dfrac{x^{5/6}}{5} + \dfrac{x^{1/2}}{3} - x^{1/6} + \tan^{-1}(x^{1/6})]+C.$

10. Let $u = \sqrt{1+2x}$. Then $u^2 = 1+2x$, $2u\,du = 2\,dx$ or $dx = u\,du$, and $2x+3 =$

$(u^2-1) + 3 = u^2+2$. $x = 0,4 \Rightarrow u = 1,3$. Thus $\displaystyle\int_0^4 \dfrac{2x+3}{\sqrt{1+2x}}\,dx = \int_1^3 \dfrac{(u^2+2)u}{u}\,du$

$= \dfrac{u^3}{3} + 2u\Big]_1^3 = 15 - \dfrac{7}{3} = \dfrac{38}{3}.$

13. Let $u = 1 + e^x$. Then $du = e^x dx$, $e^x = u-1$, and $e^{2x} = (u-1)^2$. $\displaystyle\int e^{3x}\sqrt{e^x+1}\,dx$

$= \displaystyle\int e^{2x}\sqrt{e^x+1}\,e^x dx = \int (u-1)^2\,u^{1/2}\,du = \int (u^2-2u+1)u^{1/2}\,du =$

$\displaystyle\int (u^{5/2} - 2u^{3/2} + u^{1/2})du = \dfrac{2}{7}u^{7/2} - \dfrac{4}{5}u^{5/2} + \dfrac{2}{3}u^{3/2} + C$, where $u = (1+e^x)$.

16. $\displaystyle\int \dfrac{\sin 2x}{\sqrt{1+\sin x}}\,dx = 2\int \dfrac{\sin x \cos x}{\sqrt{1+\sin x}}\,dx.$ Let $u = 1+\sin x$. Then $du = \cos x\,dx$,

$\sin x = u-1$, and the integral becomes $2\displaystyle\int \dfrac{u-1}{u^{1/2}}\,du = 2\int (u^{1/2} - u^{-1/2})du =$

$2(\dfrac{2}{3}u^{3/2} - 2u^{1/2}) + C = 4(\dfrac{(1+\sin x)^{3/2}}{3}) - (1+\sin x)^{1/2}) + C.$

19. Let $u = x-1$, $du = dx$, $x = u+1$. $x = 2,3 \Rightarrow u = 1,2$. Thus $\displaystyle\int_2^3 \dfrac{x}{(x-1)^6}\,dx =$

$\displaystyle\int_1^2 \dfrac{u+1}{u^6}\,du = \int_1^2 (u^{-5}+u^{-6})du = \dfrac{u^{-4}}{-4} + \dfrac{u^{-5}}{-5}\Big]_1^2 = -\dfrac{1}{64} - \dfrac{1}{160} + \dfrac{1}{4} + \dfrac{1}{5} = \dfrac{-5-2+80+64}{320} = \dfrac{137}{320}.$

22. Using $z = \tan(x/2)$, $\cos x = (1-z^2)/(1+z^2)$, $dx = \dfrac{2}{1+z^2}\,dz$, $\displaystyle\int \dfrac{1}{3 + 2\cos x}\,dx$

$= \displaystyle\int \dfrac{2/(1+z^2)}{3 + \dfrac{2(1-z^2)}{1+z^2}}\,dz = \int \dfrac{2\,dz}{[3(1+z^2) + 2(1-z^2)]} = 2\int \dfrac{dz}{5+z^2} = \dfrac{2}{\sqrt{5}}\tan^{-1}\dfrac{z}{\sqrt{5}} + C.$

$= \dfrac{2}{\sqrt{5}}\tan^{-1}(\dfrac{\tan(x/2)}{\sqrt{5}}) + C.$

25. $I = \displaystyle\int \dfrac{\sec x}{4 - 3\tan x}\,dx = \int \dfrac{1/\cos x}{4 - 3\sin x/\cos x}\,dx = \int \dfrac{1}{4\cos x - 3\sin x}\,dx.$

As above, let $z = \tan x/2$, etc. $I = \displaystyle\int \dfrac{1}{4(\dfrac{1-z^2}{1+z^2}) - 3(\dfrac{2z}{1+z^2})} \cdot \dfrac{2}{1+z^2}\,dz$

$= \displaystyle\int \dfrac{2}{4(1-z^2) - 6z}\,dz = \int \dfrac{-1}{2z^2+3z-2}\,dz.$ Now, as in Section 10.4, $\dfrac{-1}{2z^2+3z-2} =$

$\dfrac{-1}{(2z-1)(z+2)} = \dfrac{A}{2z-1} + \dfrac{B}{z+2} \Rightarrow -1 = A(z+2) + B(2z-1).$ Setting $z = -2$ and $1/2$

we get $-1 = -5B$, or $B = 1/5$, and $-1 = (5/2)A$, or $A = -2/5$. Thus $I =$

$\displaystyle\int (\dfrac{-2/5}{2z-1} + \dfrac{1/5}{z+1})dz = -\dfrac{1}{5}\ln|2z-1| + \dfrac{1}{5}\ln|z+1| + C = -\dfrac{1}{5}\ln|2\tan\dfrac{x}{2} - 1| +$

$\dfrac{1}{5}\ln|\tan\dfrac{x}{2} + 1| + C.$

28. With $u = \cos x$, $du = -\sin x$, $I = \int \dfrac{\sin x}{5 \cos x + \cos^2 x} \, dx = -\int \dfrac{du}{5u + u^2}$. Now,

$\dfrac{1}{5u + u^2} = \dfrac{1}{u(5+u)} = \dfrac{A}{u} + \dfrac{B}{5+u} \implies 1 = A(5+u) + Bu$. Setting $u = 0$ and -5, we

obtain $1 = 5A$, or $A = 1/5$, and $1 = -5B$, or $B = -1/5$. Thus $I = -\int \dfrac{1}{5} \left(\dfrac{1}{u} - \dfrac{1}{5+u} \right) du$

$= \dfrac{1}{5} (\ln|5+u| - \ln|u|) + C = \dfrac{1}{5} \ln \left| \dfrac{5+u}{u} \right| + C = \dfrac{1}{5} \ln \left| \dfrac{5}{u} + 1 \right| + C$

$= \dfrac{1}{5} \ln \left| \dfrac{5}{\cos x} + 1 \right| + C = \dfrac{1}{5} \ln|5 \sec x + 1| + C.$

31. Hint: Let $t = 1/u$, $dt = (-1/u^2) du$. $t = 1, x \implies u = 1, 1/x$. For the last part evaluate each integral using $\arctan 1 = \pi/4$.

34. $I = \int \csc x \, dx = \int \dfrac{1}{\sin x} \, dx = \int \dfrac{1+z^2}{2z} \dfrac{2}{1+z^2} \, dz = \int \dfrac{dz}{z} = \ln|z| + C$. Now,

$\cos x = \dfrac{1-z^2}{1+z^2} \implies \cos x + z^2 \cos x + z^2 = 1 \implies z^2 = \dfrac{1 - \cos x}{1 + \cos x} \implies$

$z = \left(\dfrac{1 - \cos x}{1 + \cos x} \right)^{1/2} \implies I = \ln|z| + C = \dfrac{1}{2} \ln \left| \dfrac{1 - \cos x}{1 + \cos x} \right| + C.$

EXERCISES 9.7, page 435

1. The presence of $\sqrt{4+9x^2}$ refers us to the portion of the table involving $\sqrt{a^2+u^2}$. The integrand, $\sqrt{4+9x^2}/x$ indicates that Formula 23 is the one to use. To convert the given integral into the desired form, we see that $a^2 = 4$, $u^2 = 9x^2$ so that $a = 2$, $u = 3x$, $du = 3 \, dx$. If we multiply and divide by 3, then $u = 3x$ is in the denominator, and $du = 3 \, dx$ is in the numerator. Then

$\int \dfrac{\sqrt{4+9x^2}}{x} \, dx = \int \dfrac{\sqrt{2^2 + (3x)^2}}{3x} \, 3 \, dx = \sqrt{2^2 + (3x)^2} - 2 \ln \left| \dfrac{2 + \sqrt{2^2 + (3x)^2}}{3x} \right| + C,$

which quickly reduces to the given answer.

4. The integrand, $x^2 \sqrt{4x^2 - 16}$, indicates that Formula 40 is the one to use. We can make the given integral compatible with that formula as above, or, alternately, by changing variables. Let $u = 2x$, $x = u/2$, $dx = du/2$. Then

$\int x^2 \sqrt{4x^2 - 16} \, dx = \int \dfrac{u^2}{4} \sqrt{u^2 - 16} \cdot \dfrac{1}{2} \, du = \dfrac{1}{8} \int u^2 \sqrt{u^2 - 16} \, du$, which is in the correct

form with $a = 4$. Using Formula 40, we obtain $\dfrac{1}{8} [\dfrac{u}{8} (2u^2 - 16) \sqrt{u^2 - 16} - \dfrac{4^4}{8} \cdot$

$\ln|u + \sqrt{u^2 - 16}| + C = \dfrac{1}{8} [\dfrac{2x}{8} (2(4x^2) - 16) \sqrt{4x^2 - 16} - \dfrac{256}{8} \ln|2x + \sqrt{4x^2 - 16}| + C$

$= \dfrac{x}{4} (x^2 - 2) \sqrt{4x^2 - 16} - 4 \ln|2x - \sqrt{4x^2 - 16}| + C.$

7. Let $u = 3x$, $dx = (1/3) du$. Then by Formula 73 with $n = 6$, $I = \dfrac{1}{3} \int \sin^6 u \, du =$

$\dfrac{1}{3} [-\dfrac{1}{6} \sin^5 u \cos u + \dfrac{5}{6} \int \sin^4 u \, du]$. By 73 again, with $n = 4$, $\int \sin^4 u \, du =$

$-\dfrac{1}{4} \sin^3 u \cos u + \dfrac{3}{4} \int \sin^2 u \, du$. Using Formula 63 for the last integral, we obtain: $I = \frac{1}{3}[-\frac{1}{6}\sin^5 u \cos u - \frac{5}{24}\sin^3 u \cos u + \frac{15}{24}(\frac{u}{2} - \frac{\sin 2u}{4})] + C$, where

$u = 3x$. (sin 2u can be replaced by 2 sin u cos u if desired.)

10. Directly from Formula 81 with a = 5, b = 3, and u = x, $\int \sin 5x \cos 3x\, dx =$

$-\frac{\cos 2x}{2(2)} - \frac{\cos 8x}{2(8)} + C$.

13. Directly from Formula 98 with a = -3, b = 2, and u = x, $\int e^{-3x} \sin 2x\, dx =$

$\frac{e^{-3x}}{(-3)^2+2^2}(-3\sin 2x - 2\cos 2x) + C$.

16. From the integrand, $1/x\sqrt{3x-2x^2}$, the formulas involving $\sqrt{2au-u^2}$ should be con-

sulted, and we see that Formula 120 fits. So, let $u = \sqrt{2}x$ so that $u^2 = 2x^2$,

$x = u/\sqrt{2}$, $dx = du/\sqrt{2}$. Then $I = \int \frac{dx}{x\sqrt{3x-2x^2}} = \int \frac{du/\sqrt{2}}{(u/\sqrt{2})\sqrt{3(u/\sqrt{2})-u^2}} =$

$\int \frac{1}{u\sqrt{\frac{3}{\sqrt{2}}u - u^2}}\, du$. Thus $2a = \frac{3}{\sqrt{2}}$, or $a = \frac{3}{2\sqrt{2}}$. By the formula,

$I = -\frac{\sqrt{(3/\sqrt{2})u-u^2}}{(3/2\sqrt{2})u} + C = -\frac{\sqrt{3x-2x^2}}{(3/2)x} + C$.

19. Writing $\int e^{2x}\cos^{-1}e^x\, dx = \int e^x \cos^{-1}e^x(e^x)dx$, we let $u = e^x$, $du = e^x dx$ to

$\int u\cos^{-1}u\, du$, which, by Formula 91, equals $\frac{2u^2-1}{4}\cos^{-1}u - \frac{u\sqrt{1-u^2}}{4} + C$, where

$u = e^x$.

22. Using Formula 61 with n = 3, u = x, a = 2, b = -1, $I = 7\int \frac{x^3}{\sqrt{2-x}}\, dx =$

$7[\frac{2x^3}{-7}\sqrt{2-x} - \frac{12}{-7}\int \frac{x^2}{\sqrt{2-x}}\, dx]$. Cancel the 7's and use Formula 56 with u = x,

a =2, b=-1 for the last integral to obtain $I = -2x^3\sqrt{2-x} +$

$12[-\frac{2}{15}(32 + 3x^2 + 8x)\sqrt{2-x}] + C$.

25. Combining Formulas 58 and 57 with u = x, a = 9, b = 2, $\int \frac{\sqrt{9+2x}}{x}\, dx = 2\sqrt{9+2x}$

$+ 9\int \frac{dx}{x\sqrt{9+2x}} = 2\sqrt{9+2x} + \frac{9}{3}\ln\left|\frac{\sqrt{9+2x}-3}{\sqrt{9+2x}+3}\right| + C$. (The first form of 57 was

used since a = 9 > 0.).

28. We begin with the rationalizing substitution $u = \sqrt{x}$, $x = u^2$, $dx = 2u\, du$.

$I = \int \frac{dx}{2x^{3/2}+5x^2} = \int \frac{2u}{2u^3+5u^4}\, du = 2\int \frac{1}{2u^2+5u^3}\, du = 2\int \frac{1}{u^2(2+5u)}\, du$. By

Formula 50 with a = 2, b = 5, $I = 2(-\frac{1}{2u} + \frac{5}{4}\ln\left|\frac{2+5u}{u}\right|) + C = -\frac{1}{\sqrt{x}}$

$+ \frac{5}{2}\ln\left|\frac{2+5\sqrt{x}}{\sqrt{x}}\right| + C$.

EXERCISES 9.8, page 442

NOTE: As in Chapter 6, in addition to the solutions of #1, 4, 7, ..., I have included the integrals from which the answers to the remaining odd-numbered problems
can be obtained in this section and in the next section as well. In these answers,
the density, ρ, is taken as unity.

1. $m = 2 + 7 + 5 = 14.$ $M_x = \sum\limits_{i=1}^{3} m_i y_i = 2(-1) + 7(0) + 5(-5) = -27.$

$M_y = \sum\limits_{i=1}^{3} m_i x_i = 2(4) + 7(-2) + 5(-8) = -46.$

$\bar{x} = \dfrac{M_y}{m} = -\dfrac{46}{14}$, $\bar{y} = \dfrac{M_x}{m} = -\dfrac{27}{14}$.

3. $m = \displaystyle\int_0^1 x^3 dx,$ $M_x = (1/2)\displaystyle\int_0^1 x^6 dx,$ $M_y = \displaystyle\int_0^1 x^4 dx.$

4.   With $\rho = 1$, $m = \text{Area} = \displaystyle\int_0^9 x^{1/2} dx = \dfrac{2}{3}x^{3/2} \Big]_0^9 = 18.$

$M_y = \displaystyle\int_0^9 x \cdot x^{1/2} dx = \dfrac{2}{5}x^{5/2} \Big]_0^9 = \dfrac{486}{5}$. $M_x =$

$\displaystyle\int_0^9 \dfrac{1}{2}(x^{1/2})^2 dx = \dfrac{x^2}{4} \Big]_0^9 = \dfrac{81}{4}$, $\bar{x} = \dfrac{486}{5(18)} = \dfrac{27}{5}$,

$\bar{y} = \dfrac{81}{4(18)} = \dfrac{9}{8}$.

5. $m = \displaystyle\int_0^\pi \sin x \, dx,$ $M_x = (1/2)\displaystyle\int_0^\pi \sin^2 x \, dx,$ $M_y = \displaystyle\int_0^\pi x \sin x \, dx.$

7. $m = A = \displaystyle\int_{-2}^1 [(1-x^2) - (x-1)] dx = \displaystyle\int_{-2}^1 (2-x-x^2) dx = [2x - \dfrac{x^2}{2} - \dfrac{x^3}{3}]_{-2}^1 = \dfrac{9}{2}$.

$M_y = \displaystyle\int_{-2}^1 x(2-x-x^2) dx = [x^2 - \dfrac{x^3}{3} - \dfrac{x^4}{4}]_{-2}^1 = -\dfrac{9}{4}$. $M_x = \dfrac{1}{2}\displaystyle\int_{-2}^1 [(1-x^2)^2 - (x-1)^2] dx$

$= \dfrac{1}{2}\displaystyle\int_{-2}^1 (x^4 - 3x^2 + 2x) dx = \dfrac{1}{2}[\dfrac{x^5}{5} - x^3 + x^2]_{-2}^1 = \dfrac{1}{2}(-\dfrac{27}{5}) = -\dfrac{27}{10}$.

$\bar{x} = -\dfrac{9}{4} \cdot \dfrac{2}{9} = -\dfrac{1}{2}$, $\bar{y} = -\dfrac{27}{10} \cdot \dfrac{2}{9} = -\dfrac{3}{5}$.

9. $m = \displaystyle\int_0^3 1/\sqrt{16+x^2} \, dx,$ $M_x = (1/2)\displaystyle\int_1^3 1/(16+x^2) \, dx,$ $M_y = \displaystyle\int_0^3 x/\sqrt{16+x^2} \, dx.$

10. $m = \displaystyle\int_1^e \dfrac{1}{x} dx = \ln x \Big]_1^e = 1.$ $M_y = \displaystyle\int_1^e x \cdot \dfrac{1}{x} dx = e-1.$ $M_x = \dfrac{1}{2}\displaystyle\int_1^e (\dfrac{1}{x})^2 dx =$

$\frac{1}{2}[-\frac{1}{x}]_1^e = \frac{1}{2}(1 - \frac{1}{e})$. $\bar{x} = e-1$, $\bar{y} = \frac{1}{2}(1 - \frac{1}{e})$.

11. $m = \int_{-1}^0 e^{2x}dx$, $M_x = (1/2) \int_{-1}^0 e^{4x}dx$, $M_y = \int_{-1}^0 xe^{2x}dx$.

13. The 3 medians have equations $y = \frac{b+c}{a} x$, $y = \frac{2b-c}{2a} x + \frac{c}{2}$, and $y = \frac{b-2c}{a} x + c$, and their point of intersection is $(\frac{a}{3}, \frac{b+c}{3})$. The area is $m = \frac{1}{2}ac$ (without integrating). The upper boundary of the region is $f(x) = \frac{b-c}{a} x + c$; the lower boundary $g(x) = \frac{b}{a} x$. $M_y = \int_0^a x(\frac{b-c}{a} x + c - \frac{b}{a} x)dx = c \int_0^a (x - \frac{x^2}{a})dx = \frac{ca^2}{6}$.

$M_x = \frac{1}{2} \int_0^a [(\frac{b-c}{a} x + c)^2 - (\frac{b}{a} x)^2]dx = \frac{c}{2} \int_0^a (\frac{c-2b}{a^2} x^2 + \frac{2(b-c)}{a} x + c)dx$

$= \frac{ac}{6}(b+c)$. $\bar{x} = \frac{a^2c}{6} \cdot \frac{2}{ac} = \frac{a}{3}$. $\bar{y} = \frac{ac}{6}(b+c) \cdot \frac{2}{ac} = \frac{b+c}{3}$.

15. $m = \int_{-a}^a \sqrt{a^2-x^2} \, dx$ (but there's an obvious way to get m without integration), $M_x = (1/2) \int_{-a}^a (a^2-x^2)dx$, $M_y = \int_{-a}^a x\sqrt{a^2-x^2} \, dx$.

16. The described region may be considered as being formed by cutting a semicircular region of radius a from a semicircular region of radius b, both centered at the origin and lying above the x-axis.

Thus $m = A = \frac{1}{2}\pi b^2 - \frac{1}{2}\pi a^2 = \pi(b^2-a^2)/2$.

Because of symmetry about the y-axis, $\bar{x} = 0$.

To compute $\bar{y}$, we need M_x. Let M_{xa} and M_{xb} denote the moments of the semi-circular regions of radii a and b, respectively, with respect to the x-axis. By #15 above, $M_{xa} = \frac{2}{3}a^3$, $M_{xb} = \frac{2}{3}b^3$. Because moments are additive $M_x + M_{xa} = M_{xb}$ since the union of the region and the semicircular region of radius a is the entire semicircular region of radius b. Thus $M_x = M_{xb} - M_{xa} = \frac{2}{3}(b^3-a^3) = \frac{2}{3}(b-a)(b^2+ab+a^2)$. Finally, $\bar{y} = \frac{M_x}{m} = \frac{(2/3)(b-a)(b^2+ab+a^2)}{(\pi/2)(b^2-a^2)} = \frac{4(b^2+ab+a^2)}{3\pi(b+a)}$.

17. $\dot{m}$ = (area of square of side 2a) + (area of circle of radius a). With x-axis placed on the top edge of the square, origin at the center (also the center of the circle), $M_x = -(1/2) \int_{-a}^{a} (-2a)^2 dx + (1/2) \int_{-a}^{a} (a^2-x^2)dx$, $M_y = 0$ by symmetry.

19. $x^{2/3} + y^{2/3} = a^{2/3} \implies y = (a^{2/3}-x^{2/3})^{3/2}$. By symmetry $\bar{x} = \bar{y}$. We will compute $\bar{y}$. $m = A = \int_0^a (a^{2/3}-x^{2/3})^{3/2}dx$. $u = x^{1/3}$, $x = u^3$, $dx = 3u^2 du$

$\implies m = 3\int_0^{\sqrt[3]{a}} (a^{2/3}-u^2)^{3/2} u^2 du$. $u = a^{1/3} \sin\theta \implies m = 3\int_0^{\pi/2} a(1 - \sin^2\theta)a^{2/3} \sin^2\theta \cdot a^{1/3} \cos\theta \, d\theta = 3a^2 \int_0^{\pi/2} \cos^4\theta \sin^2\theta \, d\theta =$

$\frac{3a^2}{8} \int_0^{\pi/2} (1 + \cos 2\theta)^2 (1 - \cos 2\theta)d\theta = \frac{3a^2}{8} \int_0^{\pi/2} (1 + \cos 2\theta - \cos^2 2\theta -$

$\cos^3 2\theta)d\theta = \frac{3a^2}{8}(\frac{\pi}{4}) = \frac{3\pi a^2}{32}$. (The integrals of the odd powers of $\cos 2\theta$ are 0; $1 - \cos^2 2\theta$ yields $\pi/4$ all by the methods of section 2.) Next, $M_y =$

$\frac{1}{2}\int_0^a f(x)^2 dx = \frac{1}{2}\int_0^a (a^{2/3}-x^{2/3})^3 dx = \frac{1}{2}\int_0^a (a^2 - 3a^{4/3}x^{2/3} + 3a^{2/3}x^{4/3} - x^2)dx$

$= \frac{1}{2}[a^2 x - 3a^{4/3}\frac{x^{5/3}}{5/3} + 3a^{2/3}\frac{x^{7/3}}{7/3} - \frac{x^3}{3}]_0^a = \frac{a^3}{2}(1 - \frac{9}{5} + \frac{9}{7} - \frac{1}{3}) = \frac{8a^3}{105}$.

Finally, $\bar{y} = \frac{M_x}{m} = \frac{8a^3}{105} \cdot \frac{32}{3\pi a^2} = \frac{256a}{315\pi}$.

EXERCISES 9.9, page 448

NOTE: As in Sec. 9.8, $\rho = 1$ and m is the volume of the solid.

1. $m = \pi \int_1^2 (\frac{1}{x})^2 dx = \pi[- \frac{1}{x}]_1^2 = \frac{\pi}{2}$.

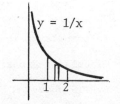

$y = 1/x$

$M_{yz} = \pi \int_1^2 x(\frac{1}{x})^2 dx = \pi \ln x]_1^2 = \pi \ln 2$.

$\bar{x} = \frac{\pi \ln 2}{\pi/2} = 2 \ln 2 \approx 1.386$.

3. $m = \pi \int_0^1 e^{2x}dx$, $M_{yz} = \pi \int_0^1 xe^{2x}dx$.

4. $m = \pi \int_0^4 (\frac{1}{\sqrt{16+x^2}})^2 dx = \frac{\pi}{4} \tan^{-1} \frac{x}{4}]_0^4 = (\frac{\pi}{4})^2$.

$$M_{yz} = \pi \int_0^4 \frac{x}{16+x^2}\, dx = \frac{\pi}{2} \ln(16+x^2)\Big]_0^4 = \frac{\pi}{2}(\ln 32 - \ln 16) = \frac{\pi}{2} \ln 2.$$

$$\bar{x} = \frac{\pi \ln 2}{2} \cdot \frac{16}{\pi^2} = \frac{8 \ln 2}{\pi} \approx 1.77.$$

5. $m = \pi \int_0^1 (x^{2/3} - x^4)\, dx$, $M_{yz} = \pi \int_0^1 (x^{5/3} - x^5)\, dx$.

7.   It is convenient to use y as the integration

variable. $m = \pi \int_2^4 (\sqrt{y^2-4})^2\, dy = \frac{32\pi}{3}$.

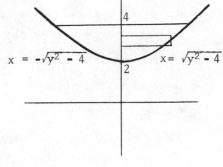

$$M_{xz} = \pi \int_2^4 y(y^2-4)\, dy = 36\pi.$$

$$\bar{y} = 36\pi \cdot \frac{3}{32\pi} = \frac{27}{8} = 3.375.$$

9. $m = 2\pi \int_0^2 xe^{2x}\, dx$, $M_{xz} = \pi \int_0^2 xe^{4x}\, dx$.

10.   Using the shell method as in Example 3, $m = 2\pi \int_{-1}^0 (-x)e^{-x}\, dx = 2\pi[(x+1)e^{-x}]_{-1}^0$

$= 2\pi$.   (Since $-1 < x < 0$, the radius of the shell is not w_i but $-w_i$.   Hence

the factor $(-x)$ in the integral.)   The moment of the shell about the xz plane

is $\frac{1}{2}$(height)·(volume) or $\frac{1}{2}e^{-w_i}(2\pi(-w_i)e^{-w_i})\Delta x_i$.   As in Chapter 6, we sum and

pass to the limit to obtain $M_{xz} = \pi \int_{-1}^0 (-x)e^{-2x}\, dx = \frac{\pi}{4}(2x+1)e^{-2x}]_{-1}^0 = \frac{\pi}{4}(1+e^2)$.

$$\bar{y} = \frac{\pi(1+e^2)}{4(2\pi)} = \frac{1+e^2}{8} \approx 1.05.$$

(Note: the integrals for m and M_{xz} can both be done by integration by parts

with $u = x$, $dv = e^{-x}dx$ or $e^{-2x}dx$, or use Formula 96 in the table of integrals.)

11. $m = 2\pi \int_0^5 x/(x^2+25)\, dx$, $M_{xz} = \pi \int_0^5 x/(x^2+25)^2\, dx$.

13.   By shells, $m = 2\pi \int_0^{\pi/2} x \cos x\, dx = 2\pi(\cos x + x \sin x)]_0^{\pi/2} = \pi(\pi-2)$.

$$M_{xz} = \int_0^{\pi/2} (1/2)y \cdot 2\pi xy\, dx = \pi \int_0^{\pi/2} x \cos^2 x\, dx = (\pi/2) \int_0^{\pi/2} x(1+\cos 2x)\, dx$$

$$= (\pi/2) \int_0^{\pi/2} x\, dx + (\pi/8) \int_0^{\pi/2} (2x)\cos 2x\, 2dx = (\pi/2)(x^3/2]_0^{\pi/2}$$

$$+ (\pi/8)(\cos 2x + 2x \sin 2x]_{0}^{\pi/2} = \pi^3/16 + (\pi/8)(\cos \pi + \pi \sin \pi - \cos 0)$$

$$= \pi^3/16 - \pi/4 = (\pi/16)(\pi^2-4). \quad \overline{y} = (\pi/16)(\pi^2-4) \cdot \frac{1}{\pi(\pi-2)} = (\pi+2)/16 \approx .3213.$$

15. $m = 2\pi \int_{0}^{\pi/2} x \cos x \, dx, \quad M_{xz} = \pi \int_{0}^{\pi/2} x \cos^2 x \, dx \quad$ (as in Example 3).

16. Let us place the base of the cone in the xz-plane such that the center of
the cone's base and of the hemisphere are at the origin and the y-axis co-
incides with the axis of the cone. Let $\overline{y}_1$ and $\overline{y}_2$ denote the y-coordinates
of the centers of mass of the cone and hemisphere, respectively, m_1 and m_2
their masses. By Example 1, $\overline{y}_1$ is located 3/4 of the way from the vertex to
the base. Here, the vertex is y = h and the base is y = 0. Thus $\overline{y}_1$ = h/4
and $m_1 = (1/3)\pi a^2 h$. By Example 2, $\overline{y}_2$ is located 3/8 of the way from the
center to the pole. Here, the center is y = 0 and the (south) pole is y =
-a. Thus $\overline{y}_2$ = -(3/8)a, and $m_2 = (2/3)\pi a^3$. By additivity of moments and
the definition of center of mass, the total moment of the solid is $m_1\overline{y}_1$ +

$m_2\overline{y}_2$. Thus $\overline{y} = \dfrac{m_1\overline{y}_1 + m_2\overline{y}_2}{m_1+m_2} = \dfrac{(1/3)\pi a^2 h \cdot h/4 + (2/3)\pi a^3 \cdot (-(3/8)a)}{(1/3)\pi a^2 h + (2/3)\pi a^3}$

$= \dfrac{h^2/4 - 3a^2/4}{h+2a} = \dfrac{h^2 - 3a^2}{4(h + 2a)}.$

19. The region is a quarter circle of radius a. Its area is $A = (1/4)\pi a^2$. When
the region is revolved about either axis, a hemisphere of radius a is swept
out whose volume is $V = \dfrac{1}{2} \cdot \dfrac{4}{3}\pi a^3 = \dfrac{2}{3}\pi a^3$. If the centroid is $(\overline{x},\overline{y})$, then by
the formula above the Theorem of Pappus, $V = 2\pi\overline{x}A$ and $V = 2\pi\overline{y}A$. (In the
first, V is the volume of the solid obtained by a revolution about the y-axis;
in the second, revolution has been about the x-axis. Here, the same value of
V can be used on both.) Thus $\overline{x} = \overline{y} = \dfrac{V}{2\pi A} = \dfrac{(2/3)\pi a^3}{2\pi(1/4)\pi a^2} = \dfrac{4}{3\pi} a \approx 0.42$ a.

EXERCISES 9.10, page 449

1. $u = \sin^{-1}x, \; dv = x \, dx \implies du = \dfrac{dx}{\sqrt{1-x^2}}, \; v = \dfrac{x^2}{2}.$

$I = \displaystyle\int x \sin^{-1}x \, dx = \dfrac{x^2}{2}\sin^{-1}x - \dfrac{1}{2}\int \dfrac{x^2}{\sqrt{1-x^2}} \, dx.$ With x =

sin θ, dx = cos θ dθ, $\sqrt{1-x^2}$ = cos θ, the last integral

is $\displaystyle\int \dfrac{\sin^2\theta \cos \theta}{\cos \theta} \, d\theta = \dfrac{1}{2}\int (1 - \cos 2\theta)d\theta = \dfrac{1}{2}(\theta - \dfrac{\sin 2\theta}{2})$

$$= \frac{1}{2}(\theta - \sin \theta \cos \theta) = \frac{1}{2}(\sin^{-1}x - x\sqrt{1-x^2}). \quad \text{Thus}$$

$$I = \frac{x^2}{2} \sin^{-1}x - \frac{1}{4} \sin^{-1}x + \frac{1}{4}x\sqrt{1-x^2} + C.$$

4. Let $y^2 = x$, $2y \, dy = dx$, $y = \sqrt{x}$. Then $\int_0^1 e^{\sqrt{x}} \, dx = 2\int_0^1 y \, e^y \, dy = 2(y-1)e^y \,]_0^1$

$= 2$. (The y integral was done by parts with $u = y$, $dv = e^y dy$.)

7. $\int \tan x \sec^5 x \, dx = \int \sec^4 x (\sec x \tan x) \, dx = \frac{\sec^5 x}{5} + C.$

10. Let $x = 4 \sin \theta$, $dx = 4 \cos \theta \, d\theta$, $\sqrt{16-x^2} = 4 \cos \theta$. Then $\int \frac{1}{x^2\sqrt{16-x^2}} \, dx =$

$$\int \frac{4 \cos \theta \, d\theta}{(16 \sin^2\theta)(4 \cos \theta)} = \frac{1}{16} \int \csc^2\theta \, d\theta = -\frac{1}{16} \cot \theta + C$$

$$= -\frac{1}{16} \frac{\sqrt{16-x^2}}{x} + C.$$

13. $\frac{x^3+1}{x(x-1)^3} = \frac{A}{x} + \frac{B}{x-1} + \frac{C}{(x-1)^2} + \frac{D}{(x-1)^3}$. $x^3+1 = A(x-1)^3 + Bx(x-1)^2 + Cx(x-1) +$

Dx. Setting $x = 1$ and then $x = 0$, we see $D = 2$, $A = -1$. Equating the x^3

coefficients: $1 = A+B = -1 + B \implies B = 2$; and the x^2 coefficients: $0 = -3A$

$-2B + C = 3-4+C \implies C = 1$. Thus $\int \frac{x^3+1}{x(x-1)^3} \, dx = -\ln|x| + 2 \ln|x-1| -$

$\frac{1}{x-1} - \frac{1}{(x-1)^2} + C$, where C is now the usual arbitrary constant of integration.

16. Let $u = x+2$. Then $du = dx$, and $x-1 = u-3$. $\int \frac{x-1}{(x+2)^5} \, dx = \int \frac{u-3}{u^5} \, du =$

$\int (u^{-4} - 3u^{-5})\,du = \frac{u^{-3}}{-3} - \frac{3u^{-4}}{-4} + C = -\frac{1}{3(x+2)^3} + \frac{3}{4(x+2)^4} + C.$

19. Let $u^3 = x+8$. Then $3u^2 = dx$, $x = u^3-8$. $I = \int \frac{\sqrt[3]{x+8}}{x} \, dx = \int \frac{u(3u^2)}{u^3-8} \, du =$

$3 \int (1 + \frac{8}{u^3-8})\,du$. Now, $u^3-8 = (u-2)(u^2+2u+4) = (u-2)[(u+1)^2+3] =$

$(z-3)(z^2+3)$ where $z = u+1$.

$\frac{1}{u^3-8} = \frac{1}{(z-3)(z^2+3)} = \frac{A}{z-3} + \frac{Bz+C}{z^2+3}$. $1 = A(z^2+3) + (Bz+C)(z-3).$

Equating coefficients gives the system

$$\left. \begin{array}{l} z^2: \quad 0 = A + B \\ z^1: \quad 0 = -3B + C \\ z^0: \quad 1 = A - C \end{array} \right\} \implies \left\{ \begin{array}{l} A = 1/4 \\ B = -1/4 \\ C = -3/4. \end{array} \right.$$

Thus $\int \frac{1}{u^3-8} \, du = \frac{1}{4} \ln|z-3| - \frac{1}{8} \ln(z^2+3) - \frac{3}{4} \cdot \frac{1}{\sqrt{3}} \tan^{-1} \frac{z}{\sqrt{3}}$. Replacing z by

$u+1$, and combining this with the first calculation for I finally gives

$I = 3u + 2 \ln|u-2| - \ln(u^2+2u+4) - 2\sqrt{3} \tan^{-1} \frac{u+1}{\sqrt{3}} + C$ where $u = \sqrt[3]{x+8}$.

22. $u = \cos(\ln x)$, $dv = dx \Rightarrow du = \dfrac{-\sin(\ln x)}{x} dx$, $v = x$. $\displaystyle\int \cos(\ln x)\,dx =$

$x \cos(\ln x) + \displaystyle\int \sin(\ln x)\,dx$. Now, $u = \sin(\ln x)$, $dv = dx \Rightarrow du = \dfrac{\cos(\ln x)}{x}$,

$v = x$. $\displaystyle\int \cos(\ln x)\,dx = x \cos(\ln x) + x \sin(\ln x) - \displaystyle\int \cos(\ln x)\,dx$.

$\therefore 2 \displaystyle\int \cos(\ln x)\,dx = x(\cos(\ln x) + \sin(\ln x)) + C$.

25. With $u = 4-x^2$, $du = -2x\,dx$, $\displaystyle\int \dfrac{x}{\sqrt{4-x^2}}\,dx = -\dfrac{1}{2}\displaystyle\int u^{-1/2}\,du = -u^{1/2} + C = -\sqrt{4-x^2} + C$.

28. $\dfrac{x^3}{x^3-3x^2+9x-27} = 1 + \dfrac{3x^2 - 9x + 27}{(x-3)(x^2+9)}$ and $\dfrac{3x^2 - 9x + 27}{(x-3)(x^2+9)} = \dfrac{A}{x-3} + \dfrac{Bx+C}{x^2+9}$.

$3x^2-9x+27 = A(x^2+9) + (Bx+C)(x-3)$. Equating coefficients yields

$$\left.\begin{array}{l} x^2:\ \ 3 = A + B \\ x^1:\ -9 = \quad\ -3B + C \\ x^0:\ 27 = 9A \quad\quad - 3C \end{array}\right\} \implies \left\{\begin{array}{l} A = \ \ 3/2 \\ B = \ \ 3/2 \\ C = -9/2. \end{array}\right.$$

Putting this all together at last we get

$\displaystyle\int \dfrac{x^3}{x^3-3x^2+9x-27}\,dx = x + \dfrac{3}{2}\ln|x-3| + \dfrac{3}{4}\ln(x^2+9) - \dfrac{3}{2}\tan^{-1}\dfrac{x}{3} + C$.

31. With $u = e^x$, $du = e^x dx$ and $\displaystyle\int e^x \sec e^x dx = \displaystyle\int \sec u\,du = \ln|\sec u + \tan u|$

$+ C = \ln|\sec e^x + \tan e^x| + C$.

34. Recalling that $\sin 2x = 2 \sin x \cos x$, $\displaystyle\int \sin 2x \cos x\,dx = 2 \displaystyle\int \sin x \cos^2 x\,dx$

$= -\dfrac{2}{3}\cos^3 x + C$.

37. With $u = e^x$, $du = e^x dx$, $\displaystyle\int e^x\sqrt{1+e^x}\,dx = \displaystyle\int (1+u)^{1/2}\,du = \dfrac{2}{3}(1+u)^{3/2} + C$

$= \dfrac{2}{3}(1+e^x)^{3/2} + C$.

40. $x^2 + 8x + 25 = (x+4)^2 + 9$. So, with $u = x+4$, $du = dx$, $3x+2 = 3(u-4) + 2 =$

$3u = 10$, and $\displaystyle\int \dfrac{3x+2}{x^2+8x+25}\,dx = \displaystyle\int \dfrac{3u-10}{u^2+9}\,du = \dfrac{3}{2}\ln(u^2+9) - \dfrac{10}{3}\tan^{-1}\dfrac{u}{3} + C$

$= \dfrac{3}{2}\ln(x^2+8x+25) - \dfrac{10}{3}\tan^{-1}\dfrac{x+4}{3} + C$.

43. $u = x$, $dv = \cot x \csc x\,dx \Rightarrow du = dx$, $v = -\csc x$. $\displaystyle\int x \cot x \csc x\,dx =$

$-x \csc x + \displaystyle\int \csc x\,dx$. Now use Formula 15.

46. $u = (\ln x)^2$, $dv = x\,dx \Rightarrow du = (2 \ln x)/x\,dx$, $v = x^2/2$. $I = \displaystyle\int x(\ln x)^2 dx =$

$(x^2/2)(\ln x)^2 - \displaystyle\int x \ln x\,dx$. In this integral we use $u = \ln x$, $dv = x\,dx \Rightarrow$

$du = (1/x)dx$, $v = x^2/2$ to obtain $I = (x^2/2)(\ln x)^2 - [(x^2/2)\ln x - \displaystyle\int x/2\,dx]$

$= (x^2/2)[(\ln x)^2 - \ln x + 1/2] + C$.

49. First write $\int \frac{e^{3x}}{1+e^x} dx = \int \frac{e^{2x}}{1+e^x} e^x dx$. Then let $u = 1+e^x$ so that $du = e^x dx$ and

$e^x = (u-1)$, and we obtain $\int \frac{(u-1)^2}{u} du = \int \frac{u^2-2u+1}{u} du = \int (u-2+1/u) du =$

$u^2/2 - 2u + \ln|u| + C$, where $u = 1+e^x$.

52. Let $u = 1 + \sin x$. Then $du = \cos x\, dx$ and $\sin x = u-1$. $\int \frac{\cos^3 x}{\sqrt{1 + \sin x}} dx$

$= \int \frac{\cos^2 x}{\sqrt{1 + \sin x}} \cos x\, dx = \int \frac{1 - \sin^2 x}{\sqrt{1 + \sin x}} \cos x\, dx = \int \frac{1-(u-1)^2}{\sqrt{u}} du$

$= \int \frac{2u-u^2}{u^{1/2}} du = \int (2u^{1/2} - u^{3/2}) du = \frac{4}{3} u^{3/2} - \frac{2}{5} u^{5/2} + C = \frac{4}{3}(1 + \sin x)^{3/2} -$

$\frac{2}{5}(1 + \sin x)^{5/2} + C$.

55. $\frac{1-2x}{x^2+12x+35} = \frac{1-2x}{(x+5)(x+7)} = \frac{A}{x+5} + \frac{B}{x+7} \Longrightarrow 1-2x = A(x+7) + B(x+5)$. Setting

$x = -7$ and -5 we get $15 = -2B$ and $11 = 2A$, whence $A = 11/2$, $B = -15/2$. The

integral then becomes $\int (\frac{11/2}{x+5} - \frac{15/2}{x+7}) dx = \frac{11}{2} \ln|x+5| - \frac{15}{2} \ln|x+7| + C$.

58. First let $u = 3x$, $dx = (1/3) du$. Then use Formulas 73 (with $n = 4$) and 63 to

obtain: $\int \sin^4 3x\, dx = \frac{1}{3} \int \sin^4 u\, du = \frac{1}{3}[- \frac{1}{4} \sin^3 u \cos u + \frac{3}{4} \int \sin^2 u\, du]$

$= - \frac{1}{12} \sin^3 u \cos u + \frac{1}{4}[\frac{1}{2}u - \frac{1}{4} \sin 2u] + C = - \frac{1}{12} \sin^3 3x \cos 3x$

$+ \frac{3}{8}x - \frac{1}{16} \sin 6x + C$.

61. $\int \frac{1}{\sqrt{7+5x^2}} dx = \frac{1}{\sqrt{5}} \int \frac{\sqrt{5}\, dx}{\sqrt{7+(\sqrt{5}x)^2}} = \frac{1}{\sqrt{5}} \ln|\sqrt{5}\, x + \sqrt{7+5x^2}| + C$ by Formula 25 with

$u = \sqrt{5}\, x$ and $a^2 = 7$.

64. $\int \cot^5 x \csc x\, dx = \int \cot^4 x(\cot x \csc x) dx = \int (\csc^2 x-1)^2(\cot x \csc x) dx =$

$-\int (u^2-1)^2 du$ (with $u = \csc x$, $du = -\cot x \csc x\, dx$) $= -\int (u^4-2u^2+1) du =$

$-\frac{u^5}{5} + \frac{2}{3}u^3 - u + C = \frac{-\csc^5 x}{5} + \frac{2}{3} \csc^3 x - \csc x + C$.

67. $\int (x^2 - \text{sech}^2 4x) dx = \frac{x^3}{3} - \frac{1}{4} \int \text{sech}^2 u\, du = \frac{x^3}{3} - \frac{1}{4} \tanh u + C$, where $u = 4x$.

70. Let $u = x^3+1$, $du = 3x^2 dx$ and $x^3 = u-1$. $\int x^5\sqrt{x^3+1}\, dx = (1/3) \int x^3\sqrt{x^3+1}(3x^2) dx$

$= (1/3) \int (u-1)\sqrt{u}\, du = \frac{1}{3} \int (u^{3/2}-u^{1/2}) du = \frac{1}{3}(\frac{2}{5}u^{5/2} - \frac{2}{3}u^{3/2}) + C$

$= \frac{2}{15}(x^3+1)^{5/2} - \frac{2}{9}(x^3+1)^{3/2} + C$.

73. Since $\tan u \cos u = \dfrac{\sin u}{\cos u} \cos u = \sin u$, $\displaystyle\int \tan 7x \cos 7x\, dx = \int \sin 7x\, dx =$

$-(1/7)\cos 7x + C$.

76. Let $x = 4 \sin\theta$, $dx = 4\cos\theta\, d\theta$, $\sqrt{16-x^2} = 4\cos\theta$. Then $I = \displaystyle\int \dfrac{1}{x^4\sqrt{16-x^2}}\, dx$

$= \displaystyle\int \dfrac{4\cos\theta}{4^4\sin^4\theta(4\cos\theta)}\, d\theta = \dfrac{1}{256}\int \dfrac{1}{\sin^4\theta}\, d\theta = \dfrac{1}{256}\int \csc^4\theta\, d\theta$. Now, by Formula

78, with $n = 4$, $I = \dfrac{1}{256}[-\dfrac{1}{3}\cot\theta\,\csc^2\theta + \dfrac{2}{3}\displaystyle\int\csc^2\theta\, d\theta]$

$= \dfrac{1}{256}[-\dfrac{1}{3}\cot\theta\,\csc^2\theta - \dfrac{2}{3}\cot\theta] + C$

$= -\dfrac{1}{768}\cot\theta\,(\csc^2\theta + 2) + C = -\dfrac{1}{768}\dfrac{\sqrt{16-x^2}}{x}(\dfrac{16}{x^2} + 2) + C$

$= -\dfrac{\sqrt{16-x^2}(8+x^2)}{384\,x^3} + C$.

79. $\displaystyle\int \dfrac{\sqrt{9-4x^2}}{x^2}\, dx = 2\int \dfrac{\sqrt{9-(2x)^2}}{(2x)^2}\, 2\, dx = 2[-\dfrac{\sqrt{9-4x^2}}{2x} - \sin^{-1}\dfrac{2x}{3}] + C$ by Formula 33

with $u = 2x$, $a^2 = 9$.

82. Let $u = x^2+5$, $du = 2x\, dx$, $x\, dx = (1/2)du$. $\displaystyle\int x(x^2+5)^{3/4}\, dx = (1/2)\int u^{3/4}\, du =$

$(1/2)(4/7)u^{7/4} + C = (2/7)(x^2+5)^{7/4} + C$.

85. Let $u = 1 + \cos x$, $du = -\sin x\, dx$. $\displaystyle\int \dfrac{\sin x}{\sqrt{1+\cos x}}\, dx = -\int u^{-1/2}\, du = -2u^{1/2}$

$+ C = -2\sqrt{1+\cos x} + C$.

88. $\displaystyle\int \sin^4 x \cos^3 x\, dx = \int \sin^4 x(1 - \sin^2 x)\cos x\, dx = \int u^4(1-u^2)\, du = \int (u^4-u^6)\, du$

$= (1/5)u^5 - (1/7)u^7 + C$, where $u = \sin x$.

91. $x^4+9x^2+20 = (x^2+4)(x^2+5) \implies f(x) = \dfrac{2x^3+4x^2+10x+13}{(x^2+4)(x^2+5)} = \dfrac{Ax+B}{x^2+4} + \dfrac{Cx+D}{x^2+5} \implies$

$2x^3+4x^2+10x+13 = (Ax+B)(x^2+5) + (Cx+D)(x^2+4) = (A+C)x^3 + (B+D)x^2 +$

$(5A+4C)x + (5B+4D)$. Equating the x^3 and x coefficients, we get the system

$A+C = 2$, $5A +4C = 10$ with solution $A = 2$, $C = 0$. Equating the x^2 and constant

coefficients, we get the system $B+D = 4$, $5B+4D = 13$ with solution $B = -3$,

$D = 7$. Thus $\displaystyle\int f(x)\, dx = \int (\dfrac{2x}{x^2+4} - \dfrac{3}{x^2+4} + \dfrac{7}{x^2+5})\, dx = \ln(x^2+4) - \dfrac{3}{2}\tan^{-1}\dfrac{x}{2}$

$+ \dfrac{7}{\sqrt{5}}\tan^{-1}\dfrac{x}{\sqrt{5}} + C$.

94. $\displaystyle\int \cot^2 x \csc x\, dx = \int (\csc^2 x - 1)\csc x\, dx = \int \csc^3 x\, dx - \int \csc x\, dx =$

$(-(1/2)\csc x \cot x + (1/2)\ln|\csc x - \cot x|) - \ln|\csc x - \cot x| + C =$

$-(1/2)(\csc x \cot x + \ln|\csc x - \cot x|) + C$. (The integral of $\csc^3 x$ is from

#2 or from Formula 72.)

97. Let $u = 2x+3$. Then $x = (1/2)(u-3)$, $dx = (1/2)du$. $\displaystyle\int \frac{x^2}{\sqrt[3]{2x+3}}\, dx = \int \frac{(1/4)(u-3)^2}{\sqrt[3]{u}} \cdot$

$(1/2)du = \dfrac{1}{8}\displaystyle\int \frac{u^2-6x+9}{u^{1/3}}\, du = \dfrac{1}{8}\displaystyle\int (u^{5/3} - 6u^{2/3} + 9u^{-1/3})\,du =$

$\dfrac{1}{8}[\dfrac{3}{8}u^{8/3} - 6(\dfrac{3}{5})u^{5/3} + 9(\dfrac{3}{2})u^{2/3}] + C$ where $u = 2x+3$.

100. Let $u = x+1$. Then $du = dx$, $u+1 = x+2$. $\displaystyle\int (x+2)^2(x+1)^{10}dx = \int (u+1)^2 u^{10}\,du =$

$\displaystyle\int (u^{12}+2u^{11}+u^{10})\,du = (1/13)u^{13} + (2/12)u^{12} + (1/11)u^{11} + C$ where $u = x+1$.

101. $V = 2\pi\displaystyle\int_0^\pi x \sin x\, dx.$

103. $y = \ln \sec x \Longrightarrow y' = \dfrac{D_x \sec x}{\sec x} = \dfrac{\sec x \tan x}{\sec x} = \tan x.$

$L_0^{\pi/3} = \displaystyle\int_0^{\pi/3} \sqrt{1 + \tan^2 x}\, dx = \int_0^{\pi/3} \sec x\, dx = \ln|\sec x + \tan x|]_0^{\pi/3} = \ln(2+\sqrt{3}).$

105. $m = \displaystyle\int_0^1 (x^2-x^3)\,dx$, $M_x = (1/2)\displaystyle\int_0^1 (x^4-x^6)\,dx$, $M_y = \displaystyle\int_0^1 (x^3-x^4)\,dx.$

106. $m = \displaystyle\int_0^{\pi/2} \cos x\, dx = \sin x]_0^{\pi/2} = 1.$ $M_x = \dfrac{1}{2}\displaystyle\int_0^{\pi/2} \cos^2 x\, dx = \dfrac{1}{4}\displaystyle\int_0^{\pi/2} (1+\cos 2x)\,dx$

$= \dfrac{1}{4}[x + \dfrac{\sin 2x}{2}]_0^{\pi/2} = \dfrac{\pi}{8}.$ $M_y = \displaystyle\int_0^{\pi/2} x \cos x\, dx.$ Let $u = x$, $dv = \cos x\, dx.$

Then $du = dx$, $v = \sin x$ and $M_y = x \sin x]_0^{\pi/2} - \displaystyle\int_0^{\pi/2} \cos x\, dx = \dfrac{\pi}{2} - 1.$

$\bar{x} = \dfrac{\pi}{2} - 1$, $\bar{y} = \dfrac{\pi}{8}.$

107. $m = \pi\displaystyle\int_0^4 x\, dx$, $M_{yz} = \pi\displaystyle\int_0^4 x^2\,dx.$

109. NOTE: we use the formula $\displaystyle\int x\, e^{ax}\, dx = \dfrac{e^{ax}}{a^2}(ax - 1)$ several times here. The shell method is employed to solve the problem.

$m = 2\pi\displaystyle\int_0^1 x\, e^{-3x}\, dx = \dfrac{2\pi}{9} e^{-3x}(-3x - 1)]_0^1 = \dfrac{2\pi}{9}(1 - 4e^{-3}).$ $M_{yz} = \dfrac{2\pi}{2}\displaystyle\int_0^1 x(e^{-3x})^2 dx$

$= \pi\displaystyle\int_0^1 xe^{-6x}dx = \dfrac{\pi}{36} e^{-6x}(-6x - 1)]_0^1 = \dfrac{\pi}{36}(1 - 7e^{-6}).$ $\bar{y} = \dfrac{\pi(1 - 7e^{-6})}{36} \cdot$

$\dfrac{9}{2\pi(1 - 4e^{-3})} = \dfrac{1 - 7e^{-6}}{8(1 - 4e^{-3})} \approx 0.15.$

CHAPTER 10

INDETERMINATE FORMS, IMPROPER INTEGRALS,

AND TAYLOR'S FORMULA

EXERCISES 10.1, page 459

1. $\lim\limits_{x\to 0} \dfrac{\sin x}{2x} = \lim\limits_{x\to 0} \dfrac{\cos x}{2} = \dfrac{\cos 0}{2} = \dfrac{1}{2}$.

4. $\lim\limits_{x\to 4} \dfrac{x-4}{(x+4)^{1/3}-2} = \lim\limits_{x\to 4} \dfrac{1}{(x+4)^{-2/3}/3} = \dfrac{3}{8^{-2/3}} = \dfrac{3}{1/4} = 12.$

7. This function is $\underline{NOT}$ indeterminate as $x \to 1$ since the denominator does not
    approach 0. Thus L'Hôpital's rule cannot be used. However, by the methods
    of Chapter 2, $\lim\limits_{x\to 1} \dfrac{x^2-3x+2}{x^2-2x-1} = \dfrac{1-3+2}{1-2-1} = \dfrac{0}{-2} = 0.$

10. $\lim\limits_{x\to 0} \dfrac{\sin x}{x - \tan x} = \lim\limits_{x\to 0} \dfrac{\cos x}{1 - \sec^2 x} = -\infty$ since $\cos x \to 1$ and $1 - \sec^2 x$ is negative
    and approaches 0.

13. $\lim\limits_{x\to 0} \dfrac{x - \sin x}{x^3} = \lim\limits_{x\to 0} \dfrac{1 - \cos x}{3x^2} = \lim\limits_{x\to 0} \dfrac{\sin x}{6x} = \lim\limits_{x\to 0} \dfrac{\cos x}{6} = \dfrac{\cos 0}{6} = \dfrac{1}{6}$.

16. $\lim\limits_{x\to 0^+} \dfrac{\cos x}{x} = \infty$ since $\cos x \to 1$ and $x > 0$ as $x \to 0^+$. (Note that L'Hôpital's
    rule cannot be used.)

19. $\lim\limits_{x\to\infty} \dfrac{x^2}{\ln x} = \lim\limits_{x\to\infty} \dfrac{2x}{1/x} = \lim\limits_{x\to\infty} 2x^2 = \infty.$

22. $\lim\limits_{x\to 0} \dfrac{2x}{\tan^{-1}x} = \lim\limits_{x\to 0} \dfrac{2}{1/(1+x^2)} = \dfrac{2}{1} = 2.$

25. The limit is ∞ since $x \cos x + e^{-x} \to 0(1) + 1 = 1$, and $x^2 \to 0$ and is positive
    as $x \to 0$. (Again, L'Hôpital's rule cannot be used.)

28. $\lim\limits_{x\to\infty} \dfrac{x^3+x+1}{3x^3+4} = \lim\limits_{x\to\infty} \dfrac{3x^2+1}{9x^2} = \lim\limits_{x\to\infty} \dfrac{6x}{18x} = \dfrac{1}{3}$.

31. If n is an integer, then after n applications of L'Hôpital's rule (possible,
    since each quotient is the ∞/∞ form), we obtain $\lim\limits_{x\to\infty} \dfrac{x^n}{e^x} = \lim\limits_{x\to\infty} \dfrac{n!}{e^x} = 0.$ If n is
    not an integer, let $k = [n] + 1$ so that $n - k < 0$. After k applications of
    the rule, $\lim\limits_{x\to\infty} \dfrac{x^n}{e^x} = \lim\limits_{x\to\infty} n(n-1)\dots(n-k+1) \dfrac{x^{n-k}}{e^x} = 0$, since $x^{n-k} \to 0$ and $e^x \to \infty$
    as $x \to \infty$.

34. $\lim\limits_{x\to 0} \dfrac{\sin^2 x + 2 \cos x - 2}{\cos^2 x - x \sin x - 1} = \lim\limits_{x\to 0} \dfrac{2 \sin x \cos x - 2 \sin x}{-2 \cos x \sin x - x \cos x - \sin x}$.

$$= \lim_{x\to 0} \frac{\sin 2x - 2\sin x}{-\sin 2x - x\cos x - \sin x} = \lim_{x\to 0} \frac{2\cos 2x - 2\cos x}{-2\cos 2x - 2\cos x + x\sin x}$$

$$= \frac{2-2}{-2-2+0} = \frac{0}{-4} = 0.$$

37. Using the identity $\frac{\tan x - \sin x}{\tan x} = 1 - \frac{\sin x}{\sin x/\cos x} = 1 - \cos x$, we have

$$\lim_{x\to 0} \frac{\tan x - \sin x}{x^3 \tan x} = \lim_{x\to 0} \frac{1-\cos x}{x^3} = \lim_{x\to 0} \frac{\sin x}{3x^2} = \lim_{x\to 0} \frac{\cos x}{6x} \text{ which does not exist}$$

since $\cos x \to 1$, $6x \to 0$.

40. $\lim_{x\to 0} \frac{2 - e^x - e^{-x}}{1 - \cos^2 x} = \lim_{x\to 0} \frac{-e^x + e^{-x}}{2\cos x \sin x} = \lim_{x\to 0} \frac{-e^x - e^{-x}}{2(\cos^2 x - \sin^2 x)} = \frac{-1-1}{2(1-0)} = \frac{-2}{2} = -1.$

43. $\lim_{x\to 0} \frac{x - \tan^{-1} x}{x \sin x} = \lim_{x\to 0} \frac{1 - 1/(1+x^2)}{x \cos x + \sin x} = \lim_{x\to 0} \frac{2x/(1+x^2)^2}{-x \sin x + 2 \cos x} = \frac{0}{0+2} = 0.$

46. $\lim_{x\to 0} \frac{x \sin^{-1} x}{x - \sin x} = \lim_{x\to 0} \frac{x/\sqrt{1-x^2} + \sin^{-1} x}{1 - \cos x}$, which is still of indeterminate form

$0/0$. Separately, we calculate $D_x \frac{x}{\sqrt{1-x^2}} = \frac{\sqrt{1-x^2} - x(-2x)/2\sqrt{1-x^2}}{(\sqrt{1-x^2})^2} = \frac{(1-x^2)+x^2}{(1-x^2)^{3/2}}$

$= \frac{1}{(1+x^2)^{3/2}}$. Continuing the limit calculation from above, using L'Hôpital's

rule, $\lim_{x\to 0} \frac{x/\sqrt{1-x^2} + \sin^{-1} x}{1 - \cos x} = \lim_{x\to 0} \frac{1/(1-x^2)^{3/2} + 1/\sqrt{1-x^2}}{\sin x}$, which does not exist

since the numerator approaches 2 and $\sin x \to 0$ as $x \to 0$.

49. $\lim_{x\to\infty} \frac{2e^{3x} + \ln x}{e^{3x} + x^2} = \lim_{x\to\infty} \frac{6e^{3x} + 1/x}{3e^{3x} + 2x} = \lim_{x\to\infty} \frac{18e^{3x} - 1/x^2}{9e^{3x} + 2} = \lim_{x\to\infty} \frac{54e^{3x} + 2/x^3}{27e^{3x}}$

$$= \lim_{x\to\infty} (2 + \frac{2}{27e^{3x} x^3}) = 2 + 0 = 2.$$

52. As $x \to 0^+$, this is of $0/0$ form, but the limit calculation is tricky. Pro-

ceeding directly, $\lim_{x\to 0^+} \frac{e^{-1/x}}{x} = \lim_{x\to 0^+} \frac{e^{-1/x}D_x(-1/x)}{1} = \lim_{x\to 0^+} \frac{e^{-1/x}}{x^2}$, still $0/0$,

but worse than before. Rather: $\lim_{x\to 0^+} \frac{e^{-1/x}}{x} = \lim_{x\to 0^+} \frac{1/x}{e^{1/x}} = \lim_{x\to 0^+} \frac{(-1/x^2)}{e^{1/x}(-1/x^2)}$

$= \lim_{x\to 0^+} \frac{1}{e^{1/x}} = 0$ since $e^{1/x} \to \infty$. However, as $x \to 0^-$, $-1/x > 0$, and $e^{-1/x} \to$

$+\infty$ and the denominator, x, approaches 0 through negative values. Hence

$\lim_{x\to 0^-} \frac{e^{-1/x}}{x} = -\infty$ and $\lim_{x\to 0} \frac{e^{-1/x}}{x}$ does not exist.

55. (a) This is a 0/0 form as $R \to 0^+$. Thus, by L'Hôpital's rule, $\lim\limits_{R\to 0^+} I =$

$$\lim_{R\to 0^+} \frac{E\, D_R(1-e^{-Rt/L})}{D_R(R)} = \lim_{R\to 0^+} \frac{E(0 - e^{-Rt/L}D_R(-Rt/L))}{1} = \lim_{R\to 0^+} \frac{Et}{L} e^{-Rt/L} =$$

$$\frac{Et}{L} \cdot e^0 = \frac{Et}{L}.$$

(b) and (c) As $L \to 0^+$ or $t \to \infty$, $-Rt/L \to -\infty$ and $e^{-Rt/L} \to 0$. Thus both

limits are evaluated directly (without L'Hôpital) to obtain $\dfrac{E(1-0)}{R} = \dfrac{E}{R}$.

58. Since $f(x) \to \infty$ as $x \to \infty$, $\lim\limits_{x\to\infty} \dfrac{f(x)}{g(x)} = \lim\limits_{x\to\infty} \dfrac{f'(x)}{g'(x)} = \dfrac{(\sin x)^{2/3}}{2x}$. Since $0 \le$

$(\sin x)^{2/3} \le 1$, and $1/2x \to 0$ as $x \to \infty$, the limit is 0 by the Sandwich

limit theorem.

EXERCISES 10.2, page 463

1. $\lim\limits_{x\to 0^+} x \ln x = \lim\limits_{x\to 0^+} \dfrac{\ln x}{1/x} = \lim\limits_{x\to 0^+} \dfrac{1/x}{-(1/x^2)} = \lim\limits_{x\to 0^+} (-x) = 0.$

4. $\lim\limits_{x\to\infty} x(e^{1/x} - 1) = \lim\limits_{x\to\infty} \dfrac{e^{1/x} - 1}{1/x} = \lim\limits_{x\to\infty} \dfrac{(-1/x^2)e^{1/x}}{(-1/x^2)} = \lim\limits_{x\to\infty} e^{1/x} = e^0 = 1.$

7. $\lim\limits_{x\to 0^+} \sin x \ln \sin x = \lim\limits_{x\to 0^+} \dfrac{\ln \sin x}{\csc x} = \lim\limits_{x\to 0^+} \dfrac{\cos x/\sin x}{-\csc x \cot x} = \lim\limits_{x\to 0^+} \dfrac{\cot x}{-\csc x \cot x}$

$= \lim\limits_{x\to 0^+} \dfrac{1}{-\csc x} = \lim\limits_{x \to 0^+} (-\sin x) = 0.$

10. $\lim\limits_{x\to\infty} e^{-x} \ln x = \lim\limits_{x\to\infty} \dfrac{\ln x}{e^x} = \lim\limits_{x\to\infty} \dfrac{1/x}{e^x} = 0.$

13. This is a 1^∞ indeterminate form. If $y = (1 + \dfrac{1}{x})^{5x}$, then $\ln y = 5x \ln(1 + 1/x)$

$= 5 \dfrac{\ln(1 + 1/x)}{1/x}$. $\lim\limits_{x\to\infty} \ln y = \lim\limits_{x\to\infty} \dfrac{5(-1/x^2)/(1+1/x)}{(-1/x^2)} = \lim\limits_{x\to\infty} \dfrac{5}{1+1/x} = 5.$ Thus

$\lim\limits_{x\to\infty} y = e^5.$

16. If $y = x^x$, then $\ln y = x \ln x$ and $\lim\limits_{x\to 0^+} \ln y = \lim\limits_{x\to 0^+} x \ln x = 0$, by #1. Thus,

$\lim\limits_{x\to 0^+} y = \lim\limits_{x\to 0^+} x^x = e^0 = 1.$

19. $(\tan x)^x$ is not indeterminate as $x \to \pi/2^-$ since $\tan x \to \infty$ and $x \to \pi/2 > 1$.

Thus $(\tan x)^x \to \infty$ as $x \to \pi/2^-$.

22. If $y = (1+3x)^{\csc x}$, $\ln y = \csc x \ln(1+3x) = \dfrac{\ln(1+3x)}{\sin x}$.

$\lim\limits_{x\to 0^+} \ln y = \lim\limits_{x\to 0^+} \dfrac{\ln(1+3x)}{\sin x} = \lim\limits_{x\to 0^+} \dfrac{3}{(1+3x)\cos x} = 3.$ Thus $\lim\limits_{x\to 0^+} y = e^3.$

25. $\lim\limits_{x\to 0} \left(\dfrac{1}{x} - \dfrac{1}{\sin x}\right) = \lim\limits_{x\to 0} \dfrac{\sin x - x}{x \sin x} = \lim\limits_{x\to 0} \dfrac{\cos x - 1}{x \cos x + \sin x} = \lim\limits_{x\to 0} \dfrac{-\sin x}{-x \sin x + 2 \cos x}$

$= \dfrac{0}{0 + 2} = 0.$

28. This is an ∞^0 indeterminate form as $x \to \infty$. $y = (1+e^x)^{e^{-x}} \implies \ln y =$

$e^{-x} \ln(1+e^x) = \dfrac{\ln(1+e^x)}{e^x}$. $\lim\limits_{x\to\infty} \ln y = \lim\limits_{x\to\infty} \dfrac{e^x/(1+e^x)}{e^x} = \lim\limits_{x\to\infty} \dfrac{1}{1+e^x} = 0.$ Thus

$\lim\limits_{x\to\infty} y = e^0 = 1.$

31. $\lim\limits_{x\to 0} \cot 2x \tan^{-1}x = \lim\limits_{x\to 0} \dfrac{\tan^{-1}x}{\tan 2x} = \lim\limits_{x\to 0} \dfrac{1/(1+x^2)}{2 \sec^2 2x} = \dfrac{1}{2}$.

34. $\lim\limits_{x\to\infty} (\sqrt{x^2+4} - \tan^{-1}x) = \infty$ since $\sqrt{x^2+4} \to \infty$, but $\tan^{-1}x \to \pi/2$ as $x \to \infty$.

37. $\dfrac{x}{x^2+2x-3} - \dfrac{4}{x+3} = \dfrac{x}{(x+3)(x-1)} - \dfrac{4}{x+3} = \dfrac{1}{x+3}\left(\dfrac{x}{x-1} - 4\right) = \dfrac{1}{x+3}\left(\dfrac{x-4x+4}{x-1}\right) = \dfrac{-3x+4}{(x+3)(x-1)}$.

As $x \to -3$, $(-3x+4) \to 13$ and the denominator $\to 0$. Thus the limit does not exist. (The right-hand limit is $-\infty$, the left-hand limit is ∞.)

40. $\lim\limits_{x\to\pi/2} \sec x \cos 3x = \lim\limits_{x\to\pi/2} \dfrac{\cos 3x}{\cos x} = \lim\limits_{x\to\pi/2} \dfrac{-3 \sin 3x}{-\sin x} = \dfrac{-3(-1)}{-1} = -3.$

43. $y = x^{1/x} \implies \ln y = \dfrac{\ln x}{x}.$ $\lim\limits_{x\to 0^+} \ln y = -\infty \implies \lim\limits_{x\to 0^+} x^{1/x} = 0.$ $\lim\limits_{x\to\infty} \ln y =$

$\lim\limits_{x\to\infty} \dfrac{\ln x}{x} = \lim\limits_{x\to\infty} \dfrac{1/x}{1} = 0 \implies \lim\limits_{x\to\infty} x^{1/x} = 1.$ Thus $y = 1$ is a horizontal

asymptote. $\ln y = \dfrac{\ln x}{x} \implies \dfrac{y'}{y} = \dfrac{x(1/x) - \ln x}{x^2} \implies y' = \dfrac{x^{1/x}(1 - \ln x)}{x^2} = 0$

at $x = e$. $x < e \implies \ln x < 1 \implies y' > 0$. $x > e \implies \ln x > 1 \implies y' < 0$.

Thus $y = f(x)$ is increasing on $(0,e]$, decreasing to the horizontal asymptote $(y = 1)$ on $[e,\infty)$ and has a local maximum at $x = e$.

46. Let $y = f(m) = (1 + r/m)^{mt}$, a 1^∞ form as $m \to \infty$. $\ln y = mt \ln(1 + r/m) =$

$t \dfrac{\ln(1 + r/m)}{1/m}$. $\lim\limits_{m\to\infty} \ln y = t \lim\limits_{m\to\infty} \dfrac{D_m(1+r/m)/(1+r/m)}{D_m(1/m)} = t \lim\limits_{m\to\infty} \dfrac{(-r/m^2)}{(1+r/m)(-1/m^2)}$

$= t \lim\limits_{m\to\infty} \dfrac{r}{1+r/m} = \dfrac{tr}{1+0} = tr.$ Thus $\lim\limits_{m\to\infty} y = e^{rt}$, and the balance (which is the

limit of Py) is Pe^{rt}.

EXERCISES 10.3, page 467

1. $\int_1^\infty \frac{1}{x^{4/3}} dx = \lim_{t\to\infty} \int_1^t x^{-4/3} dx = \lim_{t\to\infty} -3x^{-1/3} \Big]_1^t = \lim_{t\to\infty} (\frac{-3}{\sqrt[3]{t}} +3) = 0 + 3 = 3.$

4. $\int_0^\infty \frac{x}{1+x^2} dx = \lim_{t\to\infty} \int_0^t \frac{x}{1+x^2} dx = \lim_{t\to\infty} \frac{\ln(1+x^2)}{2} \Big]_0^t = \lim_{t\to\infty} (\frac{\ln(1+t^2)}{2} - \frac{\ln 1}{2}) =$

$\lim_{t\to\infty} \frac{\ln(1+t^2)}{2} = \infty.$ Thus the integral diverges.

7. $\int_0^\infty e^{-2x} dx = \lim_{t\to\infty} \int_0^t e^{-2x} dx = \lim_{t\to\infty} \frac{e^{-2x}}{-2} \Big]_0^t = \lim_{t\to\infty} (-\frac{1}{2})(e^{-2t} - 1) = \frac{1}{2}.$

10. $\int_0^\infty \frac{1}{\sqrt[3]{x+1}} dx = \lim_{t\to\infty} \int_0^t (x+1)^{-1/3} dx = \lim_{t\to\infty} (\frac{3}{2})(x+1)^{2/3} \Big]_0^t = \lim_{t\to\infty} \frac{3}{2}[(t+1)^{2/3} - 1]$

$= \infty.$ Thus the integral diverges.

13. With $u = \sin x$, $\int \frac{\cos x}{1 + \sin^2 x} dx = \int \frac{du}{1 + u^2} = \tan^{-1}u.$ Thus $\int_0^\infty \frac{\cos x}{1 + \sin^2 x} dx$

$= \lim_{t\to\infty} \tan^{-1}(\sin x)] _0^t = \lim_{t\to\infty} \tan^{-1}(\sin t) - 0$ which does not exist. As t in-

creases, sin t oscillates between -1 and +1, and $\tan^{-1}(\sin t)$ oscillates

between $-\pi/4$ and $+\pi/4$, approaching no limit. Thus the integral diverges.

15. Using (11.7) with a = 0, $\int_{-\infty}^\infty xe^{-x^2} dx = \int_{-\infty}^0 xe^{-x^2} dx + \int_0^\infty xe^{-x^2} dx.$ Now,

$\int_{-\infty}^0 xe^{-x^2} dx = \lim_{t\to-\infty} \frac{-e^{-x^2}}{2} \Big]_t^0 = \lim_{t\to\infty} (\frac{-e^0}{2} + \frac{e^{-t^2}}{2}) = -\frac{1}{2} + 0 = -\frac{1}{2}.$ The second

integral is $\int_0^\infty xe^{-x^2} dx = \lim_{t\to\infty} \frac{-e^{-x^2}}{2} \Big]_0^t = \lim_{t\to\infty} (\frac{-e^{-t^2}}{2} + \frac{e^0}{2}) = 0 + \frac{1}{2} = \frac{1}{2}.$ Since

both integrals converge, the original integral converges, and its value is

their sum. Thus $\int_{-\infty}^\infty xe^{-x^2} dx = -\frac{1}{2} + \frac{1}{2} = 0.$

16. Using (10.4) with a = 0, $\int_{-\infty}^\infty \cos^2 x\, dx = \int_{-\infty}^0 \cos^2 x\, dx + \int_0^\infty \cos^2 x\, dx.$

$\lim_{t\to\infty} \int_0^t \cos^2 x\, dx = (\frac{1}{2}) \lim_{t\to\infty} \int_0^t (1 + \cos 2x) dx = \lim_{t\to\infty} [t + \frac{\sin 2t}{2}] = \infty.$ Since at

least one of the two improper integrals on the right side diverges, the given

integral diverges.

19. $\int_0^\infty \cos x \, dx = \lim_{t\to\infty} \sin x \,]_0^t = \lim_{t\to\infty} \sin t$, which does not exist. Thus, the

integral diverges.

22. Integrating by parts ($u = x$, $dv = e^{-x}dx$), or using Formula 98, $\int xe^{-x}dx =$

$-(x+1)e^{-x} + C$. Thus $\int_0^\infty xe^{-x}dx = \lim_{t\to\infty} [-(x+1)e^{-x}]_0^t = \lim_{t\to\infty} [-(t+1)e^{-t} + 1]$

$= 0 + 1 = 1$. $(\lim_{t\to\infty} (t+1)e^{-t} = \lim_{t\to\infty} \dfrac{t+1}{e^t} = 0$ by L'Hôpital's Rule.)

25. (a) $A = \int_1^\infty \dfrac{1}{x} \, dx = \lim_{t\to\infty} \int_1^t \dfrac{1}{x} \, dx = \lim_{t\to\infty} \ln t = \infty$. Thus no value is assignable

to the area.

(b) $V = \pi \int_1^\infty \dfrac{1}{x^2} \, dx = \pi \lim_{t\to\infty} \int_1^t x^{-2} \, dx = \pi \lim_{t\to\infty} -\dfrac{1}{x} \,]_1^t = \pi$.

28. (a) $A = \int_8^\infty x^{-2/3} \, dx = \lim_{t\to\infty} 3x^{1/3} \,]_8^t = \infty$. Thus no value is assignable to the

area.

(b) $V = \pi \int_8^\infty x^{-4/3} \, dx = \pi \lim_{t\to\infty} [-3x^{-1/3} \,]_8^t = (-3\pi) \lim_{t\to\infty} (\dfrac{1}{t^{1/3}} - \dfrac{1}{8^{1/3}}) = \dfrac{3\pi}{2}$.

31. If $n \neq -1$, $\int_1^\infty x^n dx = \lim_{t\to\infty} \dfrac{x^{n+1}}{n+1}]_1^t = \lim_{t\to\infty} \dfrac{t^{n+1}}{n+1} - \dfrac{1}{n+1} = -\dfrac{1}{n+1}$ if $n+1 < 0$, ∞ if

$n+1 > 0$. If $n = -1$, $\int_1^\infty x^{-1}dx = \lim_{t\to\infty} \ln x \,]_1^t = \lim_{t\to\infty} \ln t = \infty$. Thus (a) con-

verges if $n+1 < 0$, or $n < -1$; (b) diverges if $n \geq -1$.

34. Let x be the distance between the electrons and k, the constant of propor-

tionality. Then the force function is $f(x) = k/x^2$. Since the electrons

start 1 cm. apart, $W = \int_1^\infty f(x) dx = \int_1^\infty k/x^2 dx = \lim_{t\to\infty} -\dfrac{k}{x} \,]_1^t = \lim_{t\to\infty} [-\dfrac{k}{t} + k]$

$= 0 + k = k$.

37. First we show that $\dfrac{1}{x} < \dfrac{1}{\ln x}$ on $[2,\infty)$. Let $f(x) = x - \ln x$. Then $f'(x) =$

$1 - \dfrac{1}{x} \geq 1 - \dfrac{1}{2} > 0$ and f is increasing if $x \geq 2$. Thus $f(x) \geq f(2)$ for $x \geq 2$,

or $x - \ln x \geq 2 - \ln 2 \geq 2 - \ln e = 1 > 0$, and $x > \ln x$, or $\dfrac{1}{x} < \dfrac{1}{\ln x}$ on $[2,\infty)$.

Since $\int_2^\infty \dfrac{1}{x} \, dx = \lim_{t\to\infty} \ln t - \ln 2 = \infty$, this integral diverges. With $f(x) =$

$1/x$, $g(x) = 1/\ln x$ and comparison test (ii), $\int_2^\infty \dfrac{1}{\ln x} \, dx$ diverges.

40. Hint: For all s and t, $\int_s^b + \int_b^t = (\int_s^a + \int_a^b) + (\int_b^a + \int_a^t)$.

43. $L[1] = \int_0^\infty e^{-sx} \cdot 1 \, dx = \lim_{t \to \infty} \frac{e^{-sx}}{-s}]_0^t = \lim_{t \to \infty} \frac{(1 - e^{-st})}{s} = \frac{1}{s}$ provided $s > 0$.

46. $L[\sin x] = \int_0^\infty e^{-sx} \sin x \, dx$. Using Formula 98 from the Table of Integrals with $a = -s$, $b = 1$, $u = x$ (or 2 integrations by parts), $L[\sin x] =$

$\lim_{t \to \infty} \frac{e^{-sx}}{s^2+1} (-s \sin x - \cos x)]_0^t = \lim_{t \to \infty} \frac{(1 - e^{-ts}(s \sin t + \cos t))}{s^2+1}$. If $s > 0$

then $\lim_{t \to \infty} e^{-ts} (s \sin t + \cos t) = 0$ since $|s \sin t + \cos t| \le s|\sin t| + |\cos t| \le s+1$, independent of t, whereas $\lim_{t \to \infty} e^{-ts} = 0$. The statement then follows from the Sandwich Theorem. Thus $L[\sin x] = 1/(s^2+1)$, if $s > 0$.

49. Here we will use the formulas (derived by integration by parts)

$\int xe^{-x} \, dx = -(x+1)e^{-x} + C$, $\int x^2 e^{-x} \, dx = -(x^2+2x+2)e^{-x} + C$ and the limit (via L'Hôpital's rule) $\lim_{t \to \infty} t^n e^{-t} = 0$ for any $n > 0$. (a) $\Gamma(1) = \int_0^\infty e^{-x} \, dx =$

$\lim_{t \to \infty} (1 - e^{-t}) = 1$. $\Gamma(2) = \int_0^\infty xe^{-x} dx = \lim_{t \to \infty} -(x+1)e^{-x}]_0^t = \lim_{t \to \infty} (-(t+1)e^{-t} + 1)$

$= 1$. $\Gamma(3) = \int_0^\infty x^2 e^{-x} dx = \lim_{t \to \infty} -(x^2+2x+2)e^{-x}]_0^t = \lim_{t \to \infty} (-t^2+2t+2)e^{-t} + 2) = 2$.

(b) $\Gamma(n+1) = \int_0^\infty x^n e^{-x} dx$. Let $u = x^n$, $dv = e^{-x} dx$. Then $du = nx^{n-1} dx$, $v =$

$-e^{-x}$ and $\Gamma(n+1) = \lim_{t \to \infty} -x^n e^{-x}]_0^t + \int_0^\infty nx^{n-1} e^{-x} dx = \lim_{t \to \infty} (-t^n e^{-t} + 0) + n\Gamma(n)$

$= n\Gamma(n)$.

(c) The truth of the statement $\Gamma(n+1) = n!$ was established in part (a) for $n = 1$ ($\Gamma(2) = 1$) and $n = 2$ ($\Gamma(3) = 2 = 2!$). So we assume that it is true for $n = k-1$, i.e. $\Gamma(k) = (k-1)!$ and prove that it is true for $n = k$, i.e. we must show $\Gamma(k+1) = k!$ By part (b), $\Gamma(k+1) = k\Gamma(k)$ and by the above assumption, this yields $\Gamma(k+1) = k \cdot (k-1)! = k!$, which proves the statement true for all positive integers.

EXERCISES 10.4, page 474

1. Since $1/\sqrt[3]{x}$ is continuous on $(0,8]$ and has an infinite discontinuity at 0, we

get by (10.5ii), $\int_0^8 1/\sqrt[3]{x} \, dx = \lim_{t \to 0^+} \int_t^8 x^{-1/3} \, dx = \lim_{t \to 0^+} \frac{3}{2} x^{2/3}]_t^8 =$

$\lim\limits_{t \to 0^+} \frac{3}{2}(8^{2/3} - t^{2/3}) = \frac{3}{2}(2^2 - 0) = 6.$

4. Since $1/(x+2)^{5/4}$ is continuous on $(-2,-1]$ and has an infinite discontinuity at

-2, $(10.5\text{ii}) \Longrightarrow \int_{-2}^{-1} 1/(x+2)^{5/4}\, dx = \lim\limits_{x \to -2^+} \int_{t}^{-1} (x+2)^{-5/4}\, dx = \lim\limits_{t \to -2^+} -4(x+2)^{-1/4}]_{t}^{-1}$

$= \lim\limits_{t \to -2^+} [-4 + \frac{4}{(t+2)^{1/4}}] = \infty.$ Thus the integral diverges.

7. Since the integrand is discontinuous at $x = 4$, by (10.5i) $\int_{0}^{4} \frac{1}{(4-x)^{3/2}}\, dx =$

$\lim\limits_{t \to 4^-} \int_{0}^{t} (4-x)^{-3/2}\, dx = \lim\limits_{t \to 4^-} \frac{2}{(4-x)^{1/2}}]_{0}^{t} = 2\lim\limits_{t \to 4^-} [\frac{1}{(4-t)^{1/2}} - \frac{1}{2}] = \infty.$ Thus,

the integral diverges.

10. $\int_{1}^{2} \frac{x}{x^2-1}\, dx = \lim\limits_{t \to 1^+} \int_{t}^{2} \frac{x}{x^2-1}\, dx = \lim\limits_{t \to 1^+} \frac{\ln(x^2-1)}{2}]_{t}^{2} = \lim\limits_{t \to 1^+} \frac{\ln 3 - \ln(t^2-1)}{2} = \infty,$

and the integral diverges.

13. $\int_{-2}^{0} \frac{1}{\sqrt{4-x^2}}\, dx = \lim\limits_{t \to -2^+} \sin^{-1}\frac{x}{2}]_{t}^{0} = \lim\limits_{t \to -2^+} (-\sin^{-1}\frac{t}{2}) = -\sin^{-1}(-1) = \pi/2.$

16. $x^2 - x - 2 = (x-2)(x+1)$. Thus the integrand has a discontinuity at $x = 2$ in

$[0,4]$, and by (10.6) we use $\int_{0}^{4} = \int_{0}^{2} + \int_{2}^{4}$ and examine each of the integrals.

As in Sec. 9.4 , $\frac{1}{(x-2)(x+1)} = \frac{1/3}{(x-2)} - \frac{1/3}{(x+1)}$. Thus $\int_{0}^{2} \frac{1}{x^2-x-2}\, dx =$

$\lim\limits_{t \to 2^-} \frac{1}{3}[\ln|x-2| - \ln|x+1|]_{0}^{t} = \frac{1}{3}\lim\limits_{t \to 2^-} (\ln|t-2| - \ln 2 - \ln|t+1|) = -\infty$, and the

original integral diverges since at least one of the integrals on the right

diverges.

19. $\int_{0}^{\pi/2} \tan x\, dx = \lim\limits_{t \to \pi/2^-} (-\ln|\cos x|)]_{0}^{t} = \lim\limits_{t \to \pi/2^-} (-\ln|\cos t|).$ Now, as

$t \to \pi/2^-$, $|\cos t| \to 0$ and $\ln|\cos t| \to -\infty$. Thus the above limit is ∞, and the

integral diverges.

22. The integrand, $1/x(\ln x)^2$, is continuous on $[1/e, e]$ except at $x = 1$ where

$\ln x = 0$. Thus, by (10.6) we use $\int_{1/e}^{e} = \int_{1/e}^{1} + \int_{1}^{e}$. To get the antideriva-

tive, let $u = \ln x$, $du = (1/x)dx$. Then $\int 1/x(\ln x)^2\, dx = \int 1/u^2\, du = -1/u + C$

$= -1/\ln x + C$. Then the 2nd integral above is $\int_1^e \dfrac{1}{x(\ln x)^2}\, dx = \lim\limits_{t\to 1^+} [-\dfrac{1}{\ln x}]_t^e$

$= \lim\limits_{t\to 1^+} [-\dfrac{1}{\ln e} + \dfrac{1}{\ln t}] = \infty$ since $\ln t \to 0$ and $1/\ln t \to \infty$ as $t \to 1^+$. Since at

at least one of the two integrals above diverges, the original integral diverges.

25. The integrand is continuous on $[0,\pi]$ except at $\pi/2$ since $\sin \pi/2 = 1$.

$\int_0^\pi = \int_0^{\pi/2} + \int_{\pi/2}^\pi$. For the antiderivative, let $u = 1 - \sin x$, $du = -\cos x\, dx$.

$\int \cos x/\sqrt{1 - \sin x}\, dx = -\int u^{-1/2}\, du = 2u^{1/2} + C = 2\sqrt{1 - \sin x} + C$. Thus

$\int_0^{\pi/2} \dfrac{\cos x}{\sqrt{1 - \sin x}}\, dx = \lim\limits_{t\to\pi/2^-} [-2\sqrt{1 - \sin x}]_0^t = \lim\limits_{t\to\pi/2^-} (-2\sqrt{1 - \sin t} + 2) =$

$0 + 2 = 2$. Also, $\int_{\pi/2}^\pi \dfrac{\cos x}{\sqrt{1 - \sin x}}\, dx = \lim\limits_{t\to\pi/2^+} [-2\sqrt{1 - \sin x}]_t^\pi =$

$\lim\limits_{t\to\pi/2^-} (-2 + 2\sqrt{1 - \sin t}) = -2 + 0 = -2$. The given integral is the sum of

the values of these two convergent integrals, namely, $2 + (-2) = 0$.

28. The integrand is discontinuous at $x = \pm 1$. Thus we select any number between

-1 and 1, say, 0, and $I = \int_{-1}^3 = \int_{-1}^0 + \int_0^1 + \int_1^3 = I_1 + I_2 + I_3$. To get an anti-

derivative, let $u = x^2 - 1$, $du = 2x\, dx$. Then $\int \dfrac{x}{\sqrt[3]{x^2-1}}\, dx = \dfrac{1}{2}\int u^{-1/3} du =$

$\dfrac{3}{4} u^{2/3} + C = \dfrac{3}{4}(x^2-1)^{2/3} + C$. Thus $I_1 = \lim\limits_{t\to -1^+} \dfrac{3}{4}(x^2-1)^{2/3}]_t^0$

$= \lim\limits_{t\to -1^+} (\dfrac{3}{4} - \dfrac{3}{4}(t^2-1)^{2/3}) = \dfrac{3}{4} - 0$. $I_2 = \lim\limits_{t\to 1^-} (\dfrac{3}{4}(t^2-1)^{2/3} - \dfrac{3}{4}) = 0 - \dfrac{3}{4}$.

$I_3 = \lim\limits_{t\to 1^+} (\dfrac{3}{4}(3^2-1)^{2/3} - \dfrac{3}{4}(t^2-1)^{2/3}) = \dfrac{3}{4}(8)^{2/3} = 3$. Since all 3 integrals

converge, the given integral converges and its value is $I_1 + I_2 + I_3 =$

$\dfrac{3}{4} + (-\dfrac{3}{4}) + 3 = 3$.

31. (a) $A = \int_0^1 1/\sqrt{x}\, dx = \lim\limits_{t\to 0^+} \int_t^1 x^{-1/2} dx = \lim\limits_{t\to 0^+} 2\sqrt{x}]_t^1 = \lim\limits_{t\to 0^+} (2 - 2\sqrt{t}) = 2$.

(b) $V = \pi\int_0^1 (1/\sqrt{x})^2 dx = \pi \lim\limits_{t\to 0^+} \int_t^1 \dfrac{1}{x}\, dx = \pi \lim\limits_{t\to 0^+} \ln x]_t^1 = \pi \lim\limits_{t\to 0^+} (\ln 1 - \ln t)$

$= \infty$. Thus no value can be assigned.

34. (a) $A = \int_1^2 \frac{1}{x-1}\,dx = \lim_{t \to 1^+} (\ln 1 - \ln(t-1)) = \infty$.

(b) $V = \pi \int_1^2 \frac{1}{(x-1)^2}\,dx = \pi \lim_{t \to 1^+} (\frac{1}{t-1} - 1) = \infty$.

Since both diverge, no value can be assigned in either case.

37. $1/\sqrt{x} > 0$ and $0 < \sin x \le 1$ on $(0,\pi] \implies 0 < \sin x/\sqrt{x} \le 1/\sqrt{x}$ on $(0,\pi]$.

$\int_0^\pi \frac{1}{\sqrt{x}}\,dx = \lim_{t \to 0^+} 2(\sqrt{\pi} - \sqrt{t}) = 2\sqrt{\pi}$. Thus with $f(x) = \sin x/\sqrt{x}$, $g(x) = 1/\sqrt{x}$,

and comparison test (i), $\int_0^\pi f(x)dx$ converges.

40. $0 < e^{-x} \le 1$, $1/x^{2/3} > 0 \implies 0 < e^{-x}/x^{2/3} < 1/x^{2/3}$ on $(0,1]$.

$\int_0^1 1/x^{2/3}dx = \lim_{t \to 0^+} 3(\sqrt[3]{1} - \sqrt[3]{t}) = 3$. Thus with $f(x) = e^{-x}/x^{2/3}$, $g(x) = $

$1/x^{2/3}$ and comparison test (i), $\int_0^1 f(x)dx$ converges.

EXERCISES 10.5, page 483

1. With $f(x) = \sin x$, $a = \pi/2$, $n = 3$, we have

   $f(x) = \sin x$ $f(\pi/2) = 1$

   $f'(x) = \cos x$ $f'(\pi/2) = 0$

   $f''(x) = -\sin x$ $f''(\pi/2) = -1$

   $f'''(x) = -\cos x$ $f'''(\pi/2) = 0$

   $f^{(4)}(x) = \sin x$ $f^{(4)}(z) = \sin z$.

Remembering to divide $f^{(k)}(a)$ by $k!$, we have

$\sin x = 1 - \frac{1}{2}(x - \frac{\pi}{2})^2 + \frac{\sin z}{4!}(x - \frac{\pi}{2})^4$ for some z between x and $\pi/2$.

4. With $f(x) = e^{-x}$, $a = 1$, $n = 3$, we have

   $f(x) = f''(x) = f^{(4)}(x) = e^{-x}$ $f(1) = f''(1) = e^{-1}$

                                   $f^{(4)}(z) = e^{-z}$

   $f'(x) = f'''(x) = -e^{-x}$ $f'(1) = f'''(1) = -e^{-1}$

$e^{-x} = e^{-1} - e^{-1}(x-1) + \frac{e^{-1}}{2!}(x-1)^2 - \frac{e^{-1}}{3!}(x-1)^3 + \frac{e^{-z}}{4!}(x-1)^4$

for some z between x and 1.

7. With $f(x) = 1/x$, $a = -2$, $n = 5$, we have

$f(x) = 1/x$ $f(-2) = -1/2$

$f'(x) = -1/x^2$ $f'(-2) = -1/4$

$f''(x) = 2/x^3$ $f''(-2) = -2/8$

$f'''(x) = -6/x^4$ $f'''(-2) = -6/16$

$f^{(4)}(x) = 24/x^5$ $f^{(4)}(-2) = -24/32$

$f^{(5)}(x) = -120/x^6$ $f^{(5)}(-2) = -120/64$

$f^{(6)}(x) = 720/x^7$ $f^{(6)}(z) = 720/z^7$

From the entries in the 2nd column, note that $f^{(k)}(-2)/k! = -1/2^{k+1}$ for

$k = 0,1,2,\ldots,5$. Thus $\frac{1}{x} = -\frac{1}{2} - \frac{1}{4}(x+2) - \frac{1}{8}(x+2)^2 - \frac{1}{16}(x+2)^3 - \frac{1}{32}(x+2)^4$

$- \frac{1}{64}(x+2)^5 + \frac{1}{z}(x+2)^6$, for some z between -2 and x.

10. We need here, $\sin \pi/6 = 1/2$, $\csc \pi/6 = 2$, $\cot \pi/6 = \sqrt{3}$. So, with $f(x) =$
    $\ln \sin x$, $a = \pi/6$, $n = 3$, we obtain

$f(x) = \ln \sin x$ $f(\pi/6) = \ln(1/2)$

$f'(x) = \cos x/\sin x = \cot x$ $f'(\pi/6) = \sqrt{3}$

$f''(x) = -\csc^2 x$ $f''(\pi/6) = -2^2 = -4$

$f'''(x) = 2 \csc^2 x \cot x$ $f'''(\pi/6) = 2(4)\sqrt{3} = 8\sqrt{3}$

$f^{(4)}(x) = -2(\csc^4 x + 2 \csc^2 x \cot^2 x)$. Thus

$\ln \sin x = \ln(1/2) + \sqrt{3}(x - \pi/6) - \frac{4}{2!}(x - \pi/6)^2 + \frac{8\sqrt{3}}{3!}(x - \pi/6)^3 +$

$\frac{f^{(4)}(z)}{4!} (x - \pi/6)^4$ for some z between $\pi/6$ and x.

13. In Maclaurin's formula $a = 0$. So with $n = 4$, we get

$f(x) = \ln(x+1)$ $f(0) = \ln 1 = 0$

$f'(x) = (x+1)^{-1}$ $f'(0) = 1$

$f''(x) = -(x+1)^{-2}$ $f''(0) = -1$

$f'''(x) = 2(x+1)^{-3}$ $f'''(0) = 2$

$f^{(4)}(x) = -6(x+1)^{-4}$ $f^{(4)}(0) = -6$

$f^{(5)}(x) = 24(x+1)^{-5}$ $f^{(5)}(z) = 24(z+1)^{-5}$

$\ln(x+1) = x - \frac{1}{2!}x^2 + \frac{2}{3!}x^3 - \frac{6}{4!}x^4 + \frac{24x^5}{5!(z+1)^5} = x - \frac{1}{2}x^2 + \frac{1}{3}x^3 - \frac{1}{4}x^4 +$

$\frac{x^5}{5(z+1)^5}$ for some z between x and 0.

16. $f(x) = \tan^{-1}x$ $f(0) = 0$

$f'(x) = (1+x^2)^{-1}$ $f'(0) = 1$

$f''(x) = -2x(1+x^2)^{-2}$ $f''(0) = 0$

$f'''(x) = (6x^2-2)(1+x^2)^{-3}$ $f'''(0) = -2$

$f^{(4)}(x) = 24(x-x^3)(1+x^2)^{-4}$

$\tan^{-1}x = x - \frac{2}{3!}x^3 + \frac{24(z-z^3)}{4!(1+z^2)^4}x^4 = x - \frac{1}{3}x^3 + \frac{(z-z^3)}{(1+z^2)^4}x^4$ for some z between

x and 0.

19. $f(x) = (x-1)^{-2}$ $f(0) = (-1)^{-2} = 1$

$f'(x) = -2(x-1)^{-3}$ $f'(0) = -2(-1)^{-3} = 2$

$f''(x) = 6(x-1)^{-4} = 3!(x-1)^{-4}$ $f''(0) = 3!(-1)^{-4} = 3!$

$f'''(x) = -24(x-1)^{-5} = -(4!)(x-1)^{-5}$ $f'''(0) = -(4!)(-1)^{-5} = 4!$

$f^{(4)}(x) = 120(x-1)^{-6} = 5!(x-1)^{-6}$ $f^{(4)}(0) = 5!(-1)^{-6} = 5!$

$f^{(5)}(x) = -720(x-1)^{-7} = -(6!)(x-1)^{-7}$ $f^{(5)}(0) = -6!(-1)^{-7} = 6!$

$f^{(6)}(x) = 5040(x-1)^{-8} = 7!(x-1)^{-8}$ $f^{(6)}(z) = 7!(z-1)^{-8}$

From the entries in the second column, we see that $f^{(k)}(0)/k! = (k+1)!/k! =$

k+1 for k = 0,1,...,5. Thus: $(x-1)^{-2} = 1 + 2x + 3x^2 + 4x^3 + 5x^4 + 6x^5 +$

$7(z-1)^{-8}x^6$ for some z between 0 and x. (The last coefficient is

$f^{(6)}(z)/6!$.)

22. $f(x) = e^{-x^2} \implies f'(x) = -2xe^{-x^2} \implies f''(x) = -2x(-2xe^{-x^2})-2e^{-x^2} =$

$(4x^2-2)e^{-x^2} \implies f'''(x) = (4x^2-2)(-2xe^{-x^2}) + 8xe^{-x^2} = (-8x^3+12x)e^{-x^2} \implies$

$f^{(4)}(x) = (-8x^3+12x)(-2xe^{-x^2}) + (-24x^2+12)e^{-x^2} = (16x^4-48x^2+12)e^{-x^2}$. Thus

$f(0) = 1$, $f'(0) = 0$, $f''(0)/2! = -2/2 = -1$, and $f'''(0) = 0$. Thus:

$e^{-x^2} = 1 - x^2 + (1/4!)(16z^4-48z^2+12)e^{-z^2}x^4$ for some z between 0 and x.

25. Using Exercise 1 with $x = 89^{\circ} = 90^{\circ}-1^{\circ} = \frac{\pi}{2} - \frac{\pi}{180}$, we have $x - \frac{\pi}{2} = \frac{-\pi}{180} \approx$

-0.0175 and $\sin 89^{\circ} = 1 - \frac{1}{2}(-\frac{\pi}{180})^2 + \frac{\sin z}{4!}(-\frac{\pi}{180})^4$

$\sin 89^{\circ} \approx 1 - \frac{(.0175)^2}{2} \approx 1 - \frac{.0003}{2} = 0.99985.$

$|R_n(x)| \approx \frac{|\sin z|(.0175)^4}{4!} < \frac{(.02)^4}{24} = \frac{16 \times 10^{-8}}{24} < 10^{-8}.$ (Compare the answer

obtained above with the value of $\sin 89^{\circ}$ in a 5-place table. They agree

exactly!)

28. Using Exercise 4 with x = 1.02, x-1 = .02, we have

$e^{-1.02} = e^{-1}(1 - .02 + \frac{(.02)^2}{2} - \frac{(.02)^3}{6}) + \frac{e^{-z}}{24}(.02)^4$

$e^{-1.02} \approx e^{-1}(1 - .02 + .0002 - .000001) = \frac{0.980199}{e} \approx 0.3606.$ Since 1 < z <

1.02, $e^{-z} < e^{-1} < 1$ and $|R_n(x)| = \frac{e^{-z}}{24}(.02)^4 < \frac{16 \times 10^{-8}}{24} < 10^{-8}.$

31. From Exercise 13, $\ln(x+1) = x - \frac{x^2}{2} + \frac{x^3}{3} - \frac{x^4}{4} + \frac{x^5}{5(z+1)^5}$ for some z between 0

and x. Taking x = 0.25 = 1/4 and dropping the remainder, we get

$\ln 1.25 \approx \frac{1}{4} - \frac{1/16}{2} + \frac{1/64}{3} - \frac{1/256}{4} = \frac{1}{4} - \frac{1}{32} + \frac{1}{192} - \frac{1}{1024} = 0.2500 - 0.0312 +$ 0.0052 - 0.0010 so that $\ln 1.25 \approx 0.2230$. The error in this approximation is the neglected remainder, $R_4(x)$. Since $0 < z < x = 0.25$, we have $z+1 > 1$ and, thus, $1/(z+1) < 1$. Now, $R_4(0.25) = \frac{(1/4)^5}{5(z+1)^5}$ so that $0 \leq R_4(0.25) < \frac{(1/4)^5}{5(1)^5} = \frac{1}{5(1024)} = \frac{1}{5120} < 2 \times 10^{-4}$. (3-place accuracy at least.)

34. From Exercise 12, $\log x = 1 + \frac{1}{10 \ln 10}(x-10) - \frac{1}{200 \ln 10}(x-10)^2 +$ $\frac{1}{3z^3 \ln 10}(x-10)^3$ where z is between 10 and x. Taking $x = 10.01$, so that $x-10 = .01$, and dropping the remainder, we obtain $\log 10.01 \approx 1 + \frac{1}{10 \ln 10} \cdot$ $(.01) - \frac{1}{200 \ln 10}(.01)^2 \approx 1.00043$. The error is the neglected remainder $R_3(10.01) = .01^3/3z^3 \ln 10$. Now, $10 < z < 10.01 \Rightarrow 1/z < 10 \Rightarrow 1/z^3 < 1/10^3 = 10^{-3} \Rightarrow 0 \leq R_3(10.01) < (.01^3)10^{-3}/3 \ln 10 = 10^{-9}/3 \ln 10$. Since $\ln 10 >$ 2.3, the error is $< 10^{-9}/6.9 \approx 1.4 \times 10^{-10}$. (Thus we'd have 9 place accuracy if we knew $\ln 10$ exactly to 9 places.)

35. Maclaurin's formula for $\cos x$ with $n = 3$ is $\cos x = 1 - \frac{x^2}{2} + \frac{(\cos z)x^4}{4!}$ (Compare #15). Thus if we use $\cos x \approx 1 - \frac{x^2}{2}$, the error is $\frac{|\cos z||x|^4}{24} \leq$ $\frac{1 \cdot (.1)^4}{24} = \frac{10^{-4}}{24} < 5 \times 10^{-6}$. Thus the accuracy is at least 5 places.

37. $f(x) = e^x \Rightarrow f^{(k)}(x) = e^x$ and $f^{(k)}(0) = 1$ for all k. Using $n = 2$ in Maclaurin's formula, $e^x = 1 + x + x^2/2 + R_2(x)$ where $R_2(x) = \frac{e^z}{3!}x^3$. Thus if we neglect the remainder, $e^x \approx 1 + x + x^2/2$ with error $R_2(x)$. Now, $|x| \leq 0.1$ $\Rightarrow -0.1 < x < 0.1$, and since z is between 0 and x, $-0.1 < z < 0.1$ also. Thus $e^z < e^{0.1} < e^{\ln 2} = 2$ since $\ln 2 \approx 0.693$ and e^x is an increasing function. Thus $|R_2(x)| \leq \frac{e^z|x|^3}{6} \leq \frac{2(0.1)^3}{6} = \frac{10^{-3}}{3} < 5 \times 10^{-4}$ (i.e., 3 place accuracy).

40. $f(x) = f''(x) = f^{(4)}(x) = \cosh x \Rightarrow f(0) = f''(0) = 1, f^{(4)}(z) = \cosh z$. $f'(x) = f'''(x) = \sinh x \Rightarrow f'(0) = f'''(0) = 0$. So, with $n = 3$ in Maclaurin's formula, $\cosh x = 1 + \frac{1}{2}x^2 + R_3(x)$ where $R_3(x) = (\cosh z)x^4/4!$ for some z be-between 0 and x. Neglecting the remainder yields the approximation formula. The error is $R_3(x)$. Since $\cosh z = (e^z + e^{-z})/2$ and z is between 0 and x, one exponent in $\cosh z$ is positive and one is negative. The positive exponential is < 2 as in #37 above; the negative exponential is < 1. Thus for such z and

x, $0 < \cosh z < 3/2$, and $0 < |R_3(x)| \leq \dfrac{(\cosh z)|x|^4}{24} \leq \dfrac{3}{48}(0.1)^4 = \dfrac{1}{16} \times 10^{-4} =$ 6.25×10^{-6} (at least 4 place accuracy).

EXERCISES 10.6, page 484

1. $\displaystyle\lim_{x \to 0} \frac{\ln(2-x)}{1 + e^{2x}} = \frac{\ln 2}{2}$ by the quotient limit theorem, NOT L'Hôpital's rule.

4. $\displaystyle\lim_{x \to 0} \frac{\tan^{-1}x}{\sin^{-1}x} = \lim_{x \to 0} \frac{1/(1+x^2)}{1/\sqrt{1-x^2}} = \frac{1}{1} = 1.$

7. $\displaystyle\lim_{x \to \infty} \frac{x^e}{e^x} = \lim_{x \to \infty} \frac{ex^{e-1}}{e^x} = \lim_{x \to \infty} \frac{e(e-1)x^{e-2}}{e^x} = \lim_{x \to \infty} \frac{e(e-1)(e-2)x^{e-3}}{e^x} = 0$ since $x^{e-3} \to 0$

and $e^x \to \infty$ as $x \to \infty$. (See also #31, Sec. 10.1.)

10. $\displaystyle\lim_{x \to 0} \tan^{-1}x \csc x = \lim_{x \to 0} \frac{\tan^{-1}x}{\sin x} = \lim_{x \to 0} \frac{1/(1+x^2)}{\cos x} = \frac{1}{1} = 1.$

13. $y = (e^x + 1)^{1/x} \implies \ln y = \dfrac{\ln(e^x+1)}{x}$. $\displaystyle\lim_{x \to \infty} \ln y = \lim_{x \to \infty} \frac{e^x}{e^x+1} = \lim_{x \to \infty} \frac{e^x}{e^x} = 1.$

Thus $\displaystyle\lim_{x \to \infty} y = \lim_{x \to \infty} c^{\ln y} = c^1 = c.$

16. $\displaystyle\int_4^\infty \frac{1}{x\sqrt{x}}\,dx = \lim_{t \to \infty} [-2x^{-1/2}]_4^t = -2 \lim_{t \to \infty} [\frac{1}{\sqrt{t}} - \frac{1}{2}] = 1.$

19. With the discontinuity of the integrand at $x = 0$, we write $\displaystyle\int_{-8}^1 = \int_{-8}^0 + \int_0^1.$

The 1st of these is $\displaystyle\lim_{t \to 0^-} \int_{-8}^t x^{-1/3}\,dx = \lim_{t \to 0^-} \frac{3}{2}x^{2/3}]_{-8}^t = \frac{3}{2}[0-(-8)^{2/3}] = -6.$

The second is $\displaystyle\lim_{t \to 0^+} \int_t^1 x^{-1/3}\,dx = \frac{3}{2}$. Thus the integral converges and has

value $-6 + \dfrac{3}{2} = -\dfrac{9}{2}$.

22. $\displaystyle\int_1^2 \frac{1}{x\sqrt{x^2-1}}\,dx = \lim_{t \to 1^+} \sec^{-1}x]_t^2 = \sec^{-1}2 - \sec^{-1}1 = \frac{\pi}{3} - 0 = \frac{\pi}{3}.$

25. $\displaystyle\int_0^1 \frac{\ln x}{x}\,dx = \lim_{t \to 0^+} \frac{1}{2}\ln^2 x]_t^1 = \lim_{t \to 0^+} (-\frac{1}{2})\ln^2 t = -\infty.$ Thus the integral diverges.

28.   (a) $f(x) = e^{-x^3}$ $f(0) = 1$

$f'(x) = -3x^2 e^{-x^3}$ $f'(0) = 0$

$f''(x) = (9x^4 - 6x) e^{-x^3}$ $f''(0) = 0$

$f'''(x) = (-27x^6 + 54x^3 - 6) e^{-x^3}$ $f'''(0) = -6$

$f^{(4)}(x) = (81x^8 - 324x^5 + 180x^2) e^{-x^3}$

$$e^{-x^3} = 1 - x^3 + \frac{(81z^8 - 324z^5 + 180z^2) e^{-z^3}}{24} x^4 \text{ for some } z \text{ between } 0 \text{ and } x.$$

(b) If $f(x) = 1/(1-x)$, then $f^{(k)}(x) = k!/(1-x)^{k+1}$ by an easy calculation or by #51, Sec. 3.11. It follows that $f^{(k)}(0) = k!$, and $f^{(k)}(0)/k! = 1$. Thus

$$\frac{1}{1-x} = 1 + x + x^2 + x^3 + x^4 + x^5 + x^6 + \frac{x^7}{(1-z)^8} \text{ for some } z \text{ between } 0 \text{ and } x.$$

EXERCISES 11.1, page 496

1. $a_n = \dfrac{n}{3n+2} \implies a_1 = \dfrac{1}{3+2} = \dfrac{1}{5}$, $a_2 = \dfrac{2}{6+2} = \dfrac{1}{4}$, $a_3 = \dfrac{3}{9+2} = \dfrac{3}{11}$, $a_4 = \dfrac{4}{12+2} = \dfrac{2}{7}$.

$\lim\limits_{n\to\infty} a_n = \lim\limits_{n\to\infty} \dfrac{n}{3n+2} = \lim\limits_{n\to\infty} \dfrac{1}{3 + 2/n} = \dfrac{1}{3+0} = \dfrac{1}{3}$.

4. $a_n = \dfrac{4}{8-7n} \implies a_1 = \dfrac{4}{8-7} = 4$, $a_2 = \dfrac{4}{8-14} = -\dfrac{2}{3}$, $a_3 = \dfrac{4}{8-21} = -\dfrac{4}{13}$, $a_4 = \dfrac{4}{8-28} =$

$-\dfrac{1}{5}$. $\lim\limits_{n\to\infty} \dfrac{4}{8-7n} = \lim\limits_{n\to\infty} \dfrac{4/n}{8/n - 7} = \dfrac{0}{-7} = 0.$

7. $a_1 = \dfrac{1\cdot 4}{2} = 2$, $a_2 = \dfrac{3\cdot 7}{9} = \dfrac{7}{3}$, $a_3 = \dfrac{5\cdot 10}{28} = \dfrac{25}{14}$, $a_4 = \dfrac{7\cdot 13}{65} = \dfrac{7}{5}$.

$\lim\limits_{n\to\infty} \dfrac{(2n-1)(3n+1)}{n^3+1} = \lim\limits_{n\to\infty} \dfrac{(1/n)(2-1/n)(3+1/n)}{1+1/n^3} = \dfrac{0}{1} = 0.$

10. $a_1 = \dfrac{100}{5} = 20$, $a_2 = \dfrac{200}{2\sqrt{2} + 4} = \dfrac{100}{\sqrt{2} + 2}$, $a_3 = \dfrac{300}{3\sqrt{3} + 4}$, $a_4 = \dfrac{400}{8+4} = \dfrac{100}{3}$.

$\lim\limits_{n\to\infty} \dfrac{100n}{n^{3/2} + 4} = \lim\limits_{n\to\infty} \dfrac{100/\sqrt{n}}{1 + 4/n\sqrt{n}} = 0.$

13. $a_1 = 1 + .1 = 1.1$, $a_2 = 1 + (.1)^2 = 1.01$, $a_3 = 1 + (.1)^3 = 1.001$, $a_4 = 1 +$

$(.1)^4 = 1.0001.$ $\lim\limits_{n\to\infty} 1 + (.1)^n = 1 + 0 = 1.$

16. $a_1 = 2$, $a_2 = 3/\sqrt{2}$, $a_3 = 4/\sqrt{3}$, $a_4 = 5/2.$ $\lim\limits_{n\to\infty} \dfrac{n+1}{\sqrt{n}} = \lim\limits_{n\to\infty} \sqrt{n} + \dfrac{1}{\sqrt{n}} = \infty.$

19. Since $\lim\limits_{x\to\infty} \arctan x = \pi/2$, it follows that $\lim\limits_{n\to\infty} \arctan n = \pi/2$ also.

Compare Figure 8.6.

22. $\lim\limits_{n\to\infty} \dfrac{1.0001^n}{1000} = \infty$ by (11.5) with $r = 1.0001 > 1.$

25. Let $f(x) = (4x^4+1)/(2x^2-1)$, an ∞/∞ form as $x \to \infty$. $\lim\limits_{x\to\infty} f(x) = \lim\limits_{x\to\infty} \dfrac{16x^3}{4x} = \infty$

by L'Hôpital's rule. Thus $\lim\limits_{n\to\infty} f(n) = \infty$ also.

28. Let $f(x) = e^{-x} \ln x = \ln x/e^x$. Then $\lim\limits_{x\to\infty} \dfrac{\ln x}{e^x} = \lim\limits_{x\to\infty} \dfrac{1/x}{e^x} = 0.$ Thus $\lim\limits_{n\to\infty} e^{-n} \ln n$
= 0 also.

31. Since $|\sin n| \le 1$, $|2^{-n} \sin n| \le 2^{-n} = (1/2)^n$, and $\lim\limits_{n\to\infty} (1/2)^n = 0$, it follows

that $\lim\limits_{n\to\infty} |2^{-n} \sin n| = 0$ by (11.6). Then by (11.7), $\lim\limits_{n\to\infty} 2^{-n} \sin n = 0.$

34. Let $f(x) = x \sin(1/x)$, an $\infty\cdot 0$ indeterminate form as $x \to \infty$.. $\lim\limits_{x\to\infty} f(x) =$

$$\lim_{x\to\infty} \frac{\sin(1/x)}{1/x} = \lim_{x\to\infty} \frac{(-1/x^2)\cos(1/x)}{(-1/x^2)} = \lim_{x\to\infty} \cos\frac{1}{x} = \cos 0 = 1.$$

Thus $\lim\limits_{n\to\infty} n \sin(1/n) = 1$.

37. $k \geq 2 \implies 0 < \frac{1}{k^n} \leq \frac{1}{2^n}$, and $\frac{1}{2^n} \to 0$ by (12.5i).

40. Hint: b is an upper bound for (a,b). By (12.10), there is a least upper bound, say, v, and $v \leq b$. If $v < b$, show that you can find a number w between v and b. Then w is in (a,b) but larger than the upper bound v, a contradiction. Thus v = b.

37. Let $y = f(x) = x^{1/x}$, an $\infty \cdot 0$ indeterminate form as $x \to \infty$. $\ln y = \frac{\ln x}{x} \implies$

$\lim\limits_{x\to\infty} \ln y = \lim\limits_{x\to\infty} \frac{1/x}{1} = 0 \implies \lim\limits_{x\to\infty} y = \lim\limits_{x\to\infty} f(x) = e^0 = 1$. Thus $\lim\limits_{n\to\infty} n^{1/n} = 1$.

40. This limit does not exist. To see this note that $n^2/(n^2+1) \to 1$ as $n \to \infty$ and that $(-1)^n = +1$ if n is even, -1 if n is odd. Thus if n is large and even, $a_n = (-1)^n n^2/(n^2+1)$ is close to +1, but if n is large and odd, then a_n is close to -1. Thus there is no single number which all a_n's are close to when n is large.

46. HINT: Extend #41, Sec. 1.1 to obtain $||a_n| - |L|| \leq |a_n - L|$.

49. HINT: If $L = \lim\limits_{n\to\infty} a_n$, then $|ca_n - cL| = |c||a_n - L|$.

EXERCISES 11.2, page 505

1. Since $a = 3$, $r = 1/4 < 1$, it converges with sum $3/(1 - \frac{1}{4}) = 4$.

4. Since $a = 1$, $r = e/3 < 1$, it converges with sum $1/(1-e/3) = 3/(3-e)$.

7. Writing $\sum\limits_{n=1}^{\infty} 2^{-n} 3^{n-1} = \frac{1}{2} + \frac{3}{2^2} + \frac{3^2}{2^3} + \ldots = \frac{1}{2}(1 + \frac{3}{2} + (\frac{3}{2})^2 + \ldots)$ it diverges since $r = 3/2 > 1$.

10. The series diverges since $r = \sqrt{2} > 1$.

13. The terms are obtained by multiplying those in Example 1 (where the sum was 1) by 5. Thus the series converges by (11.19ii) with $c = 5$, and its sum is 5.

16. Since $\lim\limits_{n\to\infty} \frac{n}{n+1} = 1 \neq 0$, the series diverges.

19. Since $\sum\limits_{n=1}^{\infty} 1/8^n = \frac{1}{8} + \frac{1}{8^2} + \frac{1}{8^3} + \ldots = \frac{1}{8}(1 + \frac{1}{8} + \frac{1}{8^2} + \ldots)$ is a geometric

series with $a = 1/8$, $r = 1/8 < 1$, it converges and has sum $\frac{1/8}{1-1/8} = \frac{1}{7}$. The 2nd

series is that of Example 1, convergent with sum 1. Thus the given series

converges and has sum $1/7 + 1 = 8/7$.

22. $\lim_{n \to \infty} \frac{n}{\ln(n+1)} = \lim_{n \to \infty} \frac{1}{1/(n+1)} = \infty$ (L'Hôpital) $\Rightarrow$ the series diverges.

25. $\sum (3/2)^n$ is a divergent geometric series ($r = 3/2$), and $\sum (2/3)^n$ is a con-

vergent geometric series ($r = 2/3$). Thus the given series diverges by (11.15).

28. $\sum 2^{-n} = \sum (1/2)^n$ and $\sum 2^{-3n} = \sum (2^{-3})^n = \sum (1/8)^n$ both converge as geometric

series with $r = 1/2$ and $1/8$, respectively. Thus the given series converges

by (11.19(iii)).

31. If $\sum ca_n$ converged, so would $\sum (1/c)ca_n = \sum a_n$ by (11.19(ii)). This contra-

dicts the assumed divergence of $\sum a_n$.

34. The given series, $\sum (-1)^{n+1}$ has terms $(-1)^{n+1}$ and partial sums $S_1 = 1$, $S_2 = 0$,

$S_3 = 1$, $S_4 = 0$, etc., and the series diverges both by (11.15) and the fact

that $\lim_{n \to \infty} S_n$ does not exist. When grouping is done as shown in the problem,

an entirely new series results. Its terms are $b_1 = a_1 + a_2$, $b_2 = a_3 + a_4$, etc.

so that every term is 0 and, thus, every partial sum of this different series

is 0. Thus, it is not the original series that has sum 0, but rather, it is

the new series, obtained by regrouping, that has sum 0.

37. $3.2\overline{394} = 3.2 + \frac{394}{10^4} + \frac{394}{10^7} + \frac{394}{10^{10}} + \ldots = 3.2 + \frac{1}{10^4}(394 + \frac{394}{10^3} + \frac{394}{10^6} + \ldots)$

$= 3.2 + \frac{1}{10^4} \cdot \frac{394}{1-10^{-3}}$ by (12.12) with $a = 394$ and $r = 1/10^3 = 10^{-3}$. Thus

$3.2\overline{394} = 3.2 + \frac{1}{10^4} \cdot \frac{394}{999/1000} = 3.2 + \frac{394}{9,990} = \frac{3.2(9990)+394}{9990} = \frac{32,362}{9,990}$.

40. The total distance is approximately $24 + 24(\frac{5}{6}) + 24(\frac{5}{6})^2 + \ldots = \frac{24}{1-5/6} = \frac{24}{1/6} = 144$ cm.

43. A geometric series, $a + ar + ar^2 + \ldots + ar^n + \ldots = \sum_{n=0}^{\infty} ar^n$ has sum $\frac{a}{1-r}$ if

$|r| < 1$, or $-1 < r < 1$. The given series $1 - x + x^2 - x^3 + \ldots + (-1)^n x^n + \ldots$

may be written as $\sum_{n=0}^{\infty} (-1)^n x^n = \sum_{n=0}^{\infty} (-x)^n$, a geometric series with $a = 1$ and

$r = -x$. Thus, the sum is $\frac{1}{1-(-x)} = \frac{1}{1+x}$ if $|r| = |-x| < 1 \iff |x| < 1 \iff$

$-1 < x < 1$.

46. We may write the given series as follows: $3 + (x-1) + \frac{(x-1)^2}{3} + \ldots +$

$\frac{(x-1)^n}{3^{n-1}} + \ldots = 3(1 + \frac{x-1}{3} + \frac{(x-1)^2}{3^2} + \ldots + \frac{(x-1)^n}{3^n} + \ldots)$

$= \sum_{n=0}^{\infty} 3(\frac{x-1}{3})^n$, a geometric series with $a = 3$, $r = \frac{x-1}{3}$. It converges if

$|r| = |\frac{x-1}{3}| < 1 \Longleftrightarrow |x-1| < 3 \Longleftrightarrow -3 < x-1 < 3 \Longleftrightarrow -2 < x < 4$. For such

x, the sum is $\frac{a}{1-r} = \frac{3}{1-(x-1)/3} = \frac{9}{3-(x-1)} = \frac{9}{4-x}$.

EXERCISES 11.3, page 514

1. $f(x) = (3+2x)^{-2}$ is > 0, continuous, and decreasing on $[1,\infty)$. (Decreasing

since $f'(x) = -4(3+2x)^{-2} < 0$ there.) Since $\int_1^{\infty} (3+2x)^{-2} dx = \lim_{t \to \infty} (-\frac{1}{2})\frac{1}{3+2x}]_1^t$

$= \frac{1}{10}$, the given series converges by the integral test.

4. The integral test can apply to a series $\sum_{n=2}^{\infty} f(n)$ if $f(x)$ satisfies the

hypotheses of (11.22) on $[2,\infty)$. The same proof works after a change of
variable $u = \ln x$. Here, $f(x) = 1/x(\ln x)^2$ satisfies all 3 conditions on
$[2,\infty)$. (f is decreasing either by computing $f'(x)$ or by the fact that x and

$\ln x$ are increasing.) Since $\int_2^{\infty} \frac{1}{x(\ln x)^2} dx = \lim_{t \to \infty} -\frac{1}{\ln x}]_2^t = \frac{1}{\ln 2}$, the given

series converges.

7. $f(x) = (2x+1)^{-1/3}$ is > 0, continuous and decreasing on $[1,\infty)$. ($f'(x) =$

$-(2/3)(2x+1)^{-4/3} < 0$ there.) Since $\int_1^{\infty} (2x+1)^{-1/3} dx = \lim_{t \to \infty} \frac{3}{4}[(2t+1)^{2/3} - 3^{2/3}]$

$= \infty$, the series diverges.

10. $f(x) = xe^{-x}$ is > 0, continuous and decreasing on $[1,\infty)$. ($f'(x) = (1-x)e^{-x}$

< 0 if $x > 1$.) Since $\int_1^{\infty} xe^{-x} dx = \lim_{t \to \infty} (-te^{-t} - e^{-t} + 2e^{-1}) = 2e^{-1}$, the

series converges.

13. $f(x) = x2^{-x^2}$ satisfies the hypotheses of (11.22).(It's decreasing on $[1,\infty)$

since $f'(x) = (1-2x^2)(\ln 2)2^{-x^2} < 0$ if $x \geq 1$.) Since $\int_1^{\infty} x2^{-x^2} dx =$

$\lim_{t \to \infty} \frac{1}{2 \ln 2} (-2^{-t^2}+2^{-1}) = \frac{1}{4 \ln 2}$, the series converges.

16. $f(x) = 1/x\sqrt{x^2-1}$ is > 0, continuous and decreasing on $[2,\infty)$. ($f'(x) =$

$-(2x^2-1)/x^2(x^2-1)^{3/2} < 0$ if $x \geq 2$.) Since $\int_2^\infty (1/x\sqrt{x^2-1})dx = \lim_{t\to\infty}[\sec^{-1}t -$

$\sec^{-1}2] = \frac{\pi}{2} - \frac{\pi}{3} = \frac{\pi}{6}$, the series converges.

19. Since $\frac{1}{n3^n} \leq \frac{1}{3^n}$ for $n \geq 1$, and since $\sum(\frac{1}{3})^n$ converges as a geometric series

with $r = 1/3$, the series $\sum \frac{1}{n3^n}$ converges by the Comparison Test.

22. For large n, $\sqrt{n}$ is much larger than 3, and it appears that $2/(3+\sqrt{n})$ behaves

very much like $2/\sqrt{n}$. This suggests that we compare the terms of the given

series with $1/\sqrt{n}$ (or $2/\sqrt{n}$). Thus with $a_n = 2/(3+\sqrt{n})$ and $b_n = 1/\sqrt{n}$,

$\lim_{n\to\infty} \frac{a_n}{b_n} = \lim_{n\to\infty} \frac{2\sqrt{n}}{3+\sqrt{n}} = 2$. But $\sum b_n = \sum 1/\sqrt{n}$ diverges since it is a p-series with

$p = 1/2$. Thus the given series diverges by the Limit Comparison Test.

25. For large n, neglecting the smaller powers of n, $\sqrt{4n^3-5n} \approx \sqrt{4n^3} = 2n^{3/2}$. So,

with $a_n = 1/\sqrt{4n^3-5n}$, we select $b_n = 1/2n^{3/2}$ and obtain $\lim_{n\to\infty} \frac{a_n}{b_n} =$

$\lim_{n\to\infty} \frac{2n^{3/2}}{\sqrt{4n^3-5n}} = \lim_{n\to\infty} \frac{2}{\sqrt{4-5/n^2}} = \frac{2}{\sqrt{4}} = 1$ (having divided numerator and denominator

by $n^{3/2} = \sqrt{n^3}$). Since $\sum b_n$ is $\frac{1}{2}$ times a p-series with $p = 3/2$, $\sum b_n$ converges,

and, by the Limit Comparison Test, so does $\sum a_n$.

28. $0 \leq \sin^2 n \leq 1 \implies 0 \leq \sin^2 n/2^n \leq 1/2^n$. Since $\sum 1/2^n$ converges (geometric

series, $r = 1/2$), the given series converges by the Comparison Test.

31. $-1 \leq \cos n \leq 1 \implies 1 \leq 2 + \cos n \leq 3 \implies \frac{2 + \cos n}{n^2} \leq \frac{3}{n^2}$. Since $\sum 3/n^2$ con-

verges as a p-series with $p = 2$, the given series converges by the Comparison

Test.

34. As above, if we retain the largest power of n inside the radical, it appears

that the terms of the series behave like $1/\sqrt{n^3} = 1/n^{3/2}$. Thus with

$a_n = 1/\sqrt{n(n+1)(n+2)}$ and $b_n = 1/n^{3/2}$, $\lim_{n\to\infty} a_n/b_n = 1$. But $\sum b_n$ converges as a

p-series with $p = 3/2$. Thus the given series converges by the Limit

Comparison Test.

37. $n \geq 2 \implies 1/n^n \leq 1/n^2$. Since $\sum 1/n^2$ converges $(p = 2)$, $\sum_{n=2}^\infty 1/n^n$ converges

by the Comparison Test. Since this differs from the given series only by

deleting the 1st term, the given series converges by (11.18).

40. Since $n \geq 1 \implies \ln n \geq 0$, we have $a_n = \dfrac{n + \ln n}{n^2 + 1} \geq \dfrac{n}{n^2 + 1}$. The series

$\sum n/(n^2 + 1)$ diverges either by the integral test or by the Limit Comparison
Test using $b_n = 1/n$. Thus by the Comparison Test, 2nd conclusion, the given
series diverges.

43. For sufficiently large n, $\ln n < n$ since $\displaystyle\lim_{n \to \infty} \dfrac{\ln n}{n} = 0$ (by L'Hôpital's Rule).

(In fact, it can be shown that $\ln n < n$ for all $n \geq 1$.) Thus $\dfrac{\ln n}{n^3} < \dfrac{n}{n^3} = \dfrac{1}{n^2}$.

Since $\sum 1/n^2$ converges (p = 2) so does the given series by the Comparison
Test.

46. For $n \geq 1$, $-1 \leq \sin n \leq 1$ and $2 \leq 2^n$. Thus $1 \leq \sin n + 2^n \leq 1 + 2^n$ and

$\dfrac{\sin n + 2^n}{n + 5^n} \leq \dfrac{1 + 2^n}{5^n} = (\tfrac{1}{5})^n + (\tfrac{2}{5})^n$. Since both $\sum (1/5)^n$ and $\sum (2/5)^n$ converge

(geometric series, r = 1/5, 2/5), the given series converges by the Comparison
Test.

49. Hint: For large n, $a_n/b_n < 1$, or $a_n < b_n$.

50. Hint: For some N, $n \geq N \implies a_n/b_n > 1$, or $a_n > b_n$. If S_n and T_n are the nth

partial sums of $\sum a_n$ and $\sum b_n$, respectively, and if $n > N$, $S_n = (S_n - S_N) +$

$S_N > (T_n - S_N) + S_N$. What does the divergence of $\sum b_n$ tell you about T_n as

$n \to \infty$?

52. Since the error in approximating $S = \displaystyle\sum_{n=1}^{\infty} \dfrac{1}{n^2}$ by $S_N = \displaystyle\sum_{n=1}^{N} \dfrac{1}{n^2}$ is less than

$\displaystyle\int_{N}^{\infty} \dfrac{1}{x^2}\, dx$, we seek N such that this integral is < .001. $\displaystyle\int_{N}^{\infty} \dfrac{1}{x^2}\, dx =$

$\displaystyle\lim_{t \to \infty} [-\tfrac{1}{x}]_{N}^{t} = \dfrac{1}{N} < .001 \iff N > 1000$. The smallest integer satisfying this

is N = 1001.

EXERCISES 11.4, page 518

1. $2(n+1)+1 > 2n+1 \implies \dfrac{1}{\sqrt{2(n+1)+1}} < \dfrac{1}{\sqrt{2n+1}} \implies a_{n+1} < a_n$. Since $\displaystyle\lim_{n \to \infty} a_n =$

$\displaystyle\lim_{n \to \infty} 1/\sqrt{2n+1} = 0$, the series converges by the Alternating Series Test (AST).

4. With $f(x) = \dfrac{x}{x^2 + 4}$, $f'(x) = \dfrac{4 - x^2}{(x^2 + 4)^2} < 0$ for x > 2, and the terms of the series

are decreasing for $n \geq 2$. Since $n/(n^2 + 4) \to 0$ as $n \to \infty$, the given series converges by the AST.

7. With $f(x) = \dfrac{x^2+1}{x^3+1}$, $f'(x) = \dfrac{-x(x^3+3x-2)}{(x^3+1)^2}$. The factor (x^3+3x-2) has value 2

    when $x = 1$ and increases thereafter. (Its derivative is $3x^2+3 \geq 3 > 0$.)

    Thus the numerator of $f'(x)$ is < 0 for $x \geq 1$ and $f'(x) < 0$. Thus the terms

    of the series are decreasing for $n \geq 1$ and $\lim\limits_{n\to\infty} \dfrac{n^2+1}{n^3+1} = 0$. Thus the given

    series converges by the AST.

8. Since $\lim\limits_{n\to\infty} a_n = \lim\limits_{n\to\infty} \dfrac{3n+4}{5n+7} = \dfrac{3}{5} \neq 0$, the series diverges.

10. With $f(x) = \dfrac{\sqrt{x+1}}{8x+5}$, $f'(x) = \dfrac{-8x-11}{2\sqrt{x+1}(8x+5)^2} < 0$ for $x \geq 1$. Thus the terms of the

    series decrease, and $\lim\limits_{n\to\infty} a_n = 0$.   Thus convergence by the AST.

13. With $f(x) = \dfrac{(\ln x)^k}{x}$, $f'(x) = \dfrac{x\, k(\ln x)^{k-1}/x - (\ln x)^k}{x^2} = \dfrac{(\ln x)^{k-1}}{x^2}(k - \ln x)$

    < 0 if $\ln x > k$ or $x > e^k$. Thus the terms of the series are decreasing

    from $n = [e^k] + 1$ on. Let $N = [e^k] + 1$. Next, applying L'Hôpital's rule k

    times, $\lim\limits_{x\to\infty} \dfrac{(\ln x)^k}{x} = \lim\limits_{x\to\infty} \dfrac{k(\ln x)^{k-1}/x}{1} = \lim\limits_{x\to\infty} \dfrac{k(\ln x)^{k-1}}{x} = \lim\limits_{x\to\infty} \dfrac{k(k-1)(\ln x)^{k-2}}{x}$

    $= \ldots = \lim\limits_{x\to\infty} \dfrac{k!}{x} = 0$. Thus the series $\sum\limits_{n=N}^{\infty} (-1)^n \dfrac{(\ln n)^k}{n}$ converges by the AST.

    Since the given series, which begins at $n = 2$, differs from this series by

    only a finite number of terms, it converges by (11.18).

16. We first note that the series converges by the AST since $a_n = 1/(2n)! \to 0$

    and $a_{n+1} = 1/(2(n+1))! = 1/(2n+2)! = 1/(2n+2)(2n+1)(2n)! < 1/(2n)! = a_n$.

    Recall also that if the sum, S, is approximated by the nth partial sum, S_n,

    the error is less than a_{n+1}, the first term neglected. Since we want 3

    decimal place accuracy, the error is to be less than 5×10^{-4}. Thus we seek

    n such that $a_{n+1} = 1/(2(n+1))! < 5 \times 10^{-4}$ or $(2(n+1))! > 10^4/5 = 2000$.

    Trying $n = 2$, we get $6! = 720$; but with $n = 3$, $8! = 40{,}320$. Thus, for at

    least 3 place accuracy, $S \approx S_3 = \sum\limits_{n=0}^{3} (-1)^{n+1}/(2n)! = -\dfrac{1}{0!} + \dfrac{1}{2!} - \dfrac{1}{4!} + \dfrac{1}{6!} =$

    $-1 + \dfrac{1}{2} - \dfrac{1}{24} + \dfrac{1}{720} \approx -0.540$. (Recall, $0! = 1$.)

19. Here, with $a_n = (n+1)/5^n$, we seek n such that $a_{n+1} = \dfrac{n+2}{5^{n+1}} < 5 \times 10^{-4}$ or

    $\dfrac{5^{n+1}}{n+2} > 2000$. With $n = 4$, $\dfrac{5^5}{6} = \dfrac{3125}{6} < 2000$, but with $n = 5$, $\dfrac{5^6}{7} = \dfrac{15625}{7} \approx$

    2232. Thus, to 3 place accuracy $S \approx S_5 = \sum\limits_{n=1}^{5} (-1)^{n-1}\dfrac{(n+1)}{5^n} = \dfrac{2}{5} - \dfrac{3}{25} + \dfrac{4}{125}$

    $- \dfrac{5}{625} + \dfrac{6}{3125} \approx 0.306$.

22. With $a_n = 1/\sqrt{n}$ we seek n such that $a_{n+1} = 1/\sqrt{n+1} < 5 \times 10^{-5}$, for 4 decimal

place accuracy, or $\sqrt{n+1} > 10^5/5 = 2 \times 10^4 \implies n+1 > 4 \times 10^8$. Thus

$n > 4 \times 10^8 - 1$. The smallest integer satisfying this is 4×10^8.

EXERCISES 11.5, page 525

1.   The given series converges by the AST. However, $\sum |a_n| = \sum |(-1)^{n+1}/\sqrt{n}| =$

$\sum 1/\sqrt{n}$ which is a divergent p-series (p = 1/2). Thus the given series con-

verges conditionally.

4. $\sum |a_n| = \sum |(-1)^n e^{-n}| = \sum e^{-n} = \sum (1/e)^n$ which is a convergent geometric series

(r = 1/e < 1). Thus the given series converges absolutely.

7.   With $a_n = (-1)^{n-1} \dfrac{(3n+1)}{2^n}$, $\lim\limits_{n\to\infty} \left|\dfrac{a_{n+1}}{a_n}\right| = \lim\limits_{n\to\infty} \dfrac{3n+4}{2^{n+1}} \cdot \dfrac{2^n}{3n+1} = \lim\limits_{n\to\infty} \dfrac{1}{2} \dfrac{3n+4}{3n+1} = \dfrac{1}{2}$.

Since this limit is < 1, the given series converges absolutely by the ratio

test.

10. $\lim\limits_{n\to\infty} \left|\dfrac{a_{n+1}}{a_n}\right| = \lim\limits_{n\to\infty} \dfrac{2^n}{5^{n+1}(n+2)} \cdot \dfrac{5^n(n+1)}{2^{n-1}} = \lim\limits_{n\to\infty} \dfrac{2}{5} (\dfrac{n+1}{n+2}) = \dfrac{2}{5} < 1$. Thus absolute

convergence by the ratio test.

13. Since $|a_n| = \dfrac{\sqrt{n}}{n^2+1} < \dfrac{\sqrt{n}}{n^2} = \dfrac{1}{n^{3/2}}$, and since $\sum \dfrac{1}{n^{3/2}}$ converges (p = 3/2), the

given series converges absolutely.

14. The given series converges by the AST. However, $|a_n| = \dfrac{\sqrt{n}}{n+1}$, and $\sum |a_n|$

diverges by the limit comparison test choosing $b_n = 1/\sqrt{n}$ (p = 1/2). Thus the

given series converges conditionally.

16. $|a_n| = (2n+1)/(n^2+n^3)$, and $\sum |a_n|$ converges by the limit comparison test

choosing $b_n = 1/n^2$ (p = 2). Thus it converges absolutely.

19. $|a_n| = 2/(n^3+e^n) < 2/n^3$, and $\sum |a_n|$ converges by the comparison test choosing

$b_n = 2/n^3$ (p = 3). Thus it converges absolutely.

22. $|a_n| = \dfrac{|\cos n - 1|}{n^{3/2}} \leq \dfrac{|\cos n| + 1}{n^{3/2}} \leq \dfrac{2}{n^{3/2}}$. Since $\sum 2/n^{3/2}$ converges (p = 3/2),

$\sum |a_n|$ converges by the comparison test. Thus the given series converges

absolutely.

25. $\lim\limits_{n\to\infty} \left|\dfrac{a_{n+1}}{a_n}\right| = \lim\limits_{n\to\infty} \dfrac{(n+1)!}{5^{n+1}} \cdot \dfrac{5^n}{n!} = \lim\limits_{n\to\infty} \dfrac{n+1}{5} = \infty$. Thus the series diverges by

the ratio test.

6. $\lim\limits_{n\to\infty} a_n = \lim\limits_{n\to\infty} \dfrac{\sec^{-1} n}{\tan^{-1} n} = \dfrac{\pi/2}{\pi/2} = 1.$ Thus the series diverges.

28. Since $\lim\limits_{n\to\infty} |a_n| = \lim\limits_{n\to\infty} \dfrac{n^2+3}{(2n-5)^2} = \dfrac{1}{4} \neq 0,$ $\lim\limits_{n\to\infty} a_n \neq 0$ and the series diverges.

31. $\lim\limits_{n\to\infty} \left| \dfrac{a_{n+1}}{a_n} \right| = \lim\limits_{n\to\infty} \dfrac{1\cdot 3\cdot 5\ldots(2n-1)(2n+1)}{(n+1)!} \cdot \dfrac{n!}{1\cdot 3\cdot 5\ldots(2n-1)} = \lim\limits_{n\to\infty} \dfrac{2n+1}{n+1} = 2 > 1.$

Thus the series diverges by the ratio test.

34. Since $a_n > 0$ for all n, we can drop the absolute value signs in the root test.

$\lim\limits_{n\to\infty} \sqrt[n]{a_n} = \lim\limits_{n\to\infty} \dfrac{2n}{5n+3n^{-1}} = \dfrac{2}{5} < 1.$ Thus the series converges by the root test.

37. Let $f(x) = x \tan(1/x)$, an $\infty \cdot 0$ indeterminate form as $x \to \infty$. $\lim\limits_{x\to\infty} f(x) =$

$\lim\limits_{x\to\infty} \dfrac{\tan(1/x)}{1/x} = \lim\limits_{x\to\infty} \dfrac{(-1/x^2)\sec^2(1/x)}{(-1/x^2)} = \sec^2 0 = 1.$ Thus, $\lim\limits_{n\to\infty} a_n =$

$\lim\limits_{n\to\infty} n \tan(1/n) = 1 \neq 0$, and the series diverges.

EXERCISES 11.6, page 531

1. With $u_n = \dfrac{x^n}{n+4}$, $\lim\limits_{n\to\infty} \left| \dfrac{u_{n+1}}{u_n} \right| = \lim\limits_{n\to\infty} \left| \dfrac{x^{n+1}}{n+5} \cdot \dfrac{n+4}{x^n} \right| = \lim\limits_{n\to\infty} \left| \dfrac{n+4}{n+5} \right| |x| = |x|.$ So, we

have absolute convergence by the ratio test if $|x| < 1$ or $-1 < x < 1.$ If

$x = 1$, the series is $\sum \dfrac{1}{n+4}$, which diverges. If $x = -1$, the series is

$\sum \dfrac{(-1)^n}{n+4}$ which converges by the AST. Thus the interval of convergence is $[-1,1)$.

4. With $u_n = \dfrac{(-3)^n x^{n+1}}{n}$, $\lim\limits_{n\to\infty} \left| \dfrac{u_{n+1}}{u_n} \right| = \lim\limits_{n\to\infty} \dfrac{3n}{n+1} |x| = 3|x|.$ So, we have absolute

convergence if $3|x| < 1$ or $-\dfrac{1}{3} < x < \dfrac{1}{3}$. If $x = \dfrac{1}{3}$, the series is $\sum \dfrac{(-3)^n}{n3^{n+1}}$

$= \dfrac{1}{3} \sum \dfrac{(-1)^n}{n}$, which converges by the AST. If $x = -1/3$, the series is

$\sum \dfrac{(-3)^n}{n(-3)^{n+1}} = -\dfrac{1}{3} \sum \dfrac{1}{n}$ which diverges. Thus the interval of convergence is

$(-1/3, 1/3]$.

7. With $u_n = \dfrac{n}{n^2+1} x^n$, $\lim\limits_{n\to\infty} \left| \dfrac{u_{n+1}}{u_n} \right| = \lim\limits_{n\to\infty} \dfrac{n+1}{(n+1)^2+1} \cdot \dfrac{n^2+1}{n} |x| = |x|.$ Thus, by the

ratio test we have absolute convergence if $|x| < 1$ or $-1 < x < 1.$ If $x = 1$,

the series is $\sum \dfrac{n}{n^2+1}$ which diverges by the limit comparison test ($b_n = 1/n$),

or the integral test. If x = -1, the series is $\sum \frac{n}{n^2+1} (-1)^n$, convergent by
the AST. Thus the interval of convergence is $[-1,1)$.

10. $\lim\limits_{n\to\infty} \left| \frac{u_{n+1}}{u_n} \right| = \lim\limits_{n\to\infty} \frac{10^{n+2}}{3^{2(n+1)}} \cdot \frac{3^{2n}}{10^{n+1}} |x| = \lim\limits_{n\to\infty} \frac{10}{3^2} |x| = \frac{10}{9} |x|$. Thus we have

absolute convergence if $\frac{10}{9} |x| < 1$, or $|x| < \frac{9}{10}$, or $-\frac{9}{10} < x < \frac{9}{10}$. If

$x = \pm \frac{9}{10}$, $u_n = \frac{10^{n+1}}{3^{2n}} (\pm \frac{9}{10})^n$. Since $3^{2n} = (3^2)^n = 9^n$, $u_n = \frac{10^{n+1}}{9^n} \cdot \frac{9^n}{10^n} \cdot (\pm 1)^n$.

Thus, $u_n = 10(\pm 1)^n$, which does not have a limit as $n \to \infty$. (i.e., $u_n \not\to 0$ as
$n \to \infty$.) Thus the power series diverges at each end point, and the interval of
convergence is $(-\frac{9}{10}, \frac{9}{10})$.

13. $\lim\limits_{n\to\infty} \left| \frac{u_{n+1}}{u_n} \right| = \lim\limits_{n\to\infty} \frac{(n+1)!}{100^{n+1}} \cdot \frac{100^n}{n!} |x| = \lim\limits_{n\to\infty} \frac{(n+1)}{100} |x| = \infty$ unless x = 0, in which
case the limit is 0. Thus the series converges only for x = 0.

16. $\lim\limits_{n\to\infty} \left| \frac{u_{n+1}}{u_n} \right| = \lim\limits_{n\to\infty} \frac{\sqrt[3]{n}}{\sqrt[3]{n+1}} \frac{|x|}{3} = \frac{|x|}{3} < 1$ if $\frac{|x|}{3} < 1$ or $-3 < x < 3$. If x = 3, the

series is $\sum \frac{(-1)^{n-1}}{\sqrt[3]{n}}$ which converges by the AST. If x = -3, the series is

$\sum \frac{1}{\sqrt[3]{n}}$ which diverges (p = 1/3). Thus the interval of convergence is $(-3,3]$.

19. $\lim\limits_{n\to\infty} \left| \frac{u_{n+1}}{u_n} \right| = \lim\limits_{n\to\infty} \frac{3^{2(n+1)}}{n+2} \cdot \frac{n+1}{3^{2n}} |x-2| = \lim\limits_{n\to\infty} \frac{9(n+1)}{n+2} |x-2| = 9|x-2| < 1$ if $|x-2|$

$< 1/9$ or $2 - \frac{1}{9} < x < 2 + \frac{1}{9}$. If $x = 2 + \frac{1}{9}$, $x-2 = \frac{1}{9}$, and the series is

$\sum \frac{1}{n+1}$, which diverges. (Remember $3^{2n} = (3^2)^n = 9^n$.) If $x = 2 - \frac{1}{9}$, $x-2 =$

$-1/9$ and the series is $\sum \frac{(-1)^n}{n+1}$ which converges by the AST. Thus the interval

of convergence is $[2 - \frac{1}{9}, 2 + \frac{1}{9}) = [\frac{17}{9}, \frac{19}{9})$.

22. $\lim\limits_{n\to\infty} \left| \frac{u_{n+1}}{u_n} \right| = \lim\limits_{n\to\infty} \frac{2n+1}{2n+3} |x+3| = |x+3| < 1$ if $-1 < x+3 < 1$ or $-4 < x < -2$. If

x = -2, x+3 = 1 and the series is $\sum \frac{1}{2n+1}$ which diverges. If x = -4, x+3 = -1

and the series is $\sum \frac{(-1)^n}{2n+1}$ which converges by the AST. Thus the interval of

convergence is $[-4,-2)$.

25. $\displaystyle\lim_{n\to\infty}\left|\frac{u_{n+1}}{u_n}\right| = \lim_{n\to\infty}\frac{n}{6(n+1)}\,|2x-1| = \frac{|2x-1|}{6} < 1$ if $|2x-1| < 6$ or $-6 < 2x-1 < 6$ or

$-\frac{5}{2} < x < \frac{7}{2}$. If $x = \frac{7}{2}$, $2x-1 = 6$, and the series is $\sum \frac{(-1)^n}{n}$ which converges

by the AST. If $x = -5/2$, $2x-1 = -6$, and the series is $\sum 1/n$ which diverges.

Thus the interval of convergence is $(-5/2, 7/2]$.

28. $u_n = \dfrac{2\cdot4\cdot6\cdot\ldots(2n)}{4\cdot7\cdot10\cdot\ldots(3n+1)}\,x^n \implies u_{n+1} = \dfrac{2\cdot4\cdot6\cdot\ldots(2n)(2(n+1))}{4\cdot7\cdot10\cdot\ldots(3n+1)(3(n+1)+1)}\,x^{n+1}$. Thus

$\left|\dfrac{u_{n+1}}{u_n}\right| = \dfrac{2\cdot4\cdot6\cdot\ldots(2n)(2n+2)}{4\cdot7\cdot10\cdot\ldots(3n+1)(3n+4)}\cdot\dfrac{4\cdot7\cdot10\cdot\ldots(3n+1)}{2\cdot4\cdot6\cdot\ldots(2n)}\,|x| = \dfrac{2n+2}{3n+4}\,|x|$, and

$\displaystyle\lim_{n\to\infty}\left|\frac{u_{n+1}}{u_n}\right| = \lim_{n\to\infty}\frac{2n+2}{3n+4}\,|x| = \frac{2}{3}\,|x|$. Thus, by the ratio test, the series con-

verges absolutely if $\frac{2}{3}\,|x| < 1$ or $|x| < \frac{3}{2}$, and the radius of convergence is $\frac{3}{2}$.

31. $\left|\dfrac{u_{n+1}}{u_n}\right| = \dfrac{(n+c+1)!}{(n+1)!\,(n+d+1)!}\cdot\dfrac{n!\,(n+d)!}{(n+c)!}\,|x| = \dfrac{n+c+1}{(n+1)(n+d+1)}\,|x| \to 0$ for all x as

$n \to \infty$. Thus $r = \infty$.

34. HINT: Apply the Root Test.

37. HINT: If it converged absolutely at r, then $\Sigma|a_n|r^n$ would converge. How-

ever, $\Sigma|a_n(-r)^n| = \Sigma|a_n|r^n$.

EXERCISES 11.7, page 536

1. $\dfrac{1}{1-x} = 1 + x + x^2 + \ldots = \displaystyle\sum_{n=0}^{\infty} x^n$ for $|x| < 1$. This is just the geometric

series encountered in Sec. 11.2 with $a = 1$ and $r = x$.

4. Replacing x by $4x$ in #1, $\dfrac{1}{1-4x} = \displaystyle\sum_{n=0}^{\infty}(4x)^n = \sum_{n=0}^{\infty}4^n x^n$ for $|4x| < 1$ or $|x| < 1/4$.

7. $\dfrac{x}{2-3x} = \dfrac{x}{2}\left(\dfrac{1}{1-\frac{3}{2}x}\right) = \dfrac{x}{2}\displaystyle\sum_{n=0}^{\infty}(\tfrac{3}{2}x)^n = \sum_{n=0}^{\infty}\dfrac{3^n x^{n+1}}{2^{n+1}}$ for $|\frac{3}{2}x| < 1$ or $|x| < \frac{2}{3}$, where

we replaced x by $\frac{3}{2}x$ in #1.

10. $\dfrac{3}{2x+5} = \dfrac{3}{5}\dfrac{1}{(1+\frac{2}{5}x)} = \dfrac{3}{5}\displaystyle\sum_{n=0}^{\infty}(-\tfrac{2}{5}x)^n = \sum_{n=0}^{\infty}\dfrac{3(-1)^n 2^n x^n}{5^{n+1}}$ for $|\frac{2}{5}x| < 1$ or $|x| < \frac{5}{2}$,

where we replaced x by $(-\frac{2}{5}x)$ in #1.

13. Since $e^t = 1 + t + \frac{t^2}{2!} + \frac{t^3}{3!} + \ldots + \frac{t^n}{n!} + \ldots$ for all t, replacing t by -x we

obtain $e^{-x} = 1 + (-x) + \frac{(-x)^2}{2!} + \frac{(-x)^3}{3!} + \ldots + \frac{(-x)^n}{n!} + \ldots = 1 - x + \frac{x^2}{2!} - \frac{x^3}{3!}$

$+ \ldots + \frac{(-1)^n x^n}{n!} + \ldots$.

16. $\sinh x = \frac{1}{2}(e^x - e^{-x}) = \frac{1}{2}[(1 + x + \frac{x^2}{2!} + \frac{x^3}{3!} + \ldots) - (1 - x + \frac{x^2}{2!} - \frac{x^3}{3!} + \ldots)]$

$= \frac{1}{2}[2x + \frac{2x^3}{3!} + \frac{2x^5}{5!} + \ldots + \frac{2x^{2n-1}}{(2n-1)!} + \ldots] = x + \frac{x^3}{3!} + \frac{x^5}{5!} + \ldots +$

$\frac{x^{2n-1}}{(2n-1)!} + \ldots$.

19. Replacing x by $(-x^6)$ in #1, $\frac{1}{1+x^6} = 1 - x^6 + x^{12} - \ldots$ for $|x| < 1$. Thus

$\int_0^{1/3} \frac{1}{1+x^6} dx = [x - \frac{x^7}{7} + \frac{x^{13}}{13} - \ldots]_0^{1/3} = \frac{1}{3} - \frac{1}{3^7 \cdot 7} + \frac{1}{3^{13} \cdot 13} - \ldots$. This is a

convergent alternating series. Recall that if the sum of such a series is

approximated by the partial sum of the first n terms, the error is less than

the next term, i.e. the first term neglected. Since $\frac{1}{3^7 \cdot 7} \approx 6.532 \times 10^{-5}$ and

$\frac{1}{3^{13} \cdot 13} \approx 4.825 \times 10^{-7}$, we will have 6 place accuracy if we use the first two

terms. Thus the value is $\frac{1}{3} - \frac{1}{3^7 \cdot 7} \approx 0.33333 - 0.00007 = 0.33326$, which

becomes 0.3333 when rounded off to 4 places.

22. $\frac{x^3}{1+x^5} = x^3(1 - x^5 + x^{10} - \ldots)$ for $|x| < 1$. $\int_0^{.2} \frac{x^3}{1+x^5} dx = \int_0^{.2} (x^3 - x^8 +$

$x^{13} - \ldots) dx = \frac{(.2)^4}{4} - \frac{(.2)^9}{9} + \ldots$. Since the 2nd term is $\frac{512 \times 10^{-9}}{9} <$

6×10^{-8}, we get 4 (in fact, 6) place accuracy with just the first term.

The value is $\frac{(.2)^4}{4} = .0004$ to 4 places.

25. $f(x) = (1-x^2)^{-1} \Longrightarrow f'(x) = 2x(1-x^2)^{-2}$. To obtain a series for $2x(1-x^2)^{-2}$,

we can start with the series for f(x) and differentiate it. Replacing x by

x^2 in #1, we obtain $f(x) = \frac{1}{1-x^2} = 1 + x^2 + x^4 + x^6 + \ldots + x^{2n} + \ldots$, for

$|x| < 1$, whence $f'(x) = 2x(1-x^2)^{-2} = 2x + 4x^3 + 6x^5 + \ldots + 2nx^{2n-1}$, for

$|x| < 1$.

28. $\frac{e^t - 1}{t} = [(1 + t + \frac{t^2}{2!} + \frac{t^3}{3!} + \ldots + \frac{t^n}{n!} + \ldots) - 1]/t = 1 + \frac{t}{2!} + \frac{t^2}{3!} + \ldots + \frac{t^{n-1}}{n!} +$

$\ldots$. Thus $f(x) = \int_0^x \frac{e^t - 1}{t} dt = \int_0^x (1 + \frac{t}{2!} + \frac{t^2}{3!} + \ldots + \frac{t^{n-1}}{n!} + \ldots) dt =$

$$[t + \frac{t^2}{2(2!)} + \frac{t^3}{3(3!)} + \cdots + \frac{t^n}{n(n!)} + \cdots]_0^x = x + \frac{x^2}{2(2!)} + \frac{x^3}{3(3!)} + \cdots + \frac{x^n}{n(n!)} + \cdots$$

$$= \sum_{n=1}^{\infty} \frac{x^n}{n(n!)} .$$

EXERCISES 11.8, page 545

1. We calculate: $f(x) = \cos x$ $f(0) = 1$

    $f'(x) = -\sin x$ $f'(0) = 0$

    $f''(x) = -\cos x$ $f''(0) = -1$

    $f'''(x) = \sin x$ $f'''(0) = 0$

    and the subsequent derivatives follow this pattern. Thus $\cos x =$

    $(1 - \frac{1}{2!} x^2 + \frac{1}{4!} x^4 - \frac{1}{6!} x^6 + \cdots) = \sum_{n=0}^{\infty} \frac{(-1)^n x^{2n}}{(2n)!}$. The remainder, $R_n(x)$,

    is $(\pm \sin z)x^{n+1}/(n+1)!$ if n is even or $(\pm \cos z)x^{n+1}/(n+1)!$ if n is odd. In

    either case $|R_n(x)| \leq \frac{x^{n+1}}{(n+1)!}$ which has limit 0 as $n \to \infty$ for every x by (11.41).

4. All even-numbered derivatives of $f(x) = \cosh x$ are $\cosh x$ and have value 1 at

    $x = 0$. All odd-numbered derivatives are $\sinh x$ which are all 0 at $x = 0$. Thus

    $\cosh x = (1 + \frac{x^2}{2!} + \frac{x^4}{4!} + \cdots) = \sum_{n=0}^{\infty} \frac{x^{2n}}{(2n)!}$, in agreement with (11.42g). Here,

    $R_n(x) = \frac{\sinh z}{(n+1)!} x^{n+1}$ (if n is even) or $R_n(x) = \frac{\cosh z}{(n+1)!} x^{n+1}$ (if n is odd). In

    either case $|R_n(x)| \leq \frac{e^z + e^{-z}}{2} \frac{|x|^{n+1}}{(n+1)!} \leq (\cosh z) \frac{|x|^{n+1}}{(n+1)!}$ since $|\sinh z| \leq$

    $\cosh z$. Thus $|R_n(x)| \leq (\cosh x) \frac{|x|^{n+1}}{(n+1)!}$ since z between 0 and x $\Rightarrow \cosh z \leq$

    $\cosh x$. Again by (11.41) the factor $\frac{|x|^{n+1}}{(n+1)!} \to 0$ as $n \to \infty$ and $|R_n(x)| \to 0$ for

    all x.

7. Using $e^x = (1 + x + \frac{x^2}{2!} + \cdots)$, $e^{-x} = (1 - x + \frac{x^2}{2!} - \cdots)$, and $\sinh x =$

    $(e^x - e^{-x})/2$ we obtain $\sinh x = x + \frac{x^3}{3!} + \frac{x^5}{5!} + \cdots = \sum_{n=0}^{\infty} \frac{x^{2n+1}}{(2n+1)!}$. With $u_n =$

    $\frac{x^{2n+1}}{(2n+1)!}$, $\lim_{n \to \infty} \left| \frac{u_{n+1}}{u_n} \right| = \lim_{n \to \infty} \frac{x^2}{(2n+3)(2n+2)} = 0$ for all x. Hence $r = \infty$.

10. Substituting x^2 for x in #1, we obtain $\cos(x^2) = \sum_{n=0}^{\infty} \frac{(-1)^n (x^2)^{2n}}{(2n)!} =$

    $\sum_{n=0}^{\infty} \frac{(-1)^n x^{4n}}{(2n)!}$. The ratio test yields $\lim_{n \to \infty} \left| \frac{u_{n+1}}{u_n} \right| = \lim_{n \to \infty} \frac{|x|^4}{(2n+2)(2n+1)} = 0$ for

    all x. Hence $r = \infty$.

13. We calculate: $f(x) = \sin x$ $f(\pi/4) = 1/\sqrt{2}$

$f'(x) = \cos x$ $f'(\pi/4) = 1/\sqrt{2}$

$f''(x) = -\sin x$ $f''(\pi/4) = -1/\sqrt{2}$

$f'''(x) = -\cos x$ $f'''(\pi/4) = -1/\sqrt{2}$,

and the higher derivatives follow the same pattern. Thus, the desired

Taylor's series is $\sin x = \dfrac{1}{\sqrt{2}} + \dfrac{1}{\sqrt{2}}(x - \dfrac{\pi}{4}) - \dfrac{1}{2!\sqrt{2}}(x - \dfrac{\pi}{4})^2 - \dfrac{1}{3!\sqrt{2}}(x - \dfrac{\pi}{4})^3 + \ldots$

(Note that the pattern of signs is + + - - + + - -, etc.)

16. $f(x) = e^x \implies f^{(n)}(x) = e^x$ and $f^{(n)}(-3) = e^{-3}$ for all integers $n \geq 0$. Thus

$e^x = \displaystyle\sum_{n=0}^{\infty} \dfrac{e^{-3}}{n!} (x-(-3))^n = \sum_{n=0}^{\infty} \dfrac{e^{-3}}{n!} (x+3)^n$.

19. Since powers of $(x+1)$ are required, we want the Taylor series about $c = -1$.
Thus

$f(x) = e^{2x}$ $f(-1) = e^{-2}$

$f'(x) = 2e^{2x}$ $f'(-1) = 2e^{-2}$

$\vdots$

$f^{(n)}(x) = 2^n e^{2x}$ $f^{(n)}(-1) = 2^n e^{-2}$,

and $e^{2x} = \displaystyle\sum_{n=0}^{\infty} \dfrac{2^n e^{-2}}{n!} (x+1)^n$.

22. $f(x) = \tan x$ $f(\pi/4) = 1$

$f'(x) = \sec^2 x$ $f'(\pi/4) = 2$

$f''(x) = 2\sec^2 x \tan x$ $f''(\pi/4) = 4$

$f'''(x) = 2\sec^4 x + 4\sec^2 x \tan^2 x$ $f'''(\pi/4) = 16$,

and the first four terms are

$$1 + 2(x - \frac{\pi}{4}) + \frac{4}{2!}(x - \frac{\pi}{4})^2 + \frac{16}{3!}(x - \frac{\pi}{4})^3 + \ldots$$

25. $f(x) = xe^x$ $f(-1) = -e^{-1}$

$f'(x) = (x+1)e^x$ $f'(-1) = 0$

$f''(x) = (x+2)e^x$ $f''(-1) = e^{-1}$

$f'''(x) = (x+3)e^x$ $f'''(-1) = 2e^{-1}$

$f^{(4)}(x) = (x+4)e^x$ $f^{(4)}(-1) = 3e^{-1}$,

and the first four terms of the Taylor series are

$$xe^x = -e^{-1} + \frac{e^{-1}}{2!}(x+1)^2 + \frac{2e^{-1}}{3!}(x+1)^3 + \frac{3e^{-1}}{4!}(x+1)^4 + \ldots$$

28. $e^x = \displaystyle\sum_{n=0}^{\infty} \frac{x^n}{n!} \implies e^{-1} = \sum_{n=0}^{\infty} \frac{(-1)^n}{n!}$. This series satisfies the conditions of

the AST. Thus, if we approximate the sum, $S = e^{-1}$, by the nth partial sum, S_n, the error is $< a_{n+1}$, the 1st term neglected. Thus, for 4 decimal place accuracy we seek n such that $\frac{1}{(n+1)!} < 5 \times 10^{-5}$ or $(n+1)! > 20,000$. With

$n = 6$, $7! = 5040$, but with $n = 7$, $8! = 40,320$. Thus, to 4 places, $e^{-1} \approx S_7$

$$= \sum_{n=0}^{7} (-1)^n/n! = \frac{1}{0!} - \frac{1}{1!} + \frac{1}{2!} - \frac{1}{3!} + \frac{1}{4!} - \frac{1}{5!} + \frac{1}{6!} - \frac{1}{7!} = 1 - 1 + \frac{1}{2} - \frac{1}{6} + \frac{1}{24}$$

$$- \frac{1}{120} + \frac{1}{720} - \frac{1}{5040} \approx 0.3679.$$

31. By (11.42e) with $x = 0.1$, $\tan^{-1}0.1 = \sum_{n=0}^{\infty} \frac{(-1)^n(0.1)^{2n+1}}{2n+1}$. Again using the

alternating series criterion, we seek n such that $a_{n+1} = \frac{(0.1)^{2n+3}}{2n+3} <$

5×10^{-5} or $(2n+3)10^{2n+3} > 2 \times 10^4$. With $n = 1$, the left side is 5×10^5.

Thus, to 4 places, $\tan^{-1}0.1 \approx S_1 = \sum_{n=0}^{1} \frac{(-1)^n(0.1)^{2n+1}}{2n+1} = 0.1 - \frac{0.1^3}{3} \approx 0.0997.$

34. Since, by (11.42g), the series for cosh x is a positive term series for all x, we may NOT use the alternating series criterion as in #28 and #31 above. Rather, we must determine the number of terms needed by looking at the remainder in Maclaurin's formula. It was shown in #4 above that $|R_n(x)| \leq$

$\frac{(\cosh x) x^{n+1}}{(n+1)!}$. Since $x = 0.1$, $|R_n(0.1)| \leq \frac{(\cosh 0.1)(.1)^{n+1}}{(n+1)!}$. Now we have

a problem! We are trying to estimate cosh 0.1, and this very number occurs in the upper bound for the remainder (which is, of course, the error if we use the Maclaurin polynomial of degree n to approximate cosh 0.1). We must replace cosh 0.1 by some larger number for estimation purposes. cosh 0.1 =

$(e^{0.1} + e^{-0.1})/2 < (e^{0.1} + e^{0.1})/2 = e^{0.1} < e^{\ln 2} = 2$ since $0.1 < \ln 2 \approx$

0.693. Thus $|R_n(0.1)| < \frac{2(0.1)^{n+1}}{(n+1)!}$ and this is $< 5 \times 10^{-5}$ if $\frac{(n+1)! \, 10^{n+1}}{2} >$

2×10^4. With $n = 3$, the left side is 12×10^4. Thus we need the terms out to x^3 ($n = 3$), of the Maclaurin series of cosh x. Since the coefficients of x and x^3 are 0, $\cosh 0.1 \approx 1 + \frac{(0.1)^2}{2!} = 1.0050$ to 4 places.

37. $\cos t = 1 - \frac{t^2}{2!} + \frac{t^4}{4!} - \ldots \implies \cos x^2 = 1 - \frac{x^4}{2!} + \frac{x^8}{4!} - \ldots$

$$\int_0^{.5} \cos x^2 \, dx = \int_0^{.5} (1 - \frac{x^4}{2} + \frac{x^8}{24} - \ldots) dx = 0.5 - \frac{(0.5)^5}{10} + \frac{(0.5)^9}{9(24)} - \ldots.$$

The 3rd term $= 1/2^9(216) = 1/(512)(216) < 1/(500)(200) = 10^{-5}$. Thus the first two terms are sufficient, and the value is $0.5000 - 0.00312 = 0.49688$

$\approx 0.4969.$

40. $\cos t = 1 - \frac{t^2}{2!} + \frac{t^4}{4!} - \ldots \implies \cos\sqrt{x} = 1 - \frac{x}{2!} + \frac{x^2}{4!} - \ldots \implies \int_0^{0.2} \cos\sqrt{x}\, dx =$

$\int_0^{0.2} (1 - \frac{x}{2!} + \frac{x^2}{4!} - \frac{x^6}{6!} + \ldots)\, dx = 0.2 - \frac{0.2^2}{2(2!)} + \frac{0.2^3}{3(4!)} - \frac{0.2^4}{4(6!)} + \ldots .$

Using the alternating series criterion, we note that the 4th term is

$\frac{1.6 \times 10^{-3}}{2880} < 10^{-6}$. Thus the 1st 3 terms suffice for 4 place accuracy, and

the value is $0.2000 - 0.0100 + 0.0001 = 0.1901$.

43. Using (11.42d), $\int_0^{1/2} \frac{\ln(1+x)}{x}\, dx = \int_0^{1/2} \sum_{n=0}^{\infty} (-1)^n \frac{x^n}{n+1}\, dx =$

$\sum_{n=0}^{\infty} (-1)^n \frac{x^{n+1}}{(n+1)^2}\Big]_0^{1/2} = \sum_{n=0}^{\infty} \frac{(-1)^n}{2^{n+1}(n+1)^2}$. Using the alternating series

criterion, for 4 place accuracy we seek n such that $a_{n+1} = \frac{1}{2^{n+2}(n+2)^2} <$

5×10^{-5} or $2^{n+2}(n+2)^2 > 20,000$. The left side with $n = 6$ is $256(64) =$

$16,384$ and with $n = 7$ is $512(81) = 41,472$. Thus the partial sum $S_7 =$

$\sum_{n=0}^{7}$ is required. The value is $\frac{1}{2} - \frac{1}{4 \cdot 4} + \frac{1}{8 \cdot 9} - \frac{1}{16 \cdot 16} + \frac{1}{32 \cdot 25} - \frac{1}{64 \cdot 36} +$

$\frac{1}{128 \cdot 49} - \frac{1}{256 \cdot 64} \approx 0.4484$.

46. Using (11.42c) with x replaced by $-x$, $\frac{1-e^{-x}}{x} =$

$\frac{1 - (1 - x + x^2/2! - \ldots + (-1)^n x^n/n! + \ldots)}{x} = \frac{-\sum_{n=1}^{\infty} (-1)^n x^n/n!}{x} =$

$\sum_{n=1}^{\infty} \frac{(-1)^{n+1} x^{n-1}}{n!}$. Thus $\int_0^1 \frac{1-e^{-x}}{x}\, dx = \int_0^1 \sum_{n=1}^{\infty} \frac{(-1)^{n+1} x^{n-1}}{n!}\, dx =$

$\sum_{n=1}^{\infty} \frac{(-1)^{n+1} x^n}{n \cdot n!}\Big]_0^1 = \sum_{n=1}^{\infty} \frac{(-1)^{n+1}}{n \cdot n!}$. Again we seek n such that $a_{n+1} = \frac{1}{(n+1)(n+1)!}$

$< 5 \times 10^{-5}$ or $(n+1)(n+1)! > 20,000$. $n = 6$ produces $7 \cdot 7! = 35,280$. Thus the

integral value to 4 place accuracy is given by $S_6 = \sum_{n=1}^{6} \frac{(-1)^{n+1}}{n \cdot n!} = 1 - \frac{1}{2 \cdot 2!} +$

$\frac{1}{3 \cdot 3!} - \frac{1}{4 \cdot 4!} + \frac{1}{5 \cdot 5!} - \frac{1}{6 \cdot 6!} = 1 - \frac{1}{4} + \frac{1}{18} - \frac{1}{96} + \frac{1}{600} - \frac{1}{4320} = 0.7966$.

49. $\frac{\pi}{4} = \tan^{-1}1 = \sum_{n=0}^{\infty} \frac{(-1)^n 1^{2n+1}}{2n+1} \implies \pi = \sum_{n=0}^{\infty} \frac{(-1)^n 4}{2n+1}$. Using the 1st 5 terms

$(0 \leq n \leq 4)$, $\pi \approx 4 - \frac{4}{3} + \frac{4}{5} - \frac{4}{7} + \frac{4}{9} \approx 3.34$. (Note that the actual error is

≈ 0.20. The error bound obtained by the alternating series criterion is $\frac{4}{11}$

≈ 0.36.) For 4 place accuracy we seek n such that $a_{n+1} = \frac{4}{2(n+1)+1} = \frac{4}{2n+3} <$

5×10^{-5} or $2n+3 > 80,000 \implies n > \frac{79997}{2} = 39,998.5$. The smallest integer

satisfying this is $39,999$, so let's just say $40,000$.

EXERCISES 11.9, page 549

1. (a) Using (11.43) with k = 1/2, $\sqrt{1+x} = (1+x)^{1/2} = 1 + \frac{1}{2}x + \frac{(1/2)(-1/2)}{2!} x^2$

$+ \frac{1/2(-1/2)(-3/2)}{3!} x^3 + \ldots + \frac{(1/2)(-1/2)\ldots(1/2-n+1)}{n!} x^n + \ldots$ which reduces

to the answer given. By (11.43), r = 1.

(b) Using part (a) and replacing x by $-x^3$, we have $\sqrt{1-x^3} = 1 - \frac{x^3}{2} +$

$\sum_{n=2}^{\infty} (-1)^{n-1} \frac{1\cdot3\ldots(2n-3)}{2^n n!} (-x^3)^n$ which again reduces to the answer given.

4. Using (11.43) with k = -2, $x(1+2x)^{-2} = x[1 + (-2)(2x) + \frac{(-2)(-3)(2x)^2}{2!} + \ldots$

$+ \frac{(-2)(-3)\ldots(-2-n+1)(2x)^n}{n!} + \ldots] = x[1 + \sum_{n=1}^{\infty} (-1)^n \frac{2\cdot3\ldots(n+1)2^n}{n!} x^n]$. By

(11.43), we have convergence if $|2x| < 1$ or $|x| < 1/2$. Thus r = 1/2.

7. We begin by computing $(1+x)^{-1/2} = 1 - \frac{1}{2}x + \frac{(-1/2)(-3/2)}{2!} x^2 + \ldots +$

$\frac{(-1/2)(-3/2)\ldots(-1/2 - n + 1)}{n!} x^n + \ldots = 1 + \sum_{n=1}^{\infty} (-1)^n \frac{1\cdot3\cdot5\ldots(2n-1)}{2^n n!} x^n$.

Setting $x = -t^2$, we have $\frac{1}{\sqrt{1-t^2}} = 1 + \sum_{n=1}^{\infty} (-1)^n \frac{1\cdot3\cdot5\ldots(2n-1)}{2^n n!} (-1)^n t^{2n}$.

Using $(-1)^n \cdot (-1)^n = (-1)^{2n} = 1$, we obtain $\sin^{-1}x =$

$\int_0^x \frac{1}{\sqrt{1-t^2}} dt = x + \sum_{n=1}^{\infty} \frac{1\cdot3\cdot5\ldots(2n-1)x^{2n+1}}{(2n+1) 2^n n!}$. r = 1 since the series expansion

was valid for $|x| = |t^2| < 1 \iff |t| < 1$, and integrating does not alter r.

9. (This will be done rather than #10 since it relates to #1(b) above.)

By #1(b), $\sqrt{1-x^3} = 1 - \frac{x^3}{2} - \frac{x^6}{8} - \frac{3x^9}{48} + \ldots$ and, replacing x by -x, we have

$\sqrt{1+x^3} = 1 + \frac{x^3}{2} - \frac{x^6}{8} + \frac{x^9}{16} - \ldots$ and $\int_0^{1/2} \sqrt{1+x^3} dx = [x + \frac{x^4}{8} - \frac{x^7}{56} + \frac{x^{10}}{160} - \ldots]_0^{1/2}$

$= [\frac{1}{2} + \frac{1}{2^4\cdot8} - \frac{1}{2^7\cdot56} + \frac{1}{2^{10}\cdot160} - \ldots]$. Since this is an alternating series,

the error in using only the 1st 2 terms is less than the 3rd term. Since

$\frac{1}{2^7\cdot56} = \frac{1}{7168} \approx 0.00014$, this will yield 3 place accuracy. Thus the value of

the integral to 3 places is $\frac{1}{2} + \frac{1}{2^4\cdot8} = \frac{1}{2} + \frac{1}{128} = 0.5000 + 0.0078 \approx 0.508$.

EXERCISES 11.10, page 549

1. $f(x) = \frac{\ln(x^2+1)}{x} \implies \lim_{x\to\infty} f(x) = \lim_{x\to\infty} \frac{\ln(x^2+1)}{x} = \lim_{x\to\infty} \frac{2x/(x^2+1)}{1} = 0$ by

L'Hôpital's rule. Thus $\lim\limits_{n\to\infty} \dfrac{\ln(n^2+1)}{n} = 0$ also.

4. If n is even, $(-2)^n$ is positive and becomes larger as n does. If n is odd, $(-2)^n$ is negative and becomes more so as n increases. So, even though $1/n \to 0$, the sequence behaves essentially like $(-2)^n$ which oscillates wildly, and no limit exists.

7. A preliminary analysis suggests that the terms behave like $1/\sqrt[3]{n^3} = 1/n$. Thus with $a_n = 1/\sqrt[3]{n(n+1)(n+2)}$ and $b_n = 1/n$, $\lim\limits_{n\to\infty}\dfrac{a_n}{b_n} = \lim\limits_{n\to\infty}\dfrac{n}{\sqrt[3]{n(n+1)(n+2)}} = 1$. Since $\sum b_n$ diverges (p = 1, the harmonic series), the given series diverges also.

10. $\lim\limits_{n\to\infty}\dfrac{1}{2+(1/2)^n} = \dfrac{1}{2} \neq 0 \implies$ the series diverges.

13. Since $\dfrac{n!}{\ln(n+1)} \geq \dfrac{n}{\ln(n+1)}$ for all $n \geq 1$, and since $\lim\limits_{n\to\infty}\dfrac{n}{\ln(n+1)} = \lim\limits_{n\to\infty}\dfrac{1}{1/(n+1)}$ $= \infty$ (by L'Hôpital's rule), the series diverges.

16. A preliminary analysis suggests we choose $b_n = 1/n^2$. So, with $a_n = \dfrac{n + \cos n}{n^3 + 1}$, $\lim\limits_{n\to\infty}\dfrac{a_n}{b_n} = \lim\limits_{n\to\infty}\dfrac{n^3 + n^2\cos n}{n^3 + 1} = \lim\limits_{n\to\infty}\dfrac{1 + (\cos n)/n}{1 + 1/n^3} = 1$. Since $\sum b_n$ converges (p = 2), the given series converges.

19. The series diverges since $\lim\limits_{n\to\infty}\sqrt[n]{n} = 1$, and thus, $\lim\limits_{n\to\infty} 1/\sqrt[n]{n} = 1 \neq 0$. To obtain this limit, let $y = x^{1/x}$, an ∞^0 indeterminate form as $x \to \infty$. Then $\ln y = \dfrac{1}{x}\ln x$, and $\lim\limits_{x\to\infty}\ln y = \lim\limits_{x\to\infty}\dfrac{\ln x}{x} = \lim\limits_{x\to\infty}\dfrac{1/x}{1} = 0$. Thus $\lim\limits_{x\to\infty} y = \lim\limits_{x\to\infty} x^{1/x} = e^0 = 1$, and $\lim\limits_{n\to\infty} n^{1/n} = \lim\limits_{n\to\infty}\sqrt[n]{n} = 1$ also.

22. If u_n denotes the nth term of the series, then $|u_n| = \dfrac{\sqrt[3]{n-1}}{n^2-1} \approx \dfrac{\sqrt[3]{n}}{n^2} = \dfrac{1}{n^{5/3}}$. This preliminary analysis suggests we use $b_n = 1/n^{5/3}$ in the limit comparison test. $\lim\limits_{n\to\infty}\dfrac{|u_n|}{b_n} = \lim\limits_{n\to\infty}\dfrac{n^{5/3}\sqrt[3]{n-1}}{n^2-1} = \lim\limits_{n\to\infty}\dfrac{\sqrt[3]{1-1/n}}{1-1/n^2} = 1$, having divided numerator and denominator by n^2. Since $\sum b_n$ converges (p = 5/3), so does $\sum|u_n|$, and the given series converges absolutely.

25. $\left|\dfrac{1 - \cos n}{n^2}\right| = \dfrac{|1 - \cos n|}{n^2} \leq \dfrac{1 + |\cos n|}{n^2} \leq \dfrac{2}{n^2}$. Since $\sum\dfrac{2}{n^2}$ converges (p = 2), the given series converges absolutely.

28. $\lim\limits_{n\to\infty}\left|\dfrac{u_{n+1}}{u_n}\right| = \lim\limits_{n\to\infty} \dfrac{3^n}{(n+1)^2+9} \cdot \dfrac{n^2+9}{3^{n-1}} = \lim\limits_{n\to\infty} 3\,\dfrac{n^2+9}{(n+1)^2+9} = 3(1) = 3 > 1.$ Thus the series diverges by the ratio test.

31. With $f(x) = \sqrt{\ln x}/x$ we have $f'(x) = (1-2\ln x)/2x^2\sqrt{\ln x} < 0$ for $x \geq 2$.

    Moreover, $\lim\limits_{x\to\infty} f(x) = \lim\limits_{x\to\infty} \dfrac{\sqrt{\ln x}}{x} = \lim\limits_{x\to\infty} \dfrac{1/2x\sqrt{\ln x}}{1} = 0.$ Thus, the given series,

    $\sum(-1)^n \dfrac{\sqrt{\ln n}}{n}$ converges by the AST. Now, if $n \geq 3$, $\dfrac{\sqrt{\ln n}}{n} > \dfrac{1}{n}$ ($\ln x$ is an in-

    increasing function $\Rightarrow \ln n \geq \ln 3 > \ln e = 1$). Since $\sum \dfrac{1}{n}$ diverges (harmonic

    series), $\sum\left|(-1)^n \dfrac{\sqrt{\ln n}}{n}\right| = \sum \dfrac{\sqrt{\ln n}}{n}$ diverges by the comparison test. Thus the

    original series converges conditionally.

34. $f(x) = \dfrac{x}{\sqrt{x^2-1}}$ is continuous, positive and decreasing on $[2,\infty)$. ($f'(x) =$

    $-1/(x^2-1)^{3/2} < 0$.) $\displaystyle\int_2^\infty f(x)\,dx = \lim\limits_{t\to\infty}\int_2^t x(x^2-1)^{-1/2}\,dx = \lim\limits_{t\to\infty} (x^2-1)^{1/2}\Big]_2^t =$

    $\lim\limits_{t\to\infty} (\sqrt{t^2-1} - \sqrt{3}) = \infty$, and the series diverges. (Note: divergence can be

    obtained immediately by observing $n/\sqrt{n^2-1} \to 1$ as $n \to \infty$.)

37. $f(x) = 10/\sqrt[3]{x+8}$ is positive, continuous and decreasing on $[1,\infty)$. $\displaystyle\int_1^\infty f(x)\,dx =$

    $\lim\limits_{t\to\infty}\int_1^t 10(x+8)^{-1/3}\,dx = \lim\limits_{t\to\infty} (15(t+8)^{2/3}-15(9)^{2/3}) = \infty$, and the series

    diverges.

40. The series converges by the AST. Since the 10th term, $\dfrac{1}{100(101)} < 10^{-4}$, we

    will get at least 3 place accuracy if we take only the 1st 9 terms as the

    approximation to the sum, A. Thus $A \approx \dfrac{1}{1(2)} - \dfrac{1}{4(5)} + \dfrac{1}{9(10)} - \dfrac{1}{16(17)} + \dfrac{1}{25(26)}$

    $- \dfrac{1}{36(37)} + \dfrac{1}{49(50)} - \dfrac{1}{64(65)} + \dfrac{1}{81(82)}$. $A \approx .5000 - .05000 + .0111 - .0037 +$

    $.0015 - .0008 + .0004 - .0002 + .0002 \approx .4585 \approx .458.$

43. With $u_n = \dfrac{(x+10)^n}{n2^n}$, $\lim\limits_{n\to\infty}\left|\dfrac{u_{n+1}}{u_n}\right| = \lim\limits_{n\to\infty} \dfrac{n}{2(n+1)}|x+10| = \dfrac{|x+10|}{2} < 1$ if $|x+10| <$

    2 or $-2 < x+10 < 2$ or $-12 < x < -8$. If $x = -8$, $x+10 = 2$, and the series is

    $\sum \dfrac{1}{n}$ which diverges. If $x = -12$, the series is $\sum \dfrac{(-1)^n}{n}$ which converges by the

    AST. Thus the interval of convergence is $[-12,8)$.

46. With $u_n = \dfrac{(x+5)^n}{(n+5)!}$, $\lim\limits_{n\to\infty}\left|\dfrac{u_{n+1}}{u_n}\right| = \lim\limits_{n\to\infty} \dfrac{|x+5|}{n+6} = 0$ for all x. Thus the interval

of convergence is $(-\infty, \infty)$.

49. The quickest way for this problem is to recognize that $\sin x \cos x = \frac{1}{2} \sin 2x$

$$= \frac{1}{2} \sum_{n=0}^{\infty} \frac{(-1)^n (2x)^{2n+1}}{(2n+1)!} = \sum_{n=0}^{\infty} \frac{(-1)^n 2^{2n} x^{2n+1}}{(2n+1)!} \, . \quad r = \infty \text{ by the ratio test or from}$$

the nature of the sine series. Another method for this problem would be to multiply the Maclaurin series for $\sin x$ and $\cos x$ together.

52. See the solution to #7, Sec. 11.9.

55. One way is to write $\sqrt{x} = \sqrt{4+(x-4)} = 2\sqrt{1 +(x-4)/4}$ and use #1(a), Sec. 11.9 replacing x by $(x-4)/4$ and multiplying by 2. Another way is to compute the

Taylor series of $f(x) = x^{1/2}$ about $c = 4$. This yields $f(x) = x^{1/2}$, $f'(x) =$

$\frac{1}{2}x^{-1/2}$, $f''(x) = \frac{1}{2}(-\frac{1}{2})x^{-3/2}$, $f'''(x) = \frac{1}{2}(-\frac{1}{2})(-\frac{3}{2})x^{-5/2}$, ..., $f^{(n)}(x) =$

$(\frac{1}{2})(-\frac{1}{2}) \ldots (\frac{-(2n-3)}{2}) \cdot x^{-(2n-1)/2}$ for $n \geq 2$. Evaluating these derivatives

at $x = 4$ and using the Taylor series formula, the given answer results.

58. $\sin x = x - \dfrac{x^3}{6} + \dfrac{x^5}{120} - \dfrac{x^7}{5040} + \cdots$

$\dfrac{\sin x}{\sqrt{x}} = x^{1/2} - \dfrac{x^{5/2}}{6} + \dfrac{x^{9/2}}{120} - \dfrac{x^{13/2}}{5040} + \cdots$

$\displaystyle\int_0^1 \dfrac{\sin x}{\sqrt{x}}\, dx = \dfrac{2}{3} x^{3/2} - \dfrac{2}{42} x^{7/2} + \dfrac{2}{1320} x^{11/2} -$

$$\dfrac{2}{75,600} x^{15/2} + \cdots \Big]_0^1$$

$$= \dfrac{2}{3} - \dfrac{1}{21} + \dfrac{1}{660} - \dfrac{1}{37,800} + \cdots$$

Since the 4th term of this alternating series is $< 10^{-4}$, the sum of the 1st 3 yields 3 place accuracy at least. This sum is $.6667 - .0476 + .0015 = .6206 \approx .621$.